AN OUTLINE OF PLANT GEOGRAPHY

THE MACMILLAN COMPANY
NEW YORK · BOSTON · CHICAGO · DALLAS
ATLANTA · SAN FRANCISCO

MACMILLAN & CO., Limited
LONDON · BOMBAY · CALCUTTA
MELBOURNE

THE MACMILLAN CO. OF CANADA, Ltd.
TORONTO

AN OUTLINE

OF

PLANT GEOGRAPHY

BY

DOUGLAS HOUGHTON CAMPBELL

New York

THE MACMILLAN COMPANY

1926

PRINTED IN THE UNITED STATES OF AMERICA BY
THE BERWICK & SMITH CO.

PREFACE

To the lover of Nature, whether scientist or layman, one of the greatest charms of travel is seeing the many new and interesting plants inhabiting the various parts of the world.

For a good many years the writer has had occasion to visit many countries in the quest of material for his botanical studies; and although these investigations, for the most part, have not been concerned primarily with plant distribution, nevertheless the general vegetation of the various places visited, and the relations of the different floras to each other, have always been subjects of the greatest interest.

Moreover, for some years past, these botanical excursions have been devoted to a considerable extent directly to problems of plant distribution; and although the writer can hardly lay claim to rank as a plant geographer, he has nevertheless contributed in a small way to the subject.

It is conceivable that one who is, in a way, an amateur may be more likely to appreciate the more salient features of a flora than the specialist in some particular group of such a flora; and this may be offered as an explanation of the writer's venturing into a field where he can scarcely expect to be looked upon as an expert.

In a volume of moderate size dealing with so vast a subject as plant geography, it is obvious that anything beyond a sketch is impossible; but it is hoped that the outline offered here will prove sufficiently clear and accurate to give a fairly satisfactory picture of the most notable features of the vegetation characteristic of the more important botanical regions. For the minuter details, of course, one must refer to the many treatises dealing with the floras of special countries.

For more than thirty years the writer has made excursions into many parts of the world, and the specimens, notes, sketches and photographs accumulated during these journeys, have served as the basis of the present volume. These personal data have been supplemented by free use of such standard general works as those of Drude and Schimper, as well as the descriptive floras of many

v

2137

regions, and numerous special monographs and papers dealing with plant distribution by American botanists and those of other countries. The important series of monographs "Die Vegetation der Erde" has been found especially helpful, and the well-known "Natürliche Pflanzenfamilien" of Engler and Prantl has been frequently consulted.

A considerable number of important photographs which have added materially to the value of the book, were furnished through the courtesy of colleagues and others, to all of whom the writer is greatly indebted and would express his sincere thanks. Due credit is given in each case.

It is hoped that the volume will not prove too technical to be of value to the general reader interested in the subject of plant distribution; but the writer has tried to make it sufficiently detailed to be useful, also, as a book of reference for botanists, or as a text in classes studying the general subject of plant geography.

DOUGLAS HOUGHTON CAMPBELL.

Stanford University,
February, 1926.

CONTENTS

CONTENTS   ix

AN OUTLINE OF PLANT GEOGRAPHY

OUTLINE OF PLANT GEOGRAPHY

CHAPTER I

INTRODUCTION

As one studies the existing vegetation of the Earth, one recognizes certain factors whose influence in determining the distribution of the species composing this vegetation is sufficiently clear; but there are other factors quite as potent which are by no means so obvious.

Of course for the existence of normal green plants, a certain minimum of light, heat and moisture is essential; and up to a certain point the luxuriance of vegetation is in direct ratio to the relation of these three factors, and culminates where all work together, as in the equatorial regions of both hemispheres.

The soil constituents are also very evident factors in determining the distribution of many species. Certain plants like rhododendrons and others of the heath family, are notoriously impatient of lime, and only thrive in acid soils. Others like lettuce, asparagus, clover, demand lime in the soil as a condition for their healthy growth. Heavy clay soils suit some plants, light sandy soils are indispensable for others.

Conditions in widely separated regions may be very similar, but this by no means implies a close relationship of the vegetation between these regions, although its general aspect may be much the same. Thus the rain forests of the Amazon Valley, and those of Borneo or Java, look much alike—lofty trees draped with lianas, orchids and other epiphytes, with an undergrowth of palms, huge ferns, arums and other large leaved growths like the bananas and gingers. In spite of this close general resemblance, probably there would not be a single species common to the two regions. So in the temperate parts of Europe and North America there are relatively few common species, although the floras have much in common, and are obviously related to each other.

1

The main problem of the student of plant geography is to discover, if possible, the explanation of the diverse floras of the different parts of the earth, as well as resemblances which occur in widely sundered lands.

Could we know the whole history of the evolution of the plant kingdom, this problem would be simple enough; but our knowledge of the vegetation of the earliest geological periods is almost *nil;* and it is not until a comparatively late period that we have any certain evidences of the nature of the vegetation.

As we study such relics of the ancient floras as have come to us in a fossil state, we realize that the distribution of land and water upon the earth's surface has undergone many and extensive changes. Lands once connected are now widely sundered, and regions now united were separated by great expanses of ocean. Continents have sunk beneath the ocean, and lofty mountain chains have emerged from the ancient seas.

These changes in the distribution of land and water have doubtless had much to do with the fluctuations of climate indicated by a study of the ancient rocks and fossils. These reveal the presence of luxuriant vegetation in regions now quite impossible for its existence. Within a few degrees of the poles, in both hemispheres, fossil plants have been found which must have grown in a climate at least temperate in character.

A study of these evident changes in climate and topography and the fossils that have been discovered, have thrown much light on many facts in the present distribution of plants, that otherwise would be quite incomprehensible.

While the fossil record is very incomplete, nevertheless it has greatly helped in our understanding of the relations existing between the vegetation of regions now widely separated but which we know were once connected.

However, much more must be done in the study of the fossil plants of many parts of the world before we shall be in a position to solve some of the most difficult questions of distribution which remain to be answered. It is to be hoped that in course of time with our increasing knowledge of the ancient floras of the more remote parts of the world, that we may solve some of the many puzzles in the distribution of existing plants.

The Geological Record

A study of the fossil plants shows beyond question that throughout the greater part of geological time the earth's climate was much more uniform than at present. It has been claimed [1] that the zonal climates now existing, were scarcely recognizable in the earlier geological periods, but are first clearly defined in the Pliocene—the era just preceding the succession of glaciations constituting the great ice age.

While the great fluctuations in the distribution of land and water areas during the ages undoubtedly exercised a very great influence on the prevailing climate, it is difficult to see how under any conditions, conceivable at the present day, it would be possible for such trees as magnolias, figs, walnuts and sequoias to live in the latitude of Spitzbergen and Greenland as they undoubtedly did in the Eocene.

It is true that in regions with an insular climate, such as southeastern Alaska and New Zealand there is a luxuriant vegetation in relatively high latitudes, due to heavy rain-fall and absence of severe cold; but such conditions are hardly conceivable at the present day in regions less than ten degrees from the pole.

Especially during the Carboniferous was the flora of the earth extremely uniform. "We find practically identical assemblages of plants wide spread over western Europe, central and eastern Asia, South Africa, eastern North America and probably southern South America." [2]

Even more widely spread floras occur in the Jurassic, which are known to range from Franz Josef Land, 82° N., to Graham Land, 63° S., and to extend practically completely round the world.

From the nature of the plants of these periods, one may conclude that the climate was a mild—perhaps subtropical one, and that there was very heavy precipitation. Such a climate seems to have prevailed during much of geologic time.

There were, however, periods of lower temperatures, indicated by evidences of extensive glaciation, especially during the Permian. At that period, there are abundant evidences of extensive glacia-

---

[1] Knowlton, F. H., "Evolution of Geologic Climates," *Bull. Geol. Soc. of America*, Vol. XXX, pp. 499–566, 1919.

[2] Knowlton, *loc. cit.*, p. 512.

tion, especially in the southern hemisphere, even within the tropics.

Various theories to account for the climatic conditions in geologic time have been propounded. A recent one [1] elaborated at some length assumes that prior to the Pleistocene, the climate of the earth was controlled by its own heat, the effects of solar radiation being excluded by a thick cloud envelope. Under such conditions there would be no zonal climates, but changes in climate would be due, mainly, to the relative distribution of land and water. The temperature of the oceans was much higher and more uniform than at present, and glaciation might occur anywhere, provided there was a continental area of sufficient extent to permit a loss of heat by radiation enough to reach the freezing point.

The presence of glaciers by no means implies an extremely cold climate. Today one may see growing in close proximity to extensive glaciers luxuriant forests, as in southern Alaska, or even plants of tropical origin, as in southern New Zealand, where in lat. 44°, tree-ferns, and trees and shrubs of Malayan affinities may be found close to the great Franz Josef glaciers which descend to less than 1000 feet above the sea.

The extension of many tropical genera into the temperate parts of New Zealand is very remarkable, and this fact makes one cautious about concluding that the presence of tropical genera in a fossil state necessarily implies a tropical, or even sub-tropical climate.

Succession of Plants in Geological Time

The first organisms to appear upon the earth were doubtless extremely simple in structure. Of living forms, the bacteria may offer some suggestions as to the character of the first living things. That bacteria existed at an extremely remote period is certain, as their activities are essential for the existence of all other organisms. Their extremely small size, however, makes a positive demonstration of their presence in a fossil state, a difficult matter. It is interesting to find, however, that the earliest known positive remains of plants belong to the blue-green algae, forms which probably are related to bacteria.[2] Wolcott has described from

[1] Manson, M., *The Evolution of Climates*, Baltimore, 1922.
[2] Knowlton, F. H., *loc cit.*, p. 506.

pre-Cambrian rocks of Western America a number of forms of these organisms which are supposed to be responsible for extensive limestone deposits of that region.

Most of the lower plants, however, like the algae, or sea-weeds, have very delicate tissues extremely perishable, and capable of being preserved in a fossil state, only under the most exceptional conditions; so it is not remarkable that the geological history of these plants is very incomplete, and many of the records of impressions of algae are, to say the least, doubtful.

There is good reason to believe that many of the simplest of the living algae are but little changed from their ancient relatives of the early geologic time. We are told that the ancient seas were fresh-water, and the ancestors of the living plants presumably originated in a fresh-water environment. As conditions in fresh water have not greatly changed, it is reasonable to suppose that as in the case of such simple animals as Amoeba and many flagellates, many of these primordial plants have come down to modern times with little change.

From these primitive green algae it is believed the higher green plants, including the flowering plants, have been derived.

While most of the green algae have left no recognizable fossil remains, there are some which secrete calcareous incrustations, which have enabled the geologist to recognize these in a fossil state. The oldest of these go back to the Silurian. Two types especially, Siphoneae now mostly tropical marine algae, and the Charales (Stoneworts), fresh water forms, occur without question in a fossil condition.

Two very important classes of algae, the red and brown seaweeds, are probably of more recent origin than the green algae. They are essentially salt-water plants, and it may be assumed that their main characteristics have been developed with the increasing salinity of the oceans in the later geologic time.

Of the brown algae, the remains are very doubtful in most cases, although many fossils have been attributed to this class.

Among the red algae, there are a good many—the "Corallines"—which secrete lime in quantity, and play a very important rôle as reef-builders. Corallines are found abundantly in a fossil condition, the oldest fossils attributed to this group occurring in the Silurian; but they are mostly from much more recent formations.

We may assume that the ancestors of the existing vegetation of the earth were very simple fresh-water algae.

In course of time there were manifested two divergent lines of evolution in the plant kingdom, connected directly with a change in environment.

As the seas became more and more saline, we may suppose that certain of the primitive algae adapted themselves to the denser salt water, while others confined themselves to the fresh water streams and lakes. At the present day two classes of algae, the brown and the red, are preëminently the marine plant types, aside from certain minute floating forms like the diatoms. Except for a relative small number of green algae, and a few flowering plants like the eel-grass, etc., the marine coastal flora is mainly composed of the red and brown sea-weeds.

The largest class of algae is that of the diatoms, unicellular plants of which over 10,000 species are known. Owing to their characteristic flinty shells, they are found in a fossil state in enormous quantities. In spite of their simple cell-structure, which would imply that they are primitive forms, the fossil record indicates that they are among the most recent of plant types, no certain remains being known much below the Cretaceous. As they are especially abundant at present in cold waters, being particularly numerous in the arctic and antarctic seas, it is possible that they are forms which are especially fitted to cold-water conditions and owe their great development to the refrigeration of the ocean, and the general cooling of the earth's climate which developed during the Tertiary, culminating in the Pleistocene glaciation.

Much more significant was the abandonment of the primeval aquatic habitat for life on land. This was undoubtedly the most momentous event in the history of the vegetable kingdom. The much greater range of conditions on land, involving questions of water storage and the development of mechanical or supporting tissues, as well as adaptation to greater range of temperature and other conditions, at once open up a practically unlimited field for the operation of natural selection, and marked the beginning of the reign of land plants which henceforth were to dominate the vegetation of the world.

Just when the first algae left the water and took up their abode upon the muddy bank of some ancient pond or marsh, we can never know, as we can hardly hope to find recognizable remains of the extremely delicate and perishable organisms of the very ancient formations when land life first began.

FUNGI

In addition to the algae, which are characterized by the presence of the characteristic green pigment, chlorophyll, there is a vast assemblage of plants, structurally of about the same degree of development as the algae, and perhaps derived from them. These plants, the fungi, are destitute of chlorophyll, and hence dependent on organic substances for food, and at the present time play a very important rôle in the land-vegetation of the woild.

While there is abundant evidence that fungi existed in the earlier geological formations, the record is too incomplete to throw much light on their early history. The best known fossils are parasitic forms which are found in the tissues of higher plants, and it is evident that as at present fungi were the cause of serious plant diseases.

THE FIRST LAND PLANTS

The first unmistakable land plants are first met with in the early Devonian formations, but these have already attained a structure which implies a long series of intermediate forms between them and the ancestral algae.

The Bryophytes (mosses and liverworts), which are the lowest of the existing land plants, have apparently left few recognizable traces in the ancient rocks. There is every reason to believe that these have existed for a period antedating the first known remains of land plants, but their delicate tissues are extremely perishable and positive evidence is not at present forthcoming. These plants have been rather neglected by the students of fossil plants, and possibly a more intensive search for their remains may throw light upon their early history.[1]

The early Devonian land plants belonged to a peculiar group of vascular plants, i. e., plants with woody conducting tissues—

[1] A paper by Mr. J. Walton, in the *Annals of Botany*, July, 1925, describes several liverworts from shales belonging to the Middle Coal-Measure Age, from Shropshire, in England.

sometimes separated as a distinct class—(Psilophyta). The oldest and simplest of these, the Rhyniaceae, show some very interesting resemblances to certain existing bryophytes, and support the theory that the vascular plants have come from some such bryophytic ancestors.

The later Devonian formations show the beginnings of the different classes of ferns, horsetails and club-mosses, which constitute the Pteridophytes of the present day; but there were also found in the latest Devonian certain types of seed-bearing plants as well, the Cordaitales, which, however, completely disappear before the end of the Palaeozoic.

The various plant types of the late Devonian continue into the Carboniferous where they are supplemented by a great assembly of other related forms which have been preserved in a very perfect state in immense numbers, so that we can make a pretty accurate estimate of the vegetation of the great coal period.

This flora during much of the Carboniferous was practically world wide in its distribution, and indicates a mild excessively humid climate, such as now exists in the mountain rain-forests of the tropics, and in some temperate regions like parts of New Zealand, where pteridophytes play a very important rôle in the vegetation.

Ferns, horsetails and club-mosses abounded, the two latter classes having genera which attained tree-like dimensions and were much better developed than their degenerate modern representatives. Among tree-ferns and club-mosses were seed bearing types, the Cordaitales, beginning at the end of the Devonian, which flourished in the Carboniferous. All of these Palaeozoic seed-plants disappear before the next great geological epoch— the Mesozoic—and their place is taken by forms related to existing ones and which first appear in the Permian.

The latter part of the Carboniferous and the succeeding Permian era show evidences of a decided cooling off, extensive glaciers existing, especially in the southern hemisphere. At this time, the land-masses of the southern hemisphere appear to have been in more or less intimate connection, and this "Gondwana Land," was quite separate from the northern land masses, and in it was developed a peculiar flora "Glossopteris flora" which was supposed to be a cold-climate one, and supplanted the earlier Carboniferous floras which survived for some time later in the northern hemisphere. This separation of a northern and southern flora is significant, as probably something analogous took place at a later period, resulting in the marked differences now existing between the temperate floras of the northern and southern hemispheres.

With the opening of the Mesozoic seed-bearing plants increased in numbers and importance, but were all "gymnosperms," i. e., forms with exposed seeds, like those of the living coniferous trees. The latter were represented by forms allied to the Araucarias and Kauri pines of the southern hemisphere, and the cycads and Ginkgo of the present day. The cycads are palm-like woody plants, with less than 100 species at present, inhabitants of the tropics and warm temperate regions. The only existing representatives in our territory, are two small species of Zamia in southern Florida.

Ginkgo biloba, the curious "maiden-hair tree," not infrequently seen in cultivation, is the sole survivor of a large order of trees which flourished in the early Mesozoic. The living species has been found wild in western China, but has been cultivated in China and Japan for a very long time.

The cycads reached their culmination in the middle of its Mesozoic (Jurassic) when they were a predominant feature of the vegetation. The most specialized forms had flowers suggesting those of some of the higher flowering plants, and it has even been thought that these (Angiosperms) may have originated from some of the Jurassic Cycadophytes. In the Jurassic are found also the beginning of the modern coniferous genera, pines, cypresses, cedars, etc., and the first sequoias are probably of about the same age. With the establishment of the modern conifers, the cycads become much less important and only a few of the less specialized genera have survived to the present day.

The last period of the Mesozoic, the Cretaceous, is notable as a period of extraordinary development of new life-forms, both plant and animal. The vegetation indicates a moist warm uniform climate, due, perhaps, in part to extensive invasions of the land by the oceans.

In the Cretaceous are found for the first time unmistakable remains of angiosperms, the modern type of seed-bearing plants. These are first encountered in the lower Cretaceous, where they are associated with a flora composed for the most part of ferns, cycads and conifers. The earliest fossils supposed to be angiosperms are of somwehat doubtful nature, and their relationships are obscure; but even in the lower Cretaceous there are found remains of such modern trees as oaks and willows, and in the upper Cretaceous a great many existing genera are met with. By this time most of the existing genera of conifers—pines, firs, cedars, etc.—were well established, and often much more widespread than at present. And such familiar angiospermous trees as oaks, poplars, sycamores, sweet gum (Liquidambar), magnolias, laurels and many others were found in many parts of the world.

During much of the Cretaceous there are evidences of extensive invasions of the land by the ocean, so that the distribution of the principal land masses was very different from that now existing.

In North America the Gulf of Mexico was connected with the Arctic Ocean, completely separating the western portion of this continent from the Atlantic area. Much of South America was submerged, and extensive invasions of the sea took place in Europe and Asia, and in Australia there are indications that an ancient West Australian continent was separated from the northeastern part, then probably united with New Guinea.

The end of the Cretaceous was a period of mountain building, especially in western America, and with the land elevation, North America assumed much of its present configuration.

In Europe and Asia the Tertiary was a period of mountain building, and the present conformation was attained at a later period than in America.

While the northern continents had assumed very much their existing condition before the end of the Tertiary, there were at various periods direct connections between Eurasia and North America. Remains of the land bridge still exist between Alaska and Kamtchatka, and the mainland of Siberia is separated from Alaska only by the narrow Behring's Strait.

The connections between Europe and northeastern America are much less obvious, but there is ample evidence that such connections did occur during the Tertiary.

With these changes there is evidence from the fossil plants that there was a general lowering of temperature during the Tertiary in the northern hemisphere. During the earlier period (Eocene,

Miocene) the climate of Europe was evidently sub-tropical, or at any rate mild enough for palms and other tropical types to flourish. In the Pliocene these give way to trees of northern types, oaks, beeches, etc. The marine fossils indicate that the ocean was growing colder also.

The Pliocene floras of the northern hemisphere are well known, and consist of genera which still exist, but with a very different distribution from that of Tertiary times. Many of these genera, and probably some species, have survived to the present. They are best represented at present by the forests of Atlantic North America, and those of the Himalayan regions, China and Japan in Asia.

With the pines, firs, oaks, maples, willows and poplars now found throughout the north temperate zone, were mingled other genera, at present more restricted in their range. Such are the giant sequoias of California, the bald cypress (Taxodium) of the Gulf States, hickories, walnuts, magnolias, tulip trees, sassafras and others.

The explanation of the present range of these trees is to be sought in changes of climate, and especially the changes resulting from the series of refrigerations constituting the great Pleistocene glaciation.

The effects of the extensive glaciation in the northern hemisphere upon the distribution of both plants and animals were far-reaching, and have been the subject of many investigations.

In the old world, especially in Europe, the extinction of many types, existing in the Pliocene, was brought about. Such trees as magnolias, hickories, sweet gum and others, still existing in America and eastern Asia, were completely extinguished in Europe owing to the complete glaciation north of the Alps. Their former existence is evident from abundant fossil remains in the Tertiary rocks.

In eastern America the glaciation extended only to about latitude 40° and many of these trees were able to retreat southward, later following the northward recession of the melting ice. Such characteristic Tertiary trees as the tulip-tree (Liriodendron), sweet gum (Liquidambar), sassafras, walnuts, hickories and others, still flourish in the Atlantic states and in parts of China and Japan and the Himalayas, but have quite disappeared from Europe, where they formerly lived—as their retreat was cut off by the mountain ranges to the south.

It is clear that the climate of the middle Tertiary was decidedly warmer than at present in the northern hemisphere, as most of the characteristic trees flourished far north of their present range, and there was a practically uniform circumpolar vegetation, as there is at present, but made up of elements requiring a much warmer climate than suffices for present arctic and sub-arctic vegetation.

Within the United States there seems to have been a sorting out of the Tertiary types at the time of the glacial advance. It is likely that at this time the climatic conditions in the northern states were not very different from those now prevailing, i. e., the Pacific Slope was a region of dry summers and mild wet winters; the Atlantic of hot humid summers and severe winters. Between the two regions lay the semi-arid plains between the Mississippi and the Rocky Mountains, a region unsuited, for the most part, for tree growth. As the vegetation retreated southward, before the advancing glaciers, this central area acted as a barrier to further advance, and formed a wedge on either side of which there was a migration toward the more favorable coastal regions. In this migration the species adapted to the dryer summer conditions of the West Coast have survived in the Pacific region, while those requiring more humidity now constitute the bulk of the Atlantic forest. Thus at present we find a preponderance of evergreen trees, especially conifers in the Pacific forests, while the Atlantic forest is largely composed of deciduous species.

As the glaciers retreated northward the arctic and sub-arctic plants followed closely and established themselves in their present circumpolar area. This area, once occupied by the warm temperate Tertiary flora, is now much too cold to support most of these, many of which, however, survive in the warm temperate regions of eastern Asia and North America.

In some cases, arctic species, instead of following the receding ice northward, attained the same climatic conditions by ascending the mountains until they reached an elevation where the temperature was favorable to their growth, and as the lowland climate became warmer, they moved to still higher elevations, so that these arctic refugees are now found stranded on the summits of mountains far away from their kin in the lowlands of the arctic and sub-arctic regions.

The presence of boreal species in high mountains in lower latitudes, is a familiar feature of plant distribution in Europe and the United States. A number of species for example, occur at the summit of the White Mountains which are found at sea-level in Labrador and Greenland, and the alpine summits of the Rocky Mountains and Sierra Nevada have species which inhabit the lowlands of Alaska and arctic British America.

In the northern hemisphere, therefore, it was the extensive Pleistocene glaciation which must be considered the greatest single factor in the establishment of the temperate floras of the present day.

Our knowledge of the conditions in the southern hemisphere during the Tertiary is very incomplete, and the origin of the modern south temperate floras is very uncertain.

Unlike the arctic regions, the antarctic continent is separated from the temperate zone by a broad ocean belt, so that the south temperate lands are completely isolated, and the relationships of the floras of South Africa, South America and Australasia, are much less intimate than those of Eurasia and temperate North America.

Nevertheless there is sufficient resemblance, especially between sub-antarctic South America and Australasia, to warrant the assumption of some former land connection, probably *via* some northern extension of the present antarctic continent.

The latter, at present, is practically destitute of vegetation, but there is sufficient fossil evidence, to show that within a few degrees of the pole there formerly flourished plants which must have needed a temperate climate, at least, for their existence, and fossils of a later date from Seymour Island, south of Patagonia, show remains of species closely related to some of those now found in New Zealand.

Our knowledge of these antarctic fossils is too meagre to permit any positive conclusions as to the character of the ancient antarctic flora as a whole, or to decide whether there was a continuous circumpolar Tertiary flora as in the northern hemisphere. Should such be the case, it would explain the occurrence of the same antarctic types in Patagonia and Australasia, which might be relics of an ancient wide-spread Tertiary flora derived from the antarctic continent.

In South Africa and South America there is direct communication with the lands to the north and a certain intermingling of northern and southern types; but Australia and New Zealand are completely isolated at present, and such former land connections to the north, which there is strong reason to believe once existed, have completely disappeared.

The vegetation of northeastern Australia (Queensland) and New Zealand, is evidently related to that of the Malayan Archipelago, and there is abundant evidence of former connections with the tropical regions to the north.

Western Australia was apparently completely separated from Queensland, in the Cretaceous, and it has been thought that in the ancient western continent the present extremely specialized Australian flora had its origin.

After the union of western and eastern Australia, and the establishment of the extensive land tracts which now occupy most of the great continent, it may be surmised that these western plants invaded the territory to the east, encroaching upon the Malayan rainforest flora, which has now become restricted to a relatively narrow strip near the east coast where rich soils and abundant rainfall have permitted it to survive.

In New Zealand, although the climate is a temperate one, the Malayan element is far more important than in Australia owing to the abundant and well distributed rainfall over most of the country.

There is another very important element in the New Zealand flora, especially in the south where one meets trees, shrubs and herbs whose nearest relatives are in the colder parts of South America: Patagonia and Tierra del Fuego. Some of these have also reached southeastern Australia and Tasmania.

At present, New Zealand is separated from South America by more than 90° of longitude and it is quite inconceivable that these plants have been transported over such a vast expanse of ocean.

During the Permian era, it has been held by many geologists, that the present isolated southern land masses—i. e., South Africa, South America, part of India, and Australia,—were united in a vast continent, "Gondwana Land," which also included a part of the antarctic continent. How far these connections were maintained during the Mesozoic and Tertiary seems to be very uncertain; but some such connections would seem to be necessary to account for the present distribution of these sub-antarctic plants.

Existing Factors in Distribution

Among the factors of prime importance in the distribution of the present floras of the earth, perhaps the first is the relation of the great continental masses to each other, and to the great bodies of water surrounding them.

The proximity of Eurasia and North America, especially in the North Pacific region, is reflected in the evident relationships of the northern floras throughout the northern hemisphere, while in the southern hemisphere the plants of the different continents are much less closely related, as might be expected from the isolation of the principal land-masses.

The oceans are efficient barriers to the migration of all but a small number of plants, and high mountain ranges form obstacles to the passage of plants, as do extensive arid regions such as occur in the centre of most of the continents. While mountain chains act as barriers they also may serve as highways, as for instance in the Sierra Nevada and Rocky Mountains where many arctic and sub-arctic species have migrated southward far beyond their original homes.

Many plants, however, have developed special contrivances for distributing their seeds and spores, which enable them to spread rapidly, and overcome to some degree the barriers of sea and mountain.

Many of the lower plants, including certain ferns, produce many very light spores, which retain their vitality for long periods and may be carried great distances by air-currents. Thus ferns are among the earliest plants to invade oceanic islands, where the original vegetation has been destroyed by volcanic action or otherwise.

The winged fruits and seeds of thistles, dandelions, milkweed, and many other similar plants may be borne by the wind very far from their origin and enable these weeds to spread with great rapidity, and the quickness with which they take possession of a new country when accidentally introduced by man is sufficient proof of the efficiency of their methods of seed distribution.

The winged fruits of such trees as the maple, ash and elm, are also adapted to transportation by air currents, but are too heavy to be carried long distances, except under particularly favorable circumstances.

Water transport is much less common, but nevertheless rivers, especially in flood, may transport masses of vegetation or separate fruits and seeds far from their point of origin.

Ocean currents also play a not unimportant rôle in the distribution of seeds and fruits, but this form of transportation is confined mainly to a relatively small number of maritime species. In the tropics, especially, there are a good many species, like the coconut, screw-pines, Casuarina, which usually live close to the sea-shore. These strand plants often have fruits which are provided with buoyant and water-proof envelopes which enable them to float in the salt water for a long time, without injury; and such fruits may be drifted for a very long distance before they are thrown on shore, when they quickly germinate. The coconut is the best known example, but there are others like the screw-pines, and certain leguminous species growing on the shore which have fruits adapted to water transport. In the eastern tropics, species of Barringtonia, a handsome tree belonging to the family Lecythidaceae has conspicuous fruits which are often seen floating in the sea.

Perhaps of even greater importance than air currents for transporting seeds, is the rôle played by birds and mammals in plant distribution. The many forms of adhesive fruits and seeds, like "burs," "stick-seed," "cockle-bur," etc; the bearded grains of many grasses, which adhere so tenaciously to the coats of animals—or the trousers of men—are practical demonstrations of Nature's contrivances for the dissemination of her plant children.

Occasionally there is a sticky matter by which fruits adhere, as in the mistletoe, whose glutinous berries stick to the feet or plumage of birds.

Birds undoubtedly take first place as agents of plant distribution, owing to their rapid flight. Especially in the case of plants with small edible fruits, like many kinds of berries, birds are the most important agents in spreading them. Robins, for example, devour great quantities of pulpy fruits like hawthorn berries, grapes, strawberries, etc. The seeds pass through the body undigested, and indeed in many cases, better fitted for germination than before. Owing to their powers of flight, the seeds may be discharged from the body many miles away from the parent plant, and undoubtedly such fruit-eating birds have had much to do with the rapid spread of many species.

Another way in which birds may be agents in distributing seeds and spores, is by means of mud in which seeds are imbedded. Adhering to the feet of migratory birds the mud, with its cargo of seeds, is thus carried long distances.

Finally, man, involuntarily or otherwise, has been the cause of the migration of many plants over pretty much the whole earth.[1]

MAN AND THE PLANT WORLD

Man's very existence is bound up with that of plants—whether he is a naked savage maintaining a precarious existence by means of the fruits, grains and roots he may find growing wild, or a highly civilized white man, dependent on the grains, fruits and vegetables that he has brought under cultivation.

Most of the staple food plants of civilized man are so changed by ages of cultivation that their origin is obscure; but some of them, like rice and sugar-cane, are evidently closely related to species still growing wild, and several species of wild bananas are known, some of which are probably the ancestors of the cultivated varieties. So in northern countries, the common fruits, apples, pears, cherries, plums, strawberries, etc., are evidently the improved progeny of existing wild species.

Wheat is supposed to have originated somewhere in Asia Minor, maize in Mexico, while wild potatoes of several species are common in parts of Chile and Peru.

Having brought these plants under cultivation, man has carried them with him in his wanderings, and thus has spread over the whole earth.

In addition to food plants, he had also developed many plants for their fibres, such as cotton, flax and hemp.

[1] A recent noteworthy book on plant distribution is by Dr. J. C. Willis, *Age and Area; a Study in Plant Distribution and the Origin of Species*, Cambridge, 1922.

Wherever man has settled, the original vegetation has been more or less profoundly altered. Primaeval forests once covered the sites of many a great city, and the sod of the prairies has been broken and given place to fields of corn and wheat, and the orchards and meadows of countless farms of the mid-west.

In his earliest development primitive man only took from the forest such food as he might find—fruits, nuts or roots, thus doing no more to disturb the equilibrium of the plant association than would be done by the foraging of any other animal; but as soon as he developed the most rudimentary form of agriculture, or attempted to provide grazing for animals, tame or wild, he began a warfare with the vegetable kingdom which has continued with increasing energy down to the present time.

Such primitive races of man are to be found today only in a few remote parts of the world. The Australian Blacks, and a few scanty remnants of primitive races in various tropical countries, still exist, but constitute only the merest fragment of mankind.

At a very early period in his history, man practiced a primitive form of agriculture, and so soon as he had brought under cultivation the cereals and other food plants, and had domesticated sheep and cattle, a new era was opened, and he was able to migrate far from his original home, carrying with him his cultivated food plants.

Forests were cut down to afford ground for cultivation or pasture, and the native vegetation replaced by grain fields, orchards and vineyards. Indeed the ability to carry with him food in the form of grain and herds, alone made possible the great migrations of mankind, both in former times and today.

With the facilities for transportation developed during the past century, migration has reached a stage absolutely unheard of in previous history, and the influx of millions of men into previously unoccupied regions is reflected in immense changes in the vegetation of nearly all parts of the world—far greater than in any previous period of the world's history.

Forests have been swept away until the world is menaced with a timber famine, and their place has been taken by crops of all kinds, which are entirely alien to the country and completely alter the appearance of the landscape. This disturbance of the natural vegetation is not confined to the white settler alone, but the natives of many regions, as in Central Africa, and our own western plains materially reduced the extent of forest lands, by cutting and burning—partly to increase the extent of grass-lands for grazing of cattle or wild game.

Unfortunately these primitive methods are not unknown in modern lands. The natives of our southern mountains still cut or girdle the trees to clear a corn patch, and in Australia and New Zealand sheep men burn and girdle trees to foster the growth of grass for grazing.

Of course the destruction of forests for timber or for opening land for cultivation, is necessary; but unfortunately the process has been for the most part both wasteful and injurious to the land. Particularly destructive has been the reckless clearing of mountain slopes, and the resulting washing away of the soil with floods caused by the rapid run-off which the forest cover keeps in check. The land, denuded of its good soil, remains a barren waste, while the fertile soil is carried away by the swollen streams.

The extraordinary and rapid change in the vegetation of a large area, due to man's activities is especially apparent in the United States, which a century ago was to a great extent untouched by man. The greater part of the country east of the Mississippi was covered with heavy virgin forest, and the great plains were inhabited only by scattered bands of roving Indians. Today in the eastern states the forests have given way to great cities, innumerable towns and villages, and rich farm lands, where they are not dreary deserts, the results of thriftless lumbering and forest fires.

Except for the native trees, the predominant vegetation at the present time is largely exotic. None of the staple food crops are indigenous, and the same is true for most of the common fruits, although some of the latter—like grapes and berries of various kinds,—are of native origin. Even the weeds are mostly foreigners and have driven out the native woodland plants which have retreated before these hardy invaders.

It is interesting to see, however, that given a chance, the native forest will often come back. All over the older settled regions of New England and the Middle States, the farm lands, deserted when the richer lands of the West were opened up, have already reverted to forest of the same type as that which originally covered them, while the prairies, which fifty years ago were unoccupied save by the Indians and buffalo, are now the granaries of the nation.

The deserts and mountains of this far west have as yet changed but little; but along the Pacific Coast the same changes are going on as in the Atlantic states a hundred years ago.

In California the great valleys are covered with fields of wheat, barley and alfalfa; orchards and vineyards cover the foot-hills. The climate permits the growth of many products of the warmer zones, and oranges, olives, figs and lemons thrive, as well as the apples, pears, cherries and plums of the north.

In these far western states, where a long dry summer prevails, irrigation plays an important rôle, and land naturally a desert or semi-arid, yields rich crops when water is available.

Much land in southern California, now covered with luxuriant orange orchards, and adorned with innumerable beautiful trees and shrubs brought from distant countries, was desert before the days of irrigation.

California, it is true, much more than a century ago, had introduced from Spain the orange, grape and olive, which flourished there long before it became a part of the United States.

Besides the economic plants introduced by man he has imported from all over the world a host of ornamental species which adorn his gardens. Sometimes these escape from cultivation and become quite naturalized. In the cool moist coastal regions of northern California and Oregon one meets the showy broom and foxglove of Europe—and one sees these same plants in the similar climates of central Chile and New Zealand. In the latter country the sweet briar and blackberry, introduced from England as garden plants, have escaped and become extremely troublesome weeds.

Most plants ranking as weeds, however, have been introduced accidentally, and wherever man has migrated, weeds have followed him, or been imported from divers sources. Many of the worst weeds owe their rapid dissemination to specially favorable adaptations for seed dispersal, like the wind-borne seeds of thistles and dandelions, or the hooks of burdocks and cockle bur, which stick to the coats of animals or men.

Weed seeds may come in mingled with seed grain, or in the dirt adhering to animals or in the cargo of ships and railways. Rapid transit for mankind furnishes equally quick transport for these unwelcome immigrants, and one finds the common weeds of most localities very far away from their original homes.

The thistles, burdocks, plantains, mulleins and other common weeds of the eastern United States are of European origin. In California, where the long summer is not favorable to these weeds, other species—black mustard, "filaree" (Erodium) bur clover, wild oats—have been introduced, probably from Spain, where the climate is much like that of California.

Many of these introduced plants seem to grow with increased vigor in their new home, and may largely replace the native plants.

In Australia some of the common weeds come from South Africa, Brazil, India, and one of the most troublesome, the prickly-pear cactus, is of American origin. The latter has become a very serious pest, occupying extensive tracts, especially in Queensland, and rendering them quite useless for agriculture or grazing.

Man has also been responsible for the introduction of many animal pests—injurious insects, rats and mice, rabbits, etc., which may do great damage to vegetation, and greatly affect the flora of large areas. Destructive fungi have also been introduced by human agencies, and are responsible for extensive damage to crops, or native species. A recent example of the ravages of such a fungus, is seen in the complete extermination of the native chestnut over a large part of the Atlantic states through the ravages of the fungus causing chestnut blight. It is supposed to have been introduced from China or Japan. The blister-rust of the white pine is another extremely injurious fungus which has come into the United States from Europe.

While man has been responsible for the destruction of many plants, he must also be credited with having added many new forms to those already existing. The thousands of new varieties, the result of the labors of plant breeders, are witness to man's success as a creator of new plant types.

CHAPTER II

CLIMATIC ZONES

Latitude, as might be expected, plays a very important rôle in plant-distribution, and for convenience we may recognize certain climatic zones between the poles and the equator, although, of course, these are by no means strictly limited by the parallels of latitude. These zones may be denominated: Boreal, North Temperate, Tropical, South Temperate and Austral.

The distribution of land and water is very different in the northern and southern hemispheres, and this difference is strongly reflected in the climates. It is probable, however, that this disparity has not always been so marked. At present it is particularly noticeable in the temperate zones.

At the north, all of Europe, most of Asia, North Africa and the greater part of North America lie between latitudes 25° and 60°, and land extends without a break far beyond the Arctic Circle.

In the southern hemisphere the only temperate area south of 50° is the extreme southern point of South America, while the other temperate regions, New Zealand, Australia and South Africa all lie north of 50°, and except New Zealand scarcely extend beyond 40°. To the south lies the unbroken Southern Ocean extending to the shores of the ice-bound Antarctic continent.

Due to latitude, and the proximity of the ocean, the south temperate lands, for the most part, enjoy a very mild and equable climate. Never, except at high altitudes are they subjected to the severe winter cold that prevails at corresponding latitudes in most of the north temperate zone, whose climate is, in the main, decidedly continental in character.

Melbourne, lat. 38° S. has a mean for the coldest month of 48.5°, for the warmest 67.5°; Philadelphia 39°57′ N. 32° for the coldest, 76° for the warmest; Wellington, New Zealand, 41° S., has a range only of 14.9° between the warmest and coldest months, while in Chicago, 41°53′ N., it is 48°.

The principal land-masses of the south temperate zone are

widely separated by great ocean barriers, while at the north, the two great continental masses, Eurasia and North America, are almost joined by a chain of islands, evidently indicating an even more complete connection in not very remote geologic time.

The great antarctic continent, completely isolated, and ice covered from the lofty mountains to the sea, is practically destitute of vegetation.

Very different are the conditions in the arctic regions, where far beyond the arctic circle in Greenland, Spitzbergen and Alaska, there is an abundant flora which develops rapidly during the long days of the brief summer.

Owing to the absence of any great barriers, we find that the vegetation of the higher latitudes in the northern hemisphere is relatively uniform, many species occurring throughout the range, so that the floras are very much alike in Scandinavia, Siberia and northern Canada.

There is no true antarctic flora, and the austral flora is much less developed than the corresponding vegetation of the north.

The austral or sub-antarctic flora is best developed in South America, but is also found in New Zealand and southern Australia It is quite absent from South Africa.

The sub-arctic flora merges insensibly into that of the north temperate zone, which has much the same general character throughout Eurasia and North America.

Conditions in the temperate regions of the southern hemisphere as already stated are very different and owing to the extreme isolation of South America, South Africa, and Australia, their floras are very different. It is true that there are certain correspondences pointing to former more intimate connection of the land-masses, than now exist; but the differences in the vegetation far outweigh the resemblances, and each of the three regions has an extremely individual flora, indicating a very long period of isolation.

Comparing the floras of the northern and southern hemispheres, especially in the temperate regions, it is evident that certain families and genera are either confined to one or the other, or that they predominate to such an extent as to make it pretty certain that they originated there. Thus the oaks, maples, elms, birches, poplars, sycamores, are almost exclusively northern, and the same

is true of pines and firs. The rose family, buttercups and violets
are mostly northern types, but may occur in the temperate regions
of the south. It is thought that the latter may be immigrants from
the north, which have become more or less changed by their
residence in their new habitat.

Probably of southern origin are many peculiar South American,
South African and Australian types. Among these may be
mentioned the peculiar southern conifers, the Kauri-pines
(Agathis), Araucaria and Podocarpus. The Myrtle family, which
has but few representatives in north temperate regions, is extraordinarily developed in Australia, where the genus Eucalyptus alone
has over 200 species. Two extremely peculiar families, Proteaceae
and Casuarinaceae, the former especially abundant in Australia
and South Africa, the latter mainly Australian, are quite unrepresented in the temperate regions of the north.

It is true that some of these, like Araucaria and Podocarpus,
once lived in the northern regions, from which they probably
disappeared owing to climatic changes.

It is possible that the peculiar northern and southern floras
originated at a time when there was a more or less complete separation of the mainland masses of the two hemispheres. During the
Cretaceous, at which time many existing genera are first known,
there were extensive invasions of the sea resulting in the sub-
mersion of northern South America, North Africa and much of
India, thus isolating the principal southern land-masses. About
the same time, Western Australia was probably completely
isolated, and it has been thought that many peculiar Australian
types originated in this ancient Western Australian continent.

Just what factors originally determined this segregation of the
characteristic floras of the north and south temperate zones it
would be difficult to say; but the subsequent differentiation is
undoubtedly due in large part to the very different climatic
conditions, and the much greater isolation of the southern land-
masses.

The north temperate floras for the most part are subject to a
much more severe and variable climate, but readily adapt themselves to the milder climates of the south temperate; and this may
explain the presence of such northern types as buttercups and
violets in New Zealand and Australia, while such Australian forms

as Eucalyptus and Grevillea (Proteaceae) could not adapt themselves to the rigors of a northern winter, even should they succeed in reaching these regions.[1]

In both northern and southern hemispheres there is a more or less extensive mingling of warm temperate and tropical species near the limits of the zones, and sometimes extensive migrations from one zone to the other, due to climatic or topographical reasons. Thus in New Zealand tropical genera may extend to 50°.

Vegetation reaches its maximum development within the tropics, where optimum conditions of temperature and moisture prevail. Portions of the equatorial belt, such as the great islands of the Malay Archipelago, Java, Borneo, New Guinea, the rich lowlands of the Amazon and the West Coast of Africa, exhibit the most exuberant vegetation to be found anywhere. Uniform high temperature, heavy rainfall and rich soils, combine to produce a maximum luxuriance of plant-growth, shown in dense jungles of giant trees of many species, loaded down with rampant creepers and epiphytic growths. Sometimes the shade is too dense for much undergrowth, but wherever light penetrates, there quickly develops an inpenetrable thicket of rank vegetation, and the ground is carpeted with ferns and other shade-loving plants.

It must be remembered, however, that not everywhere in the tropics does one encounter such luxuriance of growth. Regions of low rainfall, or poor soil, may consist of dreary arid grass-lands, or deserts of the most pronounced type, as in the Sahara and parts of Australia.

On the other hand, in exceptional cases due to specially favorable conditions of temperature and moisture, vegetation of decidedly tropical character may be found far beyond the actual tropics. This is particularly the case in parts of the southern hemisphere, where owing to unusually heavy rainfall, and absence of extreme cold, many tropical types have extended their range far beyond tropical latitudes, and the forests are very different from those in corresponding latitudes in the northern hemisphere.

Unlike the temperate regions of the northern hemisphere,

[1] For a fuller discussion of this question see Wallace, A. W., *Island Life*, pp. 486–487.

the tropics of the old and new worlds are widely sundered by the great oceans, and as might be anticipated, the tropical vegetation of the East and West is composed for the most part of very different elements.

There are very few common species, and to a great extent, the genera and even families differ. This is evidently the result of a very long period of isolation combined with the more intense competition which must have developed under conditions so favorable to rapid growth and multiplication.

While the superficial aspect of the equatorial forests of the old and new worlds is quite similar, nearer inspection will show a very great difference in the species of which they are composed.

THE BOREAL REGIONS

Under the name Boreal or Holarctic is included the whole of the regions lying between the Tropic of Cancer and the North Pole, but we may recognize three divisions, more or less well defined, the Arctic, Sub-arctic and North Temperate.

As might be expected from the intimate connection between the northern continents their vegetation has much in common, so that many common trees of temperate Eurasia and America, for example, are obviously related. Pines and firs, oaks, beeches, maples, willows and poplars, are characteristic of the temperate regions of both continents, and the same is true of very many shrubs and herbaceous plants.

This uniformity in the vegetation is especially marked in the arctic and sub-arctic zones, many species occurring throughout these regions, while in other cases, Eurasian species are represented in America by different, but closely related ones.

Southward the differences become more and more pronounced, owing to isolation and different climatic conditions, as well as to an intrusion of tropical or subtropical types, which differ widely in the old and new worlds.

The history of the origin and distribution of the boreal floras is revealed by a study of the abundant fossil plant remains in the Cretaceous and Tertiary rocks of both the eastern and western hemispheres.

Originating, apparently, in the far north, there is found in the early and middle Tertiary a wide-spread flora, which like the arctic and sub-arctic floras of today was very similar throughout, and occupied much the same range as the present arctic and sub-arctic vegetation.

It is clear, however, from the plants composing this "Arcto-tertiary" flora, that the climate of the far north was very much milder than at present. Trees like magnolias, laurels, gums, and other denizens of warm temperate climates lived during the middle Tertiary in Greenland and Spitzbergen where now only the hardiest of arctic plants can survive.

The arcto-tertiary flora showed a division comparable to the arctic and sub-artic zones of the present. North of 75°, the plant remains seem to be strictly boreal types, like willows, poplars, oaks, etc., but in the southern zone are found remains of palms, laurels, myrtles, now characteristic of only the warmest parts of the temperate zones.

With the increasing cold of the late Tertiary and Pleistocene, the arcto-tertiary flora which included the ancestors of most of the vegetation now occupying the north temperate regions, migrated southward, and came to occupy much lower latitudes.

This retreat was greatly accelerated by the advancing glaciers of the ice-age, and in many regions, especially in Europe and northern Asia, many forms became quite extinct, but survived in the more favorable conditions of eastern Asia and America.

With the amelioration of the climate in post-glacial time, there was a northward movement of vegetation following the retreat of the ice-sheet, and developing the modern arcto-glacial flora.

THE ARCTIC ZONE

The region surrounding the north pole is, of course, very incompletely explored; but where land occurs, it is completely ice-clad and probably quite destitute of any vegetation, except certain humble sea-weeds.

However, an unexpectedly large number of flowering plants manage to exist within a few degrees of the pole, a considerable number of species being recorded as far north as 83°.

From this region southward to where tree growth begins is the true arcto-glacial and tundra zone. Within this zone topo-

graphical conditions vary much in different regions. There are
vast expanses of barren lowlands that have apparently not been
subject to glaciation, especially in northern Siberia and parts
of northern Alaska. Most of arctic Eurasia and America, however, was covered by the great glaciers of the Ice Age, and in
these regions the lowlands are covered with lakes, swamps and
tundras—regions of frozen subsoils covered with a thick mat of
mosses and lichens among which grasses, and low prostrate
shrubs, like cranberries, rhododendrons, dwarf willows and
birches may grow. In Greenland, Iceland, Scandinavia and
Spitzbergen there are lofty mountains ice-covered to their base,
making it impossible for any plants to grow, except on the mo-
raines of the glaciers, or slopes which are free of snow for a brief
period in summer. On such exposed places, there may be an
unexpected luxuriance of vegetation, grasses and a number of
beautiful flowers—poppies, saxifrages, buttercups and others
which start into growth as soon as the snow melts.

This northernmost zone of vegetation has a growing period of
only two months, or a little more. Growth begins in June, culminates in July, and by the end of August freezing weather has
again set in.

Of course only a limited number of species can survive the
excessive cold of these regions. Vegetation consists entirely of
perennials, either herbaceous species with perennial underground
roots or root-stocks which quickly send up their leaves and flowers
during the brief period of sunshine and warmth; or else of low
prostrate shrubs, sometimes evergreen, like the cranberries or
Lapland rhododendrons, sometimes deciduous, as the dwarf willows and birches.

The degree of cold which some of these can endure is astonishing, since in some cases (as in northern Siberia), they are quite
unprotected by snow, and must survive temperatures as low as
− 60°C. (− 76°F.).

The coldest regions in which there has been found a well-marked
flora are in northern Siberia and Grinnell Land, northwest of Greenland.[1] The mean annual temperature of these regions is−16°C.
(4°F.). Even in midsummer the temperatures are very low.
In Franz Josef Land, the July mean is only 2°C., and in Spitz-

---

[1] Drude, *Handbuch der Pflanzengeographie*, pp. 352, 353.

bergen, 4°C. The period available for any plant growth is only about two months. Nevertheless there is an unexpectedly large number of species. In Spitzbergen 122 species of flowering plants are recorded, and in Greenland between 78° and 83° 88 species. At Cape Chelyuskin, the northermost point of continental Asia, 23 species of flowering plants have been noted.

The existing arcto-glacial flora was derived, presumably, from the much richer flora occupying the region to the south preceding the great ice-age. The limit of vegetation at the period of maximum glaciation was probably far south of its present latitude, but as the glaciers retreated toward the pole, the hardier species moved northward to their present habitat. Such specific changes as have taken place, were comparatively of recent date, and the arctic flora as a whole is a recent one.

The regions included in the arctic zone comprise the northern coasts of Eurasia and America with the adjacent islands, and the mountain masses immediately south. In northwest Europe, due to the invasion of the sea, and its tempering effect, the southern limits of the zone are pushed very far north, but in Russia and Siberia, and North America, arctic conditions prevail in much lower latitudes.

The limits of the strictly arctic zone have been set between the northernmost limit of vegetation—about 83°N.— regions with the July isotherm only 2°–4°C., and the regions to the south bounded by the 10°C. July isotherm.

The general type of vegetation throughout the arctic regions is very similar and most of the species extend all round the world. Where peculiar species occur in any region, they are usually closely related to wide-spread ones, and may be assumed to be of relatively recent origin. Not infrequently species which are apparently recent immigrants from the south are met with; i. e., the arctic American *Kalmia glauca*.

While the southern boundary of this zone may be said to correspond roughly with the arctic circle, it varies much in latitude, due to the differences in topography in various regions.

Thus in the great continental areas like Siberia and Canada, it lies much further south than in Scandinavia, Iceland, Greenland and western Alaska, where the proximity of the ocean water greatly tempers the climate.

In the strictly arctic regions, trees are completely wanting, and the shrubs reduced to prostrate mats, scarcely rising above the level of the ground. The bogs and tundra are largely occupied by dense growths of mosses and lichens, among which the grasses, sedges, and low shrubby growths are scattered. Where conditions are favorable there may be seen herbaceous plants, which from their perennial subterranean roots or tubers quickly start into growth in the summer and adorn the barren ground with their showy flowers. Among the characteristic flowers of the far north,

FIG. 1.—Willow thickets on the upper Killik River, North Alaska.
Photo., Dr. Philip S. Smith.

are species of buttercups, anemones, primroses, cinquefoil (Potentilla), saxifrages, poppies (*Papaver nudicaule*), and whitlow grass (Draba).

Of the woody plants, dwarf willows and birches are characteristic, and several of the heath family; e. g., Rhododendron, Cassiope, Vaccinium, Empetrum. The only conifer of the arctic regions is a dwarf juniper.

While a good many species are pretty strictly confined to the arctic zone, others like some species of cotton grass (Eriophorum) and some of the heath family, e. g., *Rhododendron lapponicum*, *Cassiope tetragona*, extend into the colder parts of the temperate zone. Other characteristic arctic species, like the pretty mountain avens (*Dryas octopetala*) and the curious arctic Pedicularis (*P. Groenlandica*), common species of the arctic lowlands, occur also as alpines in the Rocky Mountains and Sierra Nevada, while the much lower White Mountains have a few plants, e. g., *Diapensia lapponica*, natives of the far north.

We may assume that the presence of these arctic species on the mountains to the south is to be explained by the assumption that they are remnants of the wide-spread arctic flora which at the period of maximum glaciation occupied the lowlands of these lower latitudes. With the retreat of the ice-sheet, and the increasing warmth of the lowlands, some of these arctic species managed to survive by ascending the mountains until conditions were reached adapted to their needs.

Strictly arctic conditions are found in Europe only in parts of central and north Scandinavia, including parts of Lapland. In north Siberia, the most extreme arctic conditions prevail, and the lowest temperatures that have been recorded occur. In spite of this excessive cold, to which they are exposed without any snow-cover, a surprising number of species are able to survive.

The north Siberian tundra region [1] has as its commonest formation the "Moss-tundra," whose principal constitutents are mosses of the common genus Polytrichum. Among the mosses are various grasses and sedges, among them "cotton-grass" (Eriophorum), common also in cold bogs much further south. Dryas, and the heath-like *Cassiope tetragona* are characteristic of the moss-tundra.

Where there is water, true peat-bogs occur, peat mosses (Sphagnum) replacing the Polytrichum of the dry moss-tundra. On the slopes and precipices of the higher ground there is often a fairly abundant development of mats of grasses interspersed with bright flowers. Among the most notable, are species of Oxytropia, with bright yellow pea-flowers, blue Polemonium, various Saxifrages, and a showy avens (Geum). A bright blue forget-me-not (Erytrichium), is also characteristic of the Siberian arctic flora.

All of these plants grow in low compact tufts, with small leaves exposing a minimum surface to evaporation.

[1] Drude, *loc. cit.*, p. 356.

Much of the region is a desolate barren stony formation, whose sole vegetation is made up of various lichens growing on the broken rocks.

The Behring Sea tundra district is only imperfectly known; but Kjellman [1] has described 221 species from this district. Of these 53 do not extend far westward, and comprise a number of peculiar species. Others are supposed to have come from the American side of Behring Sea, and some may have been immigrants from the Baikal Mountains. Two genera also charac-

Fig. 2.—Tundra, basin of Ikpikpuk River, North Alaska.
Photo., Dr. Philip S. Smith.

teristic of western America are Claytonia and Dodecatheon, the "shooting star" of our Pacific Coast.

The western Alaska coast is much milder than corresponding latitudes on the Asiatic side, and the vegetation less pronouncedly arctic in character, although the northern part of Alaska shows climatic conditions comparable to those in Siberia. Spruces (*Picea alba*), alders and willows, extend to the polar circle, and form thickets of considerable extent, while the display of flowers is described as very remarkable. These comprise the usual arctic species, as well as species of spring beauty (Claytonia), forget-

[1] Drude, *loc. cit.*, p. 356.

me-nots and anemones. A knot-weed (Polygonum) and dock (*Rumex domestica*), have fleshy roots which are used by the natives for food.

The tundra region of Alaska and northern Canada, differs from the Siberian tundra in a much greater development of lichens, which take the place of the mosses which characterize the latter.[1] Two species of lichens, *Cetraria islandica* and *C. cucullata*, the so-called "reindeer moss," cover extensive tracts of land, and serve as the principal food of the herds of reindeer which abound in this region. With these lichens, as in the moss-tundra, are various prostrate shrubs, most of which are identical with those of the Siberian tundra, but one striking species, *Kalmia glauca*, is not found outside America.

Meadows of coarse grasses are also found in places, and in favorable localities a display of showy flowers, including a "shooting star" (Dodecatheon), one of the primrose family, especially developed in Pacific North America.

The barren islands to the north have a very meagre flora, the greater number of species being grasses.

Greenland and the adjacent regions have been more thoroughly studied than any other part of the arctic zone and belong rather to the Scandinavian region than to America. The southern part of this area is sub-arctic, and contains a good many species which hardly cross the arctic circle. One of these, the twin-flower, (*Linnaea borealis*), just reaches the arctic circle in places, and Drude[2] suggests that the northern range of this classical species, should be taken as the boundary between the arctic and sub-arctic zones.

In the sub-arctic region, thickets of willows, and in the south, alders, are a prominent feature of the vegetation. There are extensive moors covered with dwarf shrubs, and barren rocky formations where little grows except lichens. Grassy moorlands and peat-bogs occupy the more level land between the mountains and the sea, and the sandy shores are mainly occupied by a grass, *Elymus arenarius*.

Willow thickets occur as far north as 70°, and some of the herbaceous plants, e. g., Archangelica, especially in the southern portions, are of considerable size, and associated with hawkweed

[1] Drude, *loc. cit.*, p. 357.   [2] Ibid., p. 358.

(Hieracium), orchids, and other forms absent from the extreme arctic regions.

In the high northern latitudes, elevation above sea-level, apparently makes little difference in the temperature, many plants growing at altitudes of 500–600 metres or even more.

The severity of the arctic climate, and the very brief growing season, make any sort of agriculture impossible, and except for

FIG. 3.—Tundra vegetation, basin of Colville River, North Alaska.
Photo., Dr. Philip S. Smith.

the grazing afforded reindeer and musk ox, and a few edible lichens, berries and roots, the plant-life of the arctic regions offers little help to man in supporting life.

THE SUB-ARCTIC

The northernmost extension of tree-growth, the timber-line, marks the southern limit of the strictly arctic vegetation. Between the timber-line and the middle regions of the boreal area, lies a rather indefinite zone, the sub-arctic.

The number of tree species is limited, but they are often gregarious, and may form forests of great extent. Coniferous forests are a marked feature of the sub-arctic, comprising firs, spruces, pines and larches, and low-growing junipers. Of deciduous trees, birches, alders, willows and poplars characterize the more northern portions of the zone, while toward the south, oaks, beeches, hornbeams and chestnuts mark the beginning of more temperate conditions.

Like the arctic zone, the vegetation of the sub-arctic is very much alike in both hemispheres, due in part to a large intermixture of arctic species, but also to the fact that most of the sub-arctic

Fig. 4.—Northern limit of trees; white spruce, Unakserak River, lat. 68°. *Photo., Dr. Philip S. Smith.*

genera, and a good many species are common to Eurasia and America.

Throughout the zone one encounters a very characteristic forest and bog flora composed of identical or closely related species, and this flora is met with far south of the sub-arctic in the mountains, and in the colder parts of the temperate zone.

A notable feature of these northern latitudes is the abundance of club-mosses of the genus Lycopodium, most of the species occurring both in Eurasia and America. These are undoubtedly very old forms, and the same may be said of the horse-tails (Equisetum), and a number of wide-spread species of sub-arctic ferns.

Carpeting the floor of the northern evergreen forests are several familiar and attractive plants of the wintergreen family (Pyrolaceae). Several species of Pyrola, the dainty sweet scented one-flowered wintergreen (Moneses), and the "prince's pine" (Chimaphila). Associated with them are several orchids, e. g., coral-root (Corallorrhiza) and rattlesnake plantain (Goodyera). Much rarer is the beautiful *Calypso borealis*. In boggy places one may find another northern orchid, the tway-blade (Listera), and there are many other bog-plants common to the sub-arctic regions of the old and new worlds. Among these may be mentioned the sundews (Drosera), buck-bean (Menyanthes), and many grasses, sedges and rushes, as well as the species of Sphagnum and other mosses.

In the northern part of the sub-arctic, the meadows and woods have many beautiful herbaceous plants. Some of these like Hepatica and species of marsh marigold (*Caltha palustris*), cress (Cardamine), grass of Parnassus (Parnassia) dwarf cornel (*Cornus suecica*), and willow herb occur in northern Europe and in North America; more commonly the species of the old world and the new are distinct.

While forests occupy much of the sub-arctic zone, there are extensive tracts of open country, like the prairies of western Canada and the steppes of Russia and Siberia. Where moisture is abundant, swamps, bogs and lakes abound.

Within the sub-arctic zone may be included most of Scandinavia, Northern Russia, most of Siberia, Kamtchatka, Alaska and a large part of Canada and Labrador.

Like the arctic zone, the sub-arctic reaches its maximum development in Siberia where it extends, in a broad belt, from the Urals to the Pacific.[1]

The climate throughout this vast region is one of excessively cold winters and moderately warm summers, but shows a considerable range in both temperature and moisture. Much of the region is an extension of the great northern plains through which the giant rivers make their way to the Arctic Ocean, very much as in the far north of America.

To the west are the Urals, and south the great mountain ranges separating Siberia from Turkestan and Mongolia.

The Siberian flora is a poor one, composed of strictly northern types, many of which are members of the arctic flora. The monotonous forests of larch and spruce are interspersed with tundras and marsh lands, like those of the true arctic zone.

[2] Drude, *loc. cit.*, pp. 412–416.

The northernmost forest belt is made up of larch with an intermixture of pines and birches, and some spruce. Open areas are covered with tundra vegetation of quite arctic aspect, with characteristic low evergreen shrubs—Ledum, Andromeda, Rhododendron, and various others—among them the pretty twin-flower (Linnaea). Upright herbaceous plants with showy flowers—larkspur, aconite, geranium, and others—are abundant, as they are elsewhere in the sub-arctic and alpine regions.

Central Siberia, including the regions about Lake Baikal, is a country of lofty mountains, and typical Siberian flora mingles with that of the steppes of Turkestan and Mongolia. Owing to the greater moisture of much of this mountain region, as well as its proximity to the regions to the south, there is a more varied vegetation than elsewhere in Siberia. Vegetation extends high up in the mountains, plants having been collected at altitudes of 3000 to 3200 metres.

In western Siberia is a steppe region similar to that of southern Russia and the regions about the Caspian and Aral seas, but it is neither so dry nor so hot as in the latter regions.

The soil varies, being sometimes a black loam, sometimes sandy clay, and in some places alkaline.

This "birch-steppe" is so called from the groves of birches and alders which are scattered over it, somewhat like the "oak-openings" of the eastern prairies of the United States. These groves become more abundant and luxuriant in the cooler and moister climate of the north, while along the streams poplars and willows grow, and the dry steppe is replaced by prairies and bogs, which support a luxuriant growth of grasses and other herbaceous plants, including such showy flowers as Turk's-cup lilies, yellow day-lilies (Hemerocallis), anemones, and others. A giant umbellifer, *Heracleum barbatum*, is conspicuous, and much like the American "cow-parsnip" (*H. lanatum*).

Eastward from the Altai region the climate is a very severe one, and the vegetation correspondingly scanty.

The Kamtchatka peninsula forms a special province of the Siberian flora, and because of the effect of the ocean, has a much milder climate and more abundant vegetation than the adjacent mainland.

Especially interesting is the evident relationship of many species, with those of Pacific North America.

There are in parts of Kamtchatka luxuriant forests and rich meadowlands and prairies, while elsewhere there are bog-lands, conditions much resembling those of coastal Alaska. The characteristic alders, birches and willows occur as well as larches and spruces. Among the latter [1] the great tide-land spruce (*Picea Sitchensis*) of western America, and a hemlock (*Tsuga sp?*) are also suggestive of the Alaska forest. Lilies, willow-herb and other showy flowers are common, and the giant Umbelliferae, Heracleum and Angelica, are characteristic.

At elevations of about 1000 feet is a scrub forest of dwarf pines (*Pinus cembra*) mixed with junipers and alders. Here also grow two fine rhododendrons, a genus especially developed in eastern Asia.

ALASKA

The conditions in southwestern Alaska are not unlike those of northwestern Europe. Westerly winds, the numerous islands along the coast, and the deep fiords which indent it, combine to produce a climate of remarkable mildness for so high a latitude. This costal strip, moreover, is protected from the extremely severe climate of the interior by the lofty range of mountains parallel with the coast, the northern extension of the great Pacific Cordillera.

The mild climate and heavy rainfall, as well as the connection with the Pacific Coast to the south, result in a luxuriance of vegetation unequalled in any other part of the world in the same latitude, and can hardly be classed within the "sub-arctic" vegetation of other regions.

As far north as 60° and west to Kadiak Island the coastal region of Alaska supports dense forests of large trees, and a luxuriant growth of shrubs and herbaceous plants in great variety, a great contrast to the Asiatic coast in corresponding latitudes.

As the steamer makes its way through the channels between the innumerable islands of the Alaskan archipelago, they are seen to be clothed to the water's edge with a dense forest of tall evergreens, which extend to an elevation of 1000 feet or more.

The prevailing species is the Sitka spruce, also said to occur in Kamtchatka. This is the largest of all spruces, although it does

[1] Drude, *loc. cit.*, p. 417.

not attain its maximum size in Alaska. A hemlock (*Tsuga hetero-phylla*) is also abundant, and somewhat less so a cedar (*Chamae-cyparis nootkatensis*), both majestic forest trees.

Along the shore one sees masses of giant kelps (Macrocystis, Nereocystis, and others). These enormous sea-weeds are a conspicuous feature of the rocky shores of Pacific America.

The deciduous trees, alders, willows, poplars and maples, are mainly restricted to the banks of streams, the maples suggesting the proximity of a more southern flora.

FIG. 5.—Coastal forest, Southeast Alaska.

The mossy carpet of the forest floor is adorned with many of the same plants that occur in Europe and Asia, e. g., Pyrola, Linnaea, dwarf cornel and various species of Lycopodium; but in addition there are many purely American species.

Along the streams and the edge of the forest, as well as in the forest clearings is a jungle of shrubs forming impenetrable thickets. Among these are raspberries, elder, mountain ash, roses, spiraea, huckleberries and others decidedly suggestive of the temperate forests further south.

A very characteristic member of this jungle is the "Devil's

club" (*Echinopanax horrida*), whose great leaves and scarlet berries are highly ornamental, but whose hideously spiny stems, are
the terror of the woodsman, and amply justify the popular name.
This plant, and a huge aroid (*Lysichiton*), also occur in eastern
Asia, and emphasize the relations between the floras of Kamtchatka and Alaska.

Thickets of a big horse-tail (*Equisetum telmateia*) also an old-
world species, are common in low ground, and Sphagnum bogs,

FIG. 6.—Interior of Alaskan coastal forest. At right, Sitka spruce; at left,
"devil's club."

with their characteristic flora, are a common feature of the
region.

The change in the vegetation as one leaves the rainy coastal
belt and proceeds inland, is very marked. This is very clearly
seen along the railway over the White Horse Pass between Skagway and White Horse on the Yukon.

As the train ascends from Skagway, following the canyon of
the Skagway River, there is at first the luxuriant growth of trees
and shrubs characteristic of this coastal region—spruces, cedars,

and some lodge-pole pine, mingled with alders, willows, mountain-ash and birch, and various shrubs—spiraea, raspberries, roses and others. A number of pretty flowers were noted— especially an unusual abundance of the dwarf cornel (*Cornus Canadensis*).

The summit of the pass marks the timber-line, the spruces being only a few feet high, or forming prostrate mats. In early July, the creeping shoots of the dwarf arctic willow, were adorned with large and conspicuous catkins.

From the summit, the pass gradually descends to the Lake region at the headwaters of the Yukon.

This inland region, comprising parts of the Yukon Territory and Northern British Columbia, has a very different climate from that of the coast—relatively dry, and intensely cold in winter, so that the growing season is a very short one. Under such conditions it is rather surprising, therefore, to find along the Upper Yukon, a fairly abundant growth of good sized trees, mainly spruce, which furnishes lumber and fire-wood. Along the river, especially in the numerous islands, are groves of tall balsam poplars (*Populus balsamifera*), associated with thickets of alders and willows. Such forests may be seen as far north as Dawson (lat. 64°). Paper birches of fair size also occur in this region. The wide-spread lodge-pole pine (*Pinus Murrayana*), sometimes occurs in extensive stands along the Upper Yukon.

Among the characteristic shrubs, perhaps the most beautiful is a rose (*Rosa Nutkana*), very common throughout the Yukon country. Other common shrubs are species of Spiraea, Ribes, Cornus and buffalo-berry (Shepherdia). In some places a service berry (*Amelanchier sp.*) was noted. In the dryer localities a low juniper (*J. nana*) and sage-brush (*Artemisia frigida*) may be seen.

Many references have been made by visitors to these northern regions, to the profusion of showy flowers which adorn the brief summer. Some of these, like species of anemone and saxifrage, flower quickly after the snow melts; but the great majority belong to mid-summer, when they often occur in great numbers.

A good many of these northern flowers, like the fireweed (*Epilobium angustifolium*), and such woodland flowers, as Linnaea, Pyrola, and the dwarf cornel, are common throughout much of the northern United States and Canada, and the same is true of such trees as the aspens, poplars, and some of the shrubs; but many of the flowers belong entirely, or mainly to the arctic and sub-arctic zone.

Among the less familiar flowers of the Yukon country may be mentioned a very beautiful "blue-valerian" (Polemonium) which is very abundant in places, as is a species of Mertensia (*M. paniculata*), with bell-shaped flowers of the most exquisite blue. The latter is especially common at Dawson.

At White Horse, near the headwaters of the Yukon, in addition to Polemonium and Mertensia, other common plants noted were species of Aster, golden-rod, gentian, avens (Geum), rattle-weed (Astragalus) vetch, and especially some very fine blue Pentstemons.

The most striking display seen by the writer was at Lake Atlin, British Columbia.

The rocky slopes along the shore of the lake were covered with a wonderful profusion of brilliant flowers. Blue Polemonium and Pentstemons, pink roses, pale yellow Geum, orange Cotyledon, white chickweed (Arenaria) covered the broken rocky ground with sheets of vivid color.

In the moist woods, were a number of showy flowers, of which the most notable were a very handsome scarlet columbine (*Aquilegia formosà*) and a fine lupin (*Lupinus Nutkanus*).

Bogs are common and for the most part harbor the usual northern bog plants. At Carcross, on boggy hillsides along the railway between Lake Bennett and White Horse, some interesting plants were noted.

This was a moss-bog, but contained no Sphagnum. There were some interesting orchids, notably a very pretty white lady-slipper (*Cypripedium sp.*), and the round leaved orchis (*Orchis rotundifolia*). The white mountain avens (*Dryas sp.*) still showed a few flowers, and the pretty violet-like flowers, the butter-wort (Pinguicula), were at their best. The white tufts of the cotton grass, and the exquisite starry flowers of the grass of Parnassus, which was very abundant, recalled similar bogs further south.

In this neighborhood were noted some fine specimens of a large-flowered willow-herb (Epilobium) which was also very abundant in the river-bed at Skagway.

Some of the coastal plants like the Sitka spruce follow the

canyons of the rivers into the mountains, but the forests of the Yukon country are very different from those of the coastal belt. The drier forest is made up mostly of white spruce (*Picea Canadensis*), the northernmost Alaskan conifer, and associated with this are paper birch, bâlsam poplars and aspens. Two characteristic Rocky Mountain conifers reach Alaska—the lodge-pole pine (*Pinus Murrayana*) and a balsam fir (*Abies lasiocarpa*).

The swampy ground is often covered with dreary forests of black spruce (*P. Mariana*). These spruce-bogs, known locally as "muskegs" are a characteristic feature of the Canadian northwest. The sub-soil is permanently frozen, and the surface soil in consequence is saturated. Travelling between the northern Canadian Rockies and the coast of British Columbia, one becomes sufficiently familiar with these dreary spruce bogs.

As there are no high mountains east of the Rockies, the flora of the vast region between the northern Rocky Mountains and the Atlantic coast, including the basin of the Mackenzie River, the regions about Hudson Bay, and Labrador, is very much the same and quite similar to that of inland Alaska.

The arctic tundras reach their southern limit in Labrador, whose flora has a good deal in common with Greenland, and at the south merges into the forest flora of Quebec and Ontario.

In the west, the wooded area of the sub-arctic zone is confined to the more northern regions and passes gradually into the prairies of Saskatchewan, Alberta and Manitoba. Eastward the increasing precipitation permits forest growth throughout, and there is a gradual transition southward into the mixed forests of Quebec, Ontario, and the northern United States.

Immediately east of the northern Rockies lies the great plain drained by the Mackenzie and its tributaries, a region of swamps, tundras and innumerable lakes, some like the Great Slave and Athabaska, of great size, passing at the south into the prairies of western Canada.

Much of the northern district is forested, with white and black spruce, scrub pine (*P. Banksiana*), tamarack (*Larix Americana*), and balsam fir. Paper birch, balsam poplar and aspen are the common deciduous trees. Willows and alders border the streams, and other shrubs, honeysuckle, roses, currants, wild cherries, Viburnum, buffalo-berry (Shepherdia), snow-berries (Symphoricarpus) dwarf junipers, and others form an undergrowth in the forest.

The shallow water near the lake shores is a marsh, in which are bulrushes (*Scirpus sp.*) bur-reeds (Sparganium) cat-tails (Typha), various sedges and grasses, and the pond-weeds, water milfoil, and other common water-plants of northern regions. Yellow water-lilies (Nuphar) also occur.

The region between Lake Winnipeg and Hudson Bay is largely a region of swamps in which willows and tamaracks are the prevailing trees. East of Hudson Bay are the barren grounds of Labrador, a region of tundras, barren moorlands and rocky hills. At about 55°, tree-growth practically stops, but the southern part of Labrador has a forest of the same type as that of the Mackenzie region.

Newfoundland in its western portion has much in common with Labrador, but owing to the effect of the surrounding ocean, the climate, especially in the east and south is much milder, and many species are found which belong to the temperate flora, rather than that of the sub-arctic zone.[1]

---

[1] For a full account of the sub-arctic American flora, see Harshberger, J. W., *Die Vegetation der Erde*, Vol. XIII.

CHAPTER III

THE NORTH TEMPERATE ZONE

EURASIA AND NORTH AFRICA

The line between the sub-arctic and north temperate is a very ill-defined one. In western America, and western Europe, temperate conditions prevail much further north than in Asia or eastern America; but in general one may place the southern limit of the sub-arctic at about 55°.

Between this and 30°, where sub-tropical conditions begin, is a vast expanse of land. Nearly all of Europe, except parts of Scandinavia and Russia, lie between these latitudes, which include also the Mediterranean littoral of Africa, the major part of Asia south of Siberia, and practically the whole of the United States and southern Canada.

A large part of the sub-arctic flora, including all the trees, extends into the temperate zone, where the pines, firs, spruces, and larches; the poplars, birches, and willows, mingle with the beeches, maples, oaks, and other characteristic trees of the temperate zone. As all of these are represented by similar, if not identical species in Eurasia and America, the forests of the higher latitudes of the temperate zone have a general similarity of aspect, although very few species are common to the old and new worlds.

The same is true of many shrubs and herbaceous plants, e. g., roses, honeysuckles, dogwoods, raspberries, elders, viburnums, etc.; violets, lilies, buttercups, anemones, clovers, and many other familiar flowers; but there are many genera which are peculiar, or much less wide-spread. Thus America has no Narcissus, snow-drops, foxglove, broom or heath; while Europe has no mountain laurel (Kalmia), blood-root (Sanguinaria), Pentstemon or Trillium, and other lists could be extended indefinitely.

These differences become more and more pronounced as we proceed southward, until the differences become much more pronounced than the resemblances.

WESTERN AND CENTRAL EUROPE

From the Baltic on the north to the great southern barrier of the Pyrenees, Alps and Carpathians, the whole of western and Central Europe constitutes a natural botanical province throughout which are found a large number of characteristic species.

Within this area there is a good deal of difference in topography and climate, but the mountains, such as the Vosges and Harz are only of moderate height, never rising to regions of perpetual snow, and not forming barriers to the distribution of plants.

The west coast, and the British Islands enjoy a comparatively equable climate, with much less severe winters and hot summers than the more easterly parts of the area. The effect of the proximity of the ocean, and the prevailing westerly winds, together with the trend of the Gulf Stream, is evident in the very equable climates of the west coasts of the British Islands, southern Iceland, and Norway, which have extraordinarily mild winters considering their high latitude. The contrast between the cool summers and mild winters of the south of England and west Ireland, and the hot summers and frigid winters of Poland is sufficiently striking.

Much of Europe was originally forested but with the development of the dense populations now occupying it, practically all of the original forest has disappeared except in such remote regions as northern Russia or in the higher mountains.

The forests of central Europe are much poorer in species than those of temperate North America. Probably the most wide-spread tree is the Scotch pine (*Pinus sylvestris*), which extends from the sub-arctic zone to the Alps and Pyrenees, and is pretty generally distributed through the whole of central and western Europe and the British Islands. The Norway spruce (*Picea excelsa*) and silver fir (*Abies pectinata*), are also very widely spread. Less abundant is the yew (*Taxus baccata*), and the common juniper, which can hardly rank as a tree, is perhaps the most wide-spread of all conifers.

Much of the forest is composed exclusively of deciduous species. First in importance are two oaks, *Quercus pedunculata* and *Q. sessiliflora*, sometimes regarded as simply varieties of a single species, *Q. robur*. Oak forests are characteristic of a large part of western and central Europe and the British Islands.

Next in importance is the beech (*Fagus sylvatica*), common throughout northern Europe and often forming pure forests of great extent. The elm (*Ulmus campestris*), and ash (*Fraxinus excelsior*) are large and important trees, but less common than the beech and oak. Lindens and maples also occur in this area. The Norway maple (*Acer platanoides*) and the sycamore maple (*A. pseudo-platanus*), are trees of good size.

In the southern part of central Europe the chestnut (*Castanea vesca*) is an important forest tree, but is still more abundant south of the Alps and Pyrenees, and in the mountains of the Mediterranean littoral.

Among the smaller and less important trees are crab-apples, wild plums and cherries, mountain ash, hornbeam, hawthorn, and others, as well as the willows, poplars, birches and alders of the sub-arctic zone.

In regions of poor soil there are often stretches of open country of great extent, forming heaths or moorlands covered with low growing shrubs mostly belonging to the heath family; huckleberries, heather and others are sometimes mixed with the prickly gorse (Ulex) and bracken fern. The British moors when the common heather (*Calluna vulgaris*), or the golden gorse cover them with sheets of purple and gold, is a sight not soon to be forgotten.

The regions immediately adjacent to the Alps and Carpathians include some of the most beautiful scenery in Europe. South Germany, Switzerland and Austria are sufficiently familiar to European tourists.

Although the original forest has mostly disappeared, re-afforestation has been developed extensively, as in the Black Forest and many other regions; but the greater part of the country is closely cultivated, or occupied by meadows and pasture-land. The traveller passing through this region in the early summer is at once struck by the beauty of the flower-decked grass-lands. A little later, the grain fields are gay with scarlet poppies and blue cornflowers. Some of the meadow flowers like the tall buttercups and daisies, have become naturalized in the United States; but most of the European field flowers have failed to establish themselves in America, although some of them are seen in our gardens.

Among the common meadow flowers are various yellow hawkweeds (*Hieracium spp.*), as well as other Compositae, e. g.,

Centaurea, thistles, blue Salvias, and Campanulas, pink catchfly (Silene, Lychnis); cowslips, geraniums, pinks (Dianthus), orchids, and numerous Umbelliferae.

Many of the early spring flowers of the European woods and meadows, are also quite different from those of the eastern United States. It is true that in both regions, violets, spring cress, hepatica, anemones, buttercups and marsh marigolds abound; but the primroses and cowslips; the snowdrops, crocuses and narcissus, the Christmas roses and wild hyacinths and fritillaries, are absent from our eastern woods and meadows. So also are the foxgloves, scabious, poppies, and cornflowers of the early summer, except as these are occasionally escapes from the garden.

Travelling eastward down the Danube, one enters the great Hungarian Plain, reminding one strongly of our own prairie region. This resemblance is increased by the great fields of maize, which might be in Kansas or Nebraska. The climate of this region is a decidedly continental one, much like the central United States, and the most abundant shade-tree of the region is an American one, the common locust, which seems very much at home in central Europe.

To the east of the Carpathians, lie the similar plains of Rumania and southern Russia.

The forests of the Carpathian region and the Balkans, are much richer in tree-species than the rest of central Europe, and a much greater amount of the original forest still persists. Most of the northern European trees reach this region, but in addition there are a good many other species both of conifers and deciduous trees and shrubs.

Several species of oaks, e. g., the Turkey oak (*Quercus cerris*), and *Q. Austriaca*, belong to this region, and are often predominant. Beeches are abundant in some localities, but seldom occur in pure stands. With these are mingled hornbeams (Carpinus, Ostrya), elms, maples of several species, lindens, especially the silver linden (*Tilia argentea*), and chestnut. These make up a forest very much like the typical eastern American hardwood forest. Crab-apples, wild plums, cherries and pears also occur, and a number of handsome shrubs, some of which are in cultivation, are native to this region. Showy yellow brooms (*Cytisus, spp.*), roses, hawthorns, hazel, elder, barberry, buckthorn (*Rhamnus*), and in some localities, lilacs are characteristic. The smoke-bush (*Rhus cotinus*) and flowering ash (*Fraxinus ornus*) also belong to this region.

A truly alpine vegetation is richly developed in the high mountains which separate central Europe from the Mediterranean countries. The Alps, Pyrenees, and Carpathians reach high above the snow-line, and in these regions a numerous and beautiful high alpine flora is found. Many species are identical with arctic ones, but many others are peculiar to these high altitudes and each alpine district has many species peculiar to it.

Near Vienna is a mountain, Schneeberg, only about 2000 metres in height, but at the summit having a number of true alpine species. A visit to this mountain about the middle of June showed the snow was not yet all gone, and one found such typical alpine species as *Anemone alpina, Ranunculus alpestris, Soldinella, Gentiana verna, G. acaulis, Primula auricula,* and others.

Lower down the mountain were columbines, kingcups (Trollius), Clematis, forget-me-nots, *Pedicularis sp.* and other sub-alpine species. Of course in the higher Alps the number of strictly alpine forms is much greater.

In Switzerland the high alpine region above 2600 m. has according to Drude [1] 388 species, of which 150 are arctic species, the others strictly alpine.

The alpine region sometimes shows open grassy expanses, or meadows, beset with low growing plants, mostly dicotyledons, such as anemones, primroses, buttercups, gentians, etc., with relatively large and vividly colored flowers.

Monocotyledons are less abundant as alpines. Among the commonest of these (apart from grasses and sedges), are the false hellebore (Veratrum), a few species of onions (Allium), and a small number of inconspicuous orchids.

Of the dicotyledons, the Compositae, as usual, are the most abundant, for the most part familiar types like the dandelions, hawkweeds, flea-bane (Erigeron), asters, Arnica, golden-rods, mostly yellow in color, except Aster and Erigeron. To the Compositae belongs also the Edelweiss (*Leontopodium alpinum*) and the low growing thistle-like Carlinia, a very common plant of the lower elevations.

[1] *Loc. cit,* p. 378.

The many rock-plants found at the higher altitudes constitute a very characteristic type of the alpine vegetation. These
include various lichens and mosses, and a few small ferns, as
well as numerous flowering plants, many of them related to
those also found in the open meadows, such as gentians, Silene,
Campanula, etc. Other genera like the saxifrages and stone-
crops, and the little alpine poppies, are usually rock-plants.
These are densely tufted, or form rosettes of leaves close to the
ground, from which the flower-stalks arise.

The snow-line in the Alps is about 10,000 feet elevation (3250 m.)
but a considerable number of species may occur above this.
Schroeter [1] lists 110 species in this category.

Between the strictly alpine regions, and the lowlands, is an
intermediate region, varying much in elevation, and other conditions, and supporting a very rich and varied sub-alpine flora.
The beauty of the sub-alpine meadows of Switzerland and
Tyrol is proverbial.

About the end of June the meadows are solid beds of beautiful flowers in amazing variety, which almost entirely conceal
the grass amid which they are growing. A little later, the grass
grows above the mass of gay bloom, and flowers and grass are
cut down together for hay.

Among the beautiful meadow flowers noted by the writer at
Cortina, in the Dolomite region of Tyrol, toward the end of June,
were great masses of pale yellow pansies, forget-me-nots, scabious,
orchids of several species, many Umbelliferae, various clovers,
vetches, lotus, and other Papilionaceae, many campanulas, daisies,
buttercups, hawkweed, gentians, and in the lower, wet places, grass
of Parnassus (*Parnassia*), cotton-grass (Eriophorum) and an
orchis.

In the adjacent woods, were many wood-anemones (*A. nem-
orosa*), and hepatica, but the latter out of flower; kingcups
(*Trollius*), marsh-marigold, spotted orchis, lily of the valley,
Solomon's seal. The only European lady's slipper (*Cypripedium
calceolus*) also grows near Cortina as well as two lilies (*Lilium
martagon and L. bulbiferum*), but the latter was not yet in bloom.
The pretty white St. Bruno's lily (*Liliastrum*), however, was
in full flower, and very attractive.

[1] Schroeter, C., *Das Pflanzenleben der Alpen*, pp. 612–613, Zürich, 1908.

At higher elevations gentians were abundant, especially the exquisite *Gentiana verna*, and the gentianella (*G. acaulis*), the alpine rhododendrons, "alpine rose" were common, as well as an attractive fragrant pink Daphne (*D. cneorum*).

THE BRITISH ISLANDS

The climate of the British Islands is much more equable than that of continental Europe in the same latitudes. Owing to the close proximity of the Gulf Stream to the west coasts of Great Britain and Ireland, these regions, in spite of their high latitude, have very mild winters, frost being rare in the southwest of Ireland and much of western Scotland. Many plants thrive in these regions, as well as in the south of England, which cannot endure the severe winters of continental Europe. In the southwest of Ireland are a number of native plants common to Spain and the Mediterranean regions, the best known being the strawberry tree (*Arbutus Unedo*), a near relative of the Californian madroño (*A. Menziesii*).

The western regions of Great Britain and Ireland, have a very heavy rainfall, which combined with the absence of severe cold, makes these regions particularly adapted to the growth of many exotic broad-leaved evergreens, such as the laurels, rhodendendrons, and many New Zealand and Chilean evergreens. Coniferous trees of many species do remarkably well, and one may see fine specimens of Araucarias from Chile, redwoods and Douglas firs from the Pacific Coast, cedars of Lebanon, and many others.

The indigenous trees, however, are few in number, and comprise none not found also on the continent.

The meadows and woodlands are very attractive in the spring with the primroses and bluebells in the woods, and the cowslips and daisies in the meadows, the hedges white with hawthorn bloom. But all of these are common to most of temperate Europe, and Britain has very few species peculiar to it.

Much of Ireland and Scotland is occupied by bare moorlands and bogs, in which the cool damp climate induces extensive peat-formation, rendering much of the country unsuitable for agriculture.

The highest mountains of Britain scarcely exceed 4,000 feet, and there is no true alpine vegetation; but on account of the high latitude there are a few arctic and sub-arctic species which are found in the higher mountains of Scotland.

As a whole, the British flora can hardly be considered a rich one.

The Mediterranean Flora

The Mediterranean region of Europe is very effectively protected on the north by the high mountain ranges, and has a very different climate from central Europe. Very mild winters are the rule, and most of the rainfall is during the cooler half of the year, the summers being in many parts nearly or quite rainless.

In the most protected districts, like the south of Spain, southern Italy and Sicily, the climate is especially adapted to the growth of oranges and lemons, and throughout most of the Mediterranean littoral, the olive, fig, and vine flourish.

As might be expected, exotics from many lands of similar climate are at home about the Mediterranean. Palms from Egypt, California and China; Cacti and century plants from Arizona and Mexico; Eucalyptus and Acacias from Australia; pepper-trees and Bougainvillea from South America; Geraniums, Callas, Gladioli, Aloes, Mesembryanthemums, other showy flowers from South Africa, mingle with the native oaks and pines, and the roses, carnations and other familiar flowers in the gardens.

Drude [1] includes in the Mediterranean province, the islands off the west coast of Africa, i. e., Azores, Madeira and the Canaries, and all of Asia Minor as far as Persia and Mesopotamia.

The regions most familiar to travellers are those immediately bordering on the Mediterranean. The European shores are mostly mountainous, and the bold coastal scenery of the French and Italian Riviera, southern Italy, Sicily, Dalmatia and Greece includes many world famous views.

At the lower elevations the vegetation is largely evergreen. Among the commonest trees are the evergreen or Ilex oak (*Quercus Ilex*), the stone-pine (*Pinus Pinea*) and the similar *P. pinaster;*

[1] *Loc cit.*, p. 388.

olives and cypresses. Deciduous trees, e. g., elms and poplars, are by no means absent, and at moderate elevations in the mountains there are sometimes extensive chestnut forests, whose nuts are a very important article of food. In the highest mountains most of the central European trees are found.

In northern Italy, including the beautiful lake region, quite a different climate prevails from that of the sea-coast. There is a much greater range of temperature than in the maritime districts, and a much heavier precipitation, especially in the lake region. There is an abundant summer rainfall, and the climate is very much like that of the warmer Atlantic United States, so that it is not surprising to find such characteristic American trees as the tulip-tree, black walnut and various oaks growing with unusual luxuriance in the parks of Milan and the gardens of the villas about Como.

A very characteristic formation on the Riviera and elsewhere about the Mediterranean is the "Macchia" clothing the hillsides with a dense thicket of evergreen, often thorny shrubs, like the "chaparral" of the Californian mountains. The macchia is made up of a great variety of shrubs, many very ornamental. Among these are the Arbutus, laurels, heaths, rock-roses (*Cistus spp.*), brooms, and others often seen in cultivation, as well as some not so familiar.

The only native European palm, *Chamaerops humilis*, not unlike the scrub palmettos of Florida, occurs in the warmest parts of the Mediterranean littoral. It is especially common in southern Spain and Sicily.

Many showy bulbous and tuberous plants abound in the Mediterranean region, and are more or less familiar in cultivation. Among these are magnificent blue and scarlet anemones, various species of narcissus and tulips, crocuses and snowdrops, gladioli and iris, as well as some attractive ground orchids.

The Mediterranean region is preëminently the land of the vine and olive, both of which are native, and cultivated from time immemorial. Wheat is universally cultivated, and in many regions, maize is now a very important crop. Rice is also grown both in Spain and Italy. Fruits and vegetables of many kinds are an important element in the diet of all Mediterranean peoples.

Especially in the south of France, the cultivation of flowers on a commercial basis is a very important industry. Immense quantities of cut flowers are shipped from the Riviera to Paris and London, and certain fragrant flowers like violets, lavender, jasmine, etc., are grown in great numbers for the manufacture of perfume.

THE IBERIAN PENINSULA [1]

The Iberian Peninsula, Spain and Portugal, forms a very distinct botanical province in which the Mediterranean flora is predominant over much of the area, but which has also a strong element related to western and central Europe. Owing to its isolation it has an unusually high percentage of endemic species.

Except for the lofty Pyrenees separating it from France, the whole of the peninsula is bounded by the Atlantic Ocean and the Mediterranean, which exercise a great influence on the climate of the coastal regions.

The greater part of the peninsula is occupied by a plateau, between 2,000 and 3,000 feet elevation. This plateau, being largely cut off from the coast by mountains, has a very different climate. It is divided into a northern and southern portion, which differ considerably in their climate and flora.

The plateau is highest on its eastern side sloping somewhat gradually to the west, before descending to the lowlands of Portugal, which are drained by the Douro and Tagus, flowing between ranges of considerable elevation.

The southern edge of the plateau is bounded by the Sierra Morena, between which and the lofty coastal Sierra Nevada, is the broad Andalusian plain, watered by the Guadalquivir, a region of great fertility.

The northern and northwestern coasts are extremely rugged, the mountains often coming down to the sea, and this region, together with the Pyrenees, is the rainiest part of the peninsula.

Contrasted with this is the eastern or Mediterranean coast, which has for the most part a scanty rainfall, and in places is so arid as to warrant the appellation of steppes, which is also true of much of the eastern plateau. Arid conditions prevail over much

[1] For a detailed account of the flora of Spain and Portugal, see Willkomm, . M., *Pflanzenverbreitung auf der iberischen Halbinsel*, DIE VEGETATION DER ERDE, Vol. I, 1896.

PLATE I.—Olives and Carob, Island of Majorca. *Photo., Dr. H. Knoche.*

of the Ebro valley, a broad plain between the base of the Pyrenees and the range bounding the plateau to the west.

Salt marshes, sandy beaches and extensive dunes occur in certain parts of the coast, e. g., Portugal and southern Spain; but along the Mediterranean the coast is much like that of southern France and Italy.

The varied topography of the peninsula is reflected in its climate. The whole coast enjoys a mild climate, this being most evident in the extreme south, the southernmost point of continental Europe, with the warmest winter climate. The contrast between the climate of this part of Spain, and that of the bleak elevated plateau may be shown by comparing Madrid and Gibraltar. The average winter temperature for the former is 5.2°C., the summer, 29.9°C.; for Gibraltar, 12.5° and 22.6°, about the same as Los Angeles.

The rainfall varies from 1,647 mm. at Santiago in the mountains of the northwest coast, to 275 mm. at Salamanca, in the northern plateau.

This great difference in temperature and precipitation, as well as the marked differences in elevation and soil, result in a flora of great richness, with a higher degree of endemism than is found anywhere else in Europe.

This is clearly shown in the forest flora, for although only about 5% of the peninsula is forested, there are more species of trees than in any other European country.

As one enters Spain from the north, one passes through the gorges of the Pyrenees, well-wooded, and evidently having abundant rainfall. The general aspect of the forest is that of central Europe, the same deciduous trees, oak, ash, and chestnut predominating, while silver fir, Scotch and Austrian pines are the prevailing conifers. The deciduous forest and the Scotch pine are characteristic of the lower elevations, while the firs and *Pinus laricio*, are found in the higher regions.

There is an abundant alpine flora in the Pyrenees, many of the species being the same as those of the Alps; but there are also a good many endemic species as well.

While much of the vegetation of the lower slopes of the Pyrenees is evidently related to that of central Europe, there is an intermingling of forms belonging to the Mediterranean flora, such as Arbutus, the laurestinus (*Viburnum tinus*), and laurels.

Travelling southward, one soon enters the great table land which makes up the greater part of Spain. The northern part of the plateau has sufficient rainfall for the growth of grain, especially wheat and barley, and this is the great granary of Spain, reminding one of the great wheat fields of Kansas or the Dakotas. Like our prairie states, the plains are quite destitute of trees, and only in the beds of streams, does one see elms, poplars, alders and willows.

Madrid and Toledo lie in an arid region, which might be called a desert. The barren often saline soil supports only the scantiest vegetation, such as salt-bush (Atriplex and Salsola), species of plantain, Gypsophila, Lepidium, Sonchus, Lavatera, and several Leguminosae. The great stretches of gray barren plain are most depressing, and the climate extremely trying.

The southern plateau has a much better climate, and here for the first time one meets the olive, growing in veritable forests, as well as vines, figs, peaches, pomegranates and apricots, and in specially sheltered regions, oranges.

A feature of the landscape of the southern plateau is the extensive woods of evergreen cork oak (*Quercus suber*) whose bark is an important article of commerce.

It is in the coastal regions, especially at the south that one finds the most favorable condition for the growth of sub-tropical vegetation. About Seville or Gibraltar one sees the same ornamental plants that one sees in Santa Barbara or San Diego; and as in southern California, irrigation is necessary.

Besides the usual products of the Mediterranean, rice and cotton are also grown to some extent, and the date palm is more extensively grown than anywhere else in Europe.

Eucalyptus and pepper trees are common, and in Gibraltar one is struck by a curious shade tree the "Bella Sombra," a native of Argentina, closely related to the common "poke-weed" of the eastern United States.

Two conspicious American plants have escaped from cultivation and became thoroughly naturalized, the prickly-pear cactus, and the century plant (Agave), both probably introduced from Mexico. The prickly-pear is a serious pest in some places.

The extreme south of Spain, as might be expected from its close proximity to Morocco, has much in common with northern Africa, both in its climate and vegetation, the floras of the two sides of

the straits of Gibraltar being very much alike. The climate is
especially favorable for all kinds of Citrus fruits, and even bananas
will ripen in some localities; and sugar cane and cotton, are among
the products of this region. Raisins and figs are produced in large
quantities, and in the hot dry regions of the southern Mediterranean coast, date palms thrive and ripen their fruit as well as in
Morocco or Algeria.

Forests

The forests of Spain are largely restricted to the mountainous
districts. In the higher parts of the Pyrenees there are forests of

Fig. 7.—Ilex oak, Island of Majorca. *Photo., Dr. H. Knoche.*

silver fir and Norway spruce, but except for an endemic fir (*Abies
Pinsapo*) restricted to a limited area in the higher mountains of
southern Spain, the conifers are all species of pines, of which perhaps the stone pine (*P. pinea*) is the most notable. This species
and the somewhat similar *P. pinaster*, are common over most of
the Mediterranean littoral. In the south occurs also the Aleppo
pine, *P. Halepensis.*

The deciduous forests are especially characteristic of the northern mountain regions. The predominant trees are chestnuts,

beeches, and oaks of several species. Further south these are replaced by evergreen oaks, including the Ilex oak, and cork oak, and next in importance is the olive, which forms extensive woods in a wild state, and is widely planted for its fruit.

The forests, especially in the drier regions, are open, with much undergrowth, and the trees of small size; and all gradations between these open woods, and trees growing alone, or in small groups, may be met with.

Much of the drier country in Spain is covered with a more or less dense growth of shrubs and undershrubs. In the cooler districts of the northwest are extensive heaths composed entirely of species of Erica, but more commonly these shrub formations are composed of a variety of forms, such as woody labiates like lavender and rosemary; rock roses (Cistus); many species of broom and other woody Papilionaceae. The woody Labiatae are remarkably abundant and make an important element in the Spanish flora, and the genus Cistus is also represented by many species, which often forms pure stands of great extent.

Among the most showy of the Spanish shrubs are the many species of broom (Cytisus, Genista, Spartium), covered with masses of vivid golden bloom. The "Spanish broom," *Spartium junceum*, often seen in cultivation, is one of the most abundant species.

Another showy shrub, abundant along stream banks in southern Spain, is the common oleander.

The following[1] are the largest families given in order: 1. Compositae; 2. Papilionaceae; 3. Gramineae; 4. Cruciferae; 5. Labiatae.

Ths islands of the Mediterranean, viz.: the Balearic Islands, Sardinia, Corsica and Sicily, Cyprus and Crete, while showing a small percentage of endemic species, have a flora made up for the most part of wide-spread species common to the adjacent mainland.[2]

[1] Willkomm, *loc. cit.*, p. 64.
[2] Knoche, H., *Flora Balearica, Etude Phytogeographique sur les Iles Baleares*, 1923.

NORTHERN AFRICA [1]

The western Mediterranean regions of Africa, both in topography and climate, much resemble the opposite European coast, this being especially the case in Spain, which is separated from Morocco only by the narrow Straits of Gibraltar. As might be expected, a great many species in Morocco and Algeria, are

FIG. 8.—Chaparral formation, "Macchia," Island of Minorca. *Cistus monspeliensis*, dominant; *Myrtus communis, Pistacia Lentiscus, Olea sylvestris, Phyleria angustifolia. Photo., Dr. H. Knoche.*

either identical with European ones, or closely related to them. These, however, are associated with many species of undoubted African origin.

Parallel with the coast is an extensive system of mountain ranges, beginning in western Morocco, and extending to Tunis. These mountains are highest in Morocco, culminating in the Great Atlas, probably exceeding 12,000 feet elevation.

In Algeria there are two main ranges, the maritime Atlas, and the Saharan Atlas whose highest peaks are less than 8000 feet,

[1] Engler, A., *Die Pflanzenwelt Africas*, DIE VEGETATION DER ERDE, Vol. IX, 1910.

and between them is a barren plateau with an elevation of about 3,000 feet.

Back of the coast extends for fifty miles or more a broken region, the "Tell," largely covered in its original state, by a dense growth of evergreen shrubs, the "macchie" of the Italian Riviera, and composed largely of the same species.

Further inland there is a decided falling off in the rainfall, and

FIG. 9.—Dwarf palm (*Chamaerops humilis*) Cala Retjada, Majorca.
Photo., Dr. H. Knoche.

the base of the Great Atlas of Morocco is occupied by a barren steppe. In Algeria this drier zone is characterized by the presence of the Aleppo pine (*Pinus Halepensis*), two junipers and a peculiar conifer, *Callitris quadrivalvis*, the only representative of a genus, otherwise restricted to the southern hemisphere.

Where the rainfall exceeds 60 cms., woods of cork oak and olives occur on the lower slopes of the mountains, and in the drier districts extensive growths of the scrub palms occur as they do in southern Spain and Portugal. The Carob (*Ceratonia siliqua*) is also a common tree.

In moist ground, both in the lowlands and hills, elms, poplars, ash, oleander and laurel are found, and in the mountains, from 3,000 to 4,000 feet, there is developed a forest containing a variety of trees both evergreens and deciduous.

First in interest is the Atlas cedar (*Cedrus Atlantica*) often considered to be merely a variety of the cedar of Lebanon. Associated with this are several oaks (*Quercus ballota, Q. lusitanica*) species common to Spain, and also the fir *Abies Pinsapo*, also a

Fig. 10.—Aleppo pine, Cap Formentor, Majorca. *Photo., Dr. H. Knoche.*

tree found elsewhere only in Spain. The yew also occurs in these mountains, and many other types common to central Europe, e. g., holly, almond, chestnut, bird-cherry, crab-apple, honeysuckle, maple, goose-berry. Nowhere in Africa are the boreal types so abundant as in the mountains of Morocco and Algeria.

The alpine floras are poorly developed, but in the highest parts of the Atlas, there is a considerable number of alpine or subalpine species which are identical with those in the Pyrenees and Sierra Nevada of Spain, or even the western Alps. In the highest altidudes of the Great Atlas are also several endemic species.

The barren plateau region is very poor in species, the most characteristic being coarse tussock grasses, of which one, the "Halfa grass" (*Stipa tenacissima*) is of importance in paper making. The steppes may be rocky, sandy or saline, with corresponding differences in the vegetation, which is everywhere meagre. Trees are absent, and occasional shrubs, tamarisk, pistache or tall stalks of fennel, are all that break the monotony of the barren wastes.

Fig. 11.—Mt. Atlas cedar, Algeria. *Photo., Dr. W. A. Cannon.*

In the drier regions to the south the vegetation becomes more decidedly African in character, cactus-like Euphorbias, Mesembryanthemums, Acacias, and others being features of the flora.

The south side of the Saharan Atlas exposed to the hot dry winds of the Sarhara has very scanty vegetation, and the great Sahara itself is notoriously barren.

From Tripoli eastward, there are no mountains of importance and the shores of the Mediterranean are largely made up of sandy beaches and dunes. The rainfall diminishes rapidly eastward, and the desert reaches to the sea coast. In the oases, there is a limited number of plants, aside from the date-palms. Among these may be mentioned tamarisk, colocynth (*Citrullus colocynthus*), docks, capers, Reseda, mesquit (Prosopis), Cassia, Astragalus, Convolvulus and various grasses.[1]

The rich lands of the Nile delta are intensively cultivated, and yield abundant crops of clover, beans, rice, cotton, sugar and flax, as well as the usual fruits of the Mediterranean. Tamarisk, willows, acacias and the sycamore fig are common, and water-

FIG. 12.—Edge of desert, Algeria. Village with date-palms in background.
Photo., Dr. W. A. Cannon.

plants of many kinds, including the lotus (*Nymphaea lotos*) abound.

The climate of Morocco and Algeria is very similar to that of southern California. With the autumn rains, the dominant vegetation starts into life, and the lower mountain slopes and valleys are quickly covered with fresh grass and many showy flowers. There is a great development of bulbous or tuberous plants. Gladioli, Iris, Narcissus, star-of-Bethlehem, etc., which come up quickly, some like the colchicums and species of Narcissus, flowering in the autumn, others continuing through the winter and early

[1] For details of the desert floras, see Engler, *loc. cit.*, Vol. I, pp. 15–45.

spring, when the numerous annuals flower in great profusion, making brilliant masses of color, like the poppies and lupins of the California spring. Some of these, like the scarlet flax, and the Morocco toad-flax (*Linum Maroccanum*), *Convolvulus mauretanicus* and others are sometimes seen in our gardens.

The coastal regions of Algeria are very fertile, and large areas are devoted to the raising of wheat, barley and oats, as well as the

Fig. 13.—Stony desert, northern Sahara, Algeria. *Photo.*, *Dr. W. A. Cannon.*

usual vegetables, and fruits of the south of Europe. In the hotter districts, dates are extensively grown, and the vine and olive are important crops. As in southern Spain, the cork oak is of great importance.

The Atlantic Islands

The isolated island groups lying off the northwest African coast, Azores, Madeira and the Canaries, are characterized by a high degree of endemism, and the flora shows a mingling of Mediterranean and African types.

There is a marked development of the evergreen macchie, with heaths in great variety, brooms and rock-roses, as in Spain and Portugal. Much of the forest formation, however, is very different, being composed mainly of species of true laurels (Laurus, Persea, and Oreodaphne), a family very poorly represented in Europe.

In the drier regions, especially in the Canaries, [1] is a marked development of succulent plants, like stone-crops, Aloes, Euphorbias, and others, as well as many showy plants adapted to xerophytic conditions.

Two characteristic trees, the Canary Island date-palm, and pine (*Pinus Canariensis*) are extensively planted in warm temperate regions like the Riviera and California. Less frequently is seen in cultivation, the extraordinary dragon-tree (*Dracaena draco*), from Madeira and the Canaries.

THE EASTERN MEDITERRANEAN

To the east of the Mediterranean lie the lands of Palestine, Asia Minor and Mesopotamia, which Drude includes in the Mediterranean area.

This region lying between 30° and 40° N. lat. may be compared with southern California, Arizona and northern Mexico, lying in approximately the same latitudes and having very similar climatic conditions. The coastal region has the characteristic temperate Mediterranean climate, but inland are regions where the range of temperature is very great, intensely hot summers, and relatively severe winters. The region at the head of the Persian Gulf is one of the hottest known, and might be compared with Death Valley in southern California.

This region comprises elevated plateaus surrounded by lofty mountains, and the lowlands of Mesopotamia. The rainfall is for the most part scanty, and much of the region is occupied by steppes, or actual deserts, with very scanty vegetation of salt-bushes, sage-brush, various Polygonaceae and in regions where there is a marked winter rainfall, in the early spring is a growth of short-lived annuals, mostly inconspicuous species.

[1] For a complete description of the flora of the Canaries, See Knoche, H., *Vagandi Mos—Reiseskizzen cines Botanikers: I. Die Kanarischen Inseln*, Strasbourg, 1923.

The region about the Persian Gulf is supposed to be the original home of the date-palm, now so extensively cultivated in Arabia and northern Africa, and recently introduced into the hottest parts of southern California and Arizona.

Asia Minor is extraordinarily interesting historically, as the alleged cradle of the human race, and has been inhabited from earliest historic times. It is almost certain that the ancestors of the most important European cultivated plants were derived from

FIG. 14.—Sandy desert, northern Sahara. *Photo., Dr. W. A. Cannon.*

species indigenous to this region. Wheat, barley, the vine, fig and pomegranate are still represented by wild species which were the probable progenitors of all the varieties now in cultivation.

The dry steppes are surrounded by mountains, some of great elevation, like the Caucasus and Lebanon, and the highest elevations are covered with perpetual snow. These mountains in many regions, have a well-developed forest belt, and a true alpine flora.

In the mountain forests of the Balkan regions, and the Caucasus are a number of trees, absent from central Europe and the northern Mediterranean. Among these are several conifers, firs and spruces, but in addition genera quite absent from Europe. The walnut

(*Juglans regia*), Pterocarya, sweet gum (Liquidambar), honey-locust (Gleditschia), and plane-tree (*Platanus orientalis*) are all more nearly related to North American and Chinese trees, than to those of Europe. In the same category are showy rhododendrons and azaleas. All of these may be considered as relics of the ancient Tertiary flora, which became extinct in Europe.

In the Lebanon range of Palestine occur the famous cedars of Lebanon, closely related to the Atlas cedar, already referred to.

The higher mountains harbor an extensive alpine flora, many species being the same as those of the Alps, but with a large element of peculiar species.

The interior of Asia is a barren region with an intensely continental climate and meagre rainfall, so that much of it is quite unfitted for human habitation, and indeed is still unexplored. From the Caspian Sea to China, and from the Himalayas to the Altai, the country is largely barren mountains and desert uplands. For the most part it is treeless, and vast stretches are absolutely bare of any vegetation. Where conditions allow a meagre growth of stunted shrubs, they are mostly salt-bush, wormwood, and similar desert species.

In the less arid regions, especially in the western portion, there is a brief display of herbaceous plants in the spring. Among these are some fine bulbous plants, tulips, fritillaries, iris, and others which soon ripen their seeds, die down and remain dormant for most of the year.

Southward, however, following the great Himalayan range, there is developed an extremely rich temperate flora, which links that of the Mediterranean with temperate China and Japan.

THE HIMALAYAN REGIONS

The great Himalayan region constitutes one of the most important botanical areas of the world. This loftiest of all mountain ranges is a link between the Mediterranean lands and eastern Asia, and the flora is a remarkable mingling of types belonging to both regions.

The lower elevations of the Himalaya, rising from the great Indian plain, have a truly tropical flora made up mostly of strictly Indian types; but above the tropical belt there are successive

PLATE II.—Forest at base of Himalaya, Darjiling railway.

zones passing through all degrees of temperate and arctic climate to the regions of everlasting snow and ice.

The temperate zone begins at about 5,000 feet elevation, but the distribution of the temperate flora is controlled both by elevation and moisture. In the eastern parts of the Himalaya are regions of excessive rainfall, reaching a maximum in the lower ranges about the head of the Bay of Bengal. Westward there is a marked diminution in rainfall, and a corresponding falling off in the luxuriance of the forests. This is true also on the northern slopes, which descend to the great Tibetan highlands, among the most desolate and forbidding regions of the world.

The western Himalayan temperate forests have much in common with those of Europe. Oaks, ashes, elms, poplars, maples and other familiar genera, predominate, giving place at higher elevations to willows, alders and other sub-arctic and arctic forms, which are replaced at still higher altitudes by a genuine arctic-alpine flora which reaches to the limits of vegetation.

Coniferous trees, pines, firs, larch, yew and cypress are common, and the Atlas and Lebanon cedars are represented by the beautiful Deodar. Of the pines, *Pinus longifolia*, and *P. excelsa* are the most important. Walnuts, horse-chestnuts and plane-trees are reminiscent of the forests of Asia minor and the Balkans.

Eastward, as we have seen, the rainfall increases rapidly, and this is accompanied by a decided change in the flora. Conifers are much less prominent, and the European element is to a great extent superseded by species related to those of Japan and China which in turn have a strong relationship with many American species. A forest of this type may be seen in the neighborhood of Darjiling, whose unrivalled panorama of the main range of the Himalaya is world famous.

Darjiling lies at an elevation of about 7,000 feet, and has an annual rainfall of 120 inches, so that the forest is a very luxuriant one. It is a mixed forest of deciduous and evergreen angiospermous trees. Oaks are perhaps the most abundant trees, but with these are associated maples, laurels, birches, chestnuts, and especially characteristic are several species of magnolias and tree rhododendrons. Magnolias are quite absent from Europe and western Asia, but a conspicuous feature of the eastern Asiatic and North American floras. Both Magnolia and Rhododendron comprise some

PLATE III.—Forest below Darjiling, about 4,000 (?) feet elevation; at left, *Duabanga Sonneratioides.*

of the most beautiful known flowering trees and shrubs, the latter reaching their finest development in the Himalayas where they may become trees of some size. One of the finest of these is *R. arboreum*, a spreading tree as large as a good sized apple tree, and in the spring adorned with clusters of blood-red flowers, once seen never to be forgotten.

Crab-apples, cherries, hydrangeas, dogwoods, cotoneasters, barberries, roses, spiraeas, are among the many ornamental shrubs which abound in the Himalayan forests.

Among the evergreen shrubs which are distinctly east Asiatic, are several members of the tea family, Thea, Camellia, Gordonia. This family is also represented in the south Atlantic United States.

The very humid climate induces an abundant growth of mosses and ferns, and also many epiphytes, among which are some very handsome orchids, including many species of Dendrobium, some of which are highly prized in cultivation.

Hooker [1] gives a very graphic account of the transition from the strictly tropical vegetation of the "Terai" the forest region at the foot of the mountains, to the temperate flora as one approaches Darjiling.

At 4,000 feet he notes the appearance of raspberries, deciduous oaks and birches, maples, violets, chickweed, strawberries, geraniums, and other temperate plants, but with these are growing tree-ferns, and such tropical forms as palms, figs, peppers, bamboos, bananas, climbing arums, and many epiphytic orchids, some of these tropical forms extending well into the temperate regions. Owing to the great humidity and mild temperature prevailing here, this region has a much more uniform climate than prevails at similar altitudes in the western Himalaya.

The region beyond the summit of the main range, Sikkim, was carefully studied by Hooker, who states that this district is most remarkable as a meeting place for representatives of most of the plant-types characteristic of the temperate regions of both the old and new worlds. In addition are many species belonging to the Indo-Malayan flora. Of American genera not occurring in Europe, he mentions the following; Buddleia, Magnolia, Sassafras, Hydrangea, Aralia, Trillium, while characteristic Chinese and

[1] *Himalayan Journal*, I, p. 99.

PLATE IV. — Tree-ferns near Darjiling; Mt. Kinchinjunga in background.

Japanese genera were Camellia, Deutzia, Aucuba, Skimmea and Enkianthus.

The recent discoveries of palaentologists in Mongolia, pointing to that region as the original home of the ancestors of most of the large mammalia of both hemispheres, suggest that possibly somewhere in central Asia was also the region from which were derived the ancestors of all the boreal floras.

EASTERN ASIA

The temperate regions of eastern Asia are comprised in the Chinese Empire, Corea, and Japan.

As might be inferred from its vast extent China possesses a very extensive and varied flora. The southern portion lies within the tropics, and the flora is Indo-Malayan in character, like that of the adjacent Himalayan and Burmese regions.

The mountains of the south and west, however, have a very rich flora of a more temperate character, being part of the Himalayan-Tibetan region. It is these mountain regions from which have come so many beautiful Chinese plants which adorn our gardens.

China, being such an ancient and densely populated country, has little to offer the botanist except in the more remote regions. Most of the land has been so long closely cultivated that it is quite impossible to find any trace of the original vegetation. Moreover the mountains have been stripped of their forests, resulting in extensive denudation, so that the student of the indigenous Chinese flora must seek the remote, and thinly settled mountain regions of the south and west.

In the valley of the Yangstse Kiang, the upper forest is said to be composed largely of conifers. At 6000 feet elevation there are firs, spruces, larch, not unlike the European forests at similar altitudes, but composed of different species. Below is a mixed forest of conifers and deciduous trees similar to that in northern Japan and the eastern United States. The common European genera are all present, but with these are many types absent from Europe, but represented in North America. Such characteristic American trees as the sweet gum (Liquidambar), tupelo (Nyssa), tulip-tree (Liriodendron), Magnolia, Catalpa and others, have Chinese representatives, and there are many

PLATE V.—Valley in South Central China, Shansi Province, 32° N. lat. *Photo., Dr. Bailey Willis.*

shrubs and herbaceous plants having a similar distribution. Witch hazel (Hamamelis), Sassafras, Virginia creeper (Ampelopsis), bittersweet (Celastrus), honey-locust (Gleditschia) Hydrangea, Wistaria, mandrake (Podophyllum), moon-seed (Menispermum), are a few of these Asiatic-American genera.

All of the European genera of conifers occur in China, and there are several genera peculiar to China and Japan. Among these Cryptomeria, Sciadopitys, Cunninghamia, Glyptostrobus, and the Yew-like Cephalotaxus. Another of the Yew-family, Torreya, has two species, two others being found in California and Florida.

The most peculiar tree, however, is the Ginkgo, a single species which is the only survivor of a very primitive type which flourished in the early Mesozoic. This tree, like the "Tree of heaven" (Ailanthus), and the white mulberry, is sometimes seen in the United States, where it seems to be quite at home, as do many ornamental plants, like Wistaria, Forsythia, Weigela, Daphne, peony and other ornamental garden shrubs and herbaceous plants.

China and the temperate Himalaya seem to have been the centre of development of the rhododendrons and azaleas, of which China is said to possess over a hundred species, compared to four in all of Europe. The wetter regions, especially in the south, are extraordinarily rich in ferns, and the warmer parts have many species of bamboos.

China is supposed to be the original home of the peach, forms of which occur wild, and it is possible that the orange is the product of one of the wild species of Citrus which are found in southern China; but the different citrus fruits have been so long in cultivation, that their origin is very uncertain.

While most of southern and central China has usually an adequate rainfall, the northwest portions merging into Mongolia are arid, and much of the country is a dry steppe or even desert, with an extremely severe climate exhibiting great extremes of heat and cold. Indeed all of China has a pronounced continental climate.

Many of our choicest garden plants have come from China. A Chinese rose, *R. Chinensis*, crossed with other species has furnished the tea roses, and many others, and the fine climbing

Fig. 15.—Ginkgo, a peculiar Chinese tree, Stanford University.
Photo., Dr. L. L. Burlingame.

roses, the Banksia, Cherokee, and Fortune's yellow are of Chinese origin. Peonies, Dicentra, lilies, among herbaceous plants, Wistaria, lilacs, Deutzia, Spiraeas of several species, azaleas, Daphne, flowering plums and crab-apples and peaches are a few of the contributions of China to our gardens.

JAPAN

The chain of islands forming Japan extends for about fifteen degrees of latitude 30°–45°, corresponding therefore to the Atlantic States between Maine and northern Florida, and showing much the same range of climate. However, due to insular conditions, the Japanese climate is somewhat more uniform, and very decidedly milder than the adjacent coast of the Asiatic mainland in the same latitudes.

The influence of the sea is also shown in a more abundant and better distributed rainfall, Japan being quite destitute of any arid regions, the country naturally being well wooded throughout. In spite of the dense population of the lowlands, there is everywhere an abundance of trees, probably planted in most cases, but the Japanese are such skilful landscape artists that it is quite impossible to tell where nature leaves off and art begins.

The Japanese love of beautiful scenery has made all the most attractive parts of the country readily accessible, and it is easy to get into the mountains where the interesting native vegetation may be seen in all its wild luxuriance.

In southern Japan there is an admixture of Malayan types like bamboos, Cycas, palms and others; but the flora as a whole is a temperate one and has much in common with the eastern United States. In the northern island, Hokkaido, which is much less densely populated, there is still a good deal of lowland forest, which is entirely boreal in its constituents.

The southernmost island, Kiushiu [1] shows the largest percentage of Malayan types. The forest is made up almost entirely of broad-leaved evergreens, of which the most abundant are several species of evergreen oaks. Another characteristic tree is the camphor (*Cinnamomum camphora*), and other members of the laurel family. Camellias and others of the tea family

[1] Schimper, A. F. W., *Pflanzengeographie*, pp. 516–518, 1898.

PLATE VI.—Gorge of a tributary of the Yangtse River, South Central China, elevation 3,200 feet. *Photo., Dr. Bailey Willis.*

are abundant, and the handsome *Pittosporum tobira*, often seen
in Californian gardens. The magnolia family is also well represented. More suggestive of the tropics are several epiphytic orchids (Dendrobium, Malaxis and others), as well as a good many
epiphytic ferns. Begonias, peppers, and several members of the
banana family (Scitamineae) are also reminiscent of the tropics.

Fig. 16.—Two favorite garden flowers from Japan; *Anemone Japonica,
Lilium auratum.*

Owing to the close cultivation of the land there is not much to
be seen of the native vegetation in the densely populated areas
near Yokohama and Kyoto. Along the roadside banks and
ditches, a few wild plants find a foothold, one of the most peculiar, in summer, being Houttuynia, closely related to the lizard-
tail (Saururus) of eastern America, but having four white bracts
subtending the spike of flowers.

Not infrequently one catches a glimpse from the car windows of the great golden-banded lily (*Lilium auratum*), growing on the embankment. This magnificent flower, one of the most prized of garden plants, is common in the country near Yokohama. One of the writer's most vivid recollections of Japan is that of thousands of these splendid lilies adorning the steep sides of a gorge, on the road to the well-known resort Miyanoshita, in the Hakone mountains.

The principal cities of Japan are in the southern part of the main island, in about the latitude of the Carolinas. The summer is hot and rainy, with a correspondingly luxuriant vegetation. The winters are comparatively mild, so that bamboos, hardy palms, oleanders, Gardenia and bananas grow freely in the open, and rice is the staple crop.

The Japanese are world-famous as horticulturists, and their gardens are marvels of landscape art. The beauty of the flowering cherries and wistaria in the spring; the iris, lotus and morning glories of the summer; the exhibition of chrysanthemums in autumn have been the admiration of thousands of visitors to this beautiful land.

Along the roadsides and about the temples and parks, the most abundant tree is a pine (*P. densiflora*), whose picture one sees in nearly every landscape adorning screen or fan. The Ginkgo, from China, already referred to, is often planted about the Japanese temples, where there are gigantic specimens many centuries old.

To see the native vegetation in perfection one must visit the mountains, which are only thinly populated. Nikko, the famous resort some hundred miles from Tokyo, affords a convenient base from which to study the lower mountain vegetation. The magnificent tombs and shrines for which Nikko is celebrated are in a grove of giant cedars (Cryptomeria) which strongly suggest the Californian redwoods. The rainfall is very heavy—about 150 inches annually, and the region is heavily forested with mostly deciduous trees, and abounds in beautiful flowering shrubs and herbaceous plants.

A walk through this forest to Chuzengi some 2,000 feet above Nikko, gives a good idea of the general character of the vegetation of this part of Japan. There are some evergreens, pines and firs, but deciduous trees predominate. Maples are especially abundant and beautiful, and beeches and oaks are common. Among the showy flowering shrubs and small trees, are dogwood (Benthamia),

PLATE VII.—Temple grove, Nikko, Japan. The trees are the Japanese cedar (*Cryptomeria Japonica*). *Photo., courtesy of Dr. D. S. Jordan.*

82

much like the American flowering dogwood, syringa (Philadelphus), Deutzia and Weigela. Above all are the azaleas which in the early summer are a blaze of scarlet and crimson.

Between Chuzenji and Yumoto, between 4,000 and 5,000 feet elevation, are extensive grassy moorlands, which in midsummer are full of beautiful purple and white iris.

The northern Island, Hokkaido, has a much colder climate, and the general character of the vegetation is astonishingly like that of the northeastern United States. Nearly all the trees, elms, oaks, maples, beeches, magnolias, and others, are very similar to American species, and this is true also of many shrubs and herbaceous plants, some of them being actually identical. Thus the poison ivy (*Rhus toxicodendron*) is very common and a wild grape (*Vitis labrusca*) is identical with the American fox-grape. The sensitive fern (*Onoclea sensibilis*), the maiden-hair fern, and the cinnamon fern, (*Osmunda cinnamomea*) are old acquaintances, and a long list of other familiar plants could be cited. In many cases, where species are not identical, the Japanese plant has a closely related species in America. Thus our trailing arbutus (*Epigaea repens*) has its counterpart in the Japanese *E. Asiatica*.[1]

Japan is rich in coniferous trees, most of which it shares with China. The hemlocks (Tsuga), Douglas fir (Pseudotsuga), and white cedar (Chamaecyparis) of the American forest, also have their representatives in Japan.

Like the eastern American deciduous forests, those of Japan are magnificent in their autumnal dress. As in America, maples take first place in this display, but sumacs, Ampelopsis, ashes, oaks, elms, and beeches contribute their quota, while the evergreens form a background for the gayly colored deciduous trees.

SIBERIA

Conditions in eastern Siberia are not favorable for tree growth, and the trees are said to be much inferior to those in corresponding latitudes in America. In Kamtchatka and Sachalien, however, conditions are more favorable, and sometimes there is a good growth of forest.

[1] For a full discussion of the remarkable similarities between the vegetation of Japan and Atlantic North America see Asa Gray's essay on the subject, *Scientific Papers of Asa Gray*, Vol. II, p. 125, 1889.

CHAPTER IV

THE NORTH TEMPERATE ZONE—*(Continued)*

ATLANTIC AND CENTRAL UNITED STATES AND CANADA

The temperate regions of North America are very extensive, comprising southern Canada, southeastern Alaska, and all the United States except southern Florida.

This vast area is extremely diversified as to topography, and this together with great differences in climate, results in a very rich and varied flora. This territory lies, for the most part between latitude 50° and 30°, and extends from the Atlantic to the Pacific, a distance of over 3,000 miles.

Nearly parallel with the Atlantic Coast is the Appalachian mountain system extending from Canada to Georgia. In its northern portion it approaches the coast, and the coastal belt is more or less broken by lower hills; but southward from New Jersey there is a more or less pronounced coastal plain which broadens toward the south and is coextensive with the flat lands of the northern shores of the Gulf of Mexico.

The Appalachians are nowhere of great height, the loftiest peaks, like Mt. Washington in New Hampshire and Mt. Mitchell in North Carolina, being less than 7,000 feet elevation, and too low to possess a true alpine flora; nor are they of sufficient height to act as an efficient barrier between the coastal plain, and the regions to the west.

Between the Appalachians and the Rocky mountains is the great plain drained by the Mississippi and its tributaries, and destitute of any mountain ranges of importance. To the north is the region of the Great Lakes, draining into the Atlantic through the St. Lawrence.

This vast region has no barriers to plant migration, beyond climatic ones. From the Mississippi to the Atlantic coast is a region of ample rainfall, and the country originally was almost entirely covered with forest, in which deciduous trees predominated. Many of these, like the white and red oaks, elm, walnut, and others are found practically throughout this whole region.

In the western sections of this area the rainfall is less, and there occur expanses of open grass-land or prairies, more or less intermingled with patches of forest. Still further west the true prairie formation prevails.

In Canada and the northeast and central states, e. g., Michigan, Wisconsin and Minnesota, are regions of extensive glaciation, abounding in lakes and peat bogs. This is a transition region between the sub-arctic and the true temperate zone, and has many sub-arctic species, and the forest is composed to a considerable extent of conifers.

West of the Mississippi is a region of treeless plains—prairies with close turf in the east, merging by degrees into the drier prairies and steppes of the regions adjoining the Rocky Mountains. Trees are for the most part confined to the banks of streams, or the bottoms of gullies worn down by the streams.

The western third of North America is very different from the east. It is a region of lofty mountains and elevated plateaus. The main range of the Rocky Mountains, extending from New Mexico into northwest Canada, has elevations of over 14,000 feet, and between this and the great Pacific Cordillera are extensive elevated plateaus, and secondary mountain systems. Much of this plateau region is arid, and may be a true desert, as in the vicinity of the Great Salt Lake, and portions of Nevada and eastern Washington.

Extending the whole length of the continent, parallel with the Pacific Coast, is the great Cordillera which with few breaks, stretches from Alaska to Patagonia, and sharply sets off the coastal region of the Pacific from the rest of the continent.

The whole of the great mountain region from the Rockies to the Pacific, is very different climatically and floristically from Atlantic North America, and here alone are the mountains high enough to have perpetual snow, and to develop a true alpine flora. Especially on the majestic snow-clad cones of the great volcanic peaks, Shasta, Hood, Tacoma, are these conditions especially favorable.

In southern California, Arizona and New Mexico, there are

extensive steppes or deserts, really part of the great Mexican plateau, and in climate and vegetation perhaps rather sub-tropical than temperate.

As a whole the climate of temperate North America is decidedly continental in character, the range of temperature being large, especially in the dry plains of the interior. In Montana, the following extreme temperatures have been recorded,[1] viz:—65° and 117° F., a range of 182°!

The temperature of the sea-board, both Atlantic and Pacific, is naturally influenced by the proximity of the ocean, but this is much more marked on the Pacific coast, where the prevailing westerly winds traverse the ocean, whose temperature varies but little, and the high mountains to the east protect the coastal belt from the effects of extreme temperature changes of the interior regions.

The whole Pacific coast has a remarkably equable climate, mild winters and cool summers. The January isotherm of 0°C, which on the Atlantic coast is in the neighborhood of New York and Philadelphia, (lat. 40°), on the Pacific is pushed north as far as Sitka, in Alaska (lat. 58°). In San Francisco there is only a difference of ten degrees Fahrenheit, between the coldest and warmest months (50°–60°); in Washington, nearly in the same latitude, the difference is more than four times as great (32°–78°). The differences are even greater in the interior of the country.

In general, the climate of the eastern third of the United States is one of hot humid summers and cold winters. Except for a small part of southern Florida, no part of the eastern states is immune from occasional killing frosts; while over the greater part of the area the winter is a season of absolute cessation of all plant activity, and in the interior more than half the year is a dead season for pretty much all vegetation.

In the northern tier of states vegetation rarely starts before April, of course becoming earlier as one proceeds southward, and the coastal region has a decidedly earlier spring and more protracted autumn than inland stations in the same latitude.

At the south, spring is somewhat gradual, but toward the north the transition from winter to summer is much more abrupt, and

[1] Kirkwood, J. E., *Forest Distribution in the Northern Rocky Mountains*, University of Montana Studies, p. 49, 1922.

the foliage of the deciduous trees seems to expand almost over night. Where the deciduous forest prevails, the spring is marked by a profusion of delicate herbaceous perennials, such as violets, spring-beauty, blood-root, anemones, etc., which spring up very quickly and flower before the leaves of the trees expand. They soon mature their fruit, and in a few weeks have mostly disappeared, remaining dormant until the next spring.

A feature of these deciduous forests is the magnificent display in the autumn when the varied species show a wonderful variety of brilliant colors in the ripening foliage. The gorgeous dyes of the sugar and scarlet maples; the crimson, purple and scarlet of the gums; the gold, russet and wine reds of the oaks, hickories, dogwoods and ash, and the blood-red sumacs, huckleberries, and many other shrubs, combine to make an unrivalled display of splendid color.

While temperature is a very important factor in plant distribution, moisture is perhaps even more so. The whole eastern United States is a well watered country, abundantly blessed with great rivers and lakes, and consequently having an ample rainfall. The precipitation is heaviest in the southern coastal regions and the slopes of the southern mountains; but throughout the region east of the Mississippi there is a rainfall of 30–60 inches, and nearly the whole country was covered originally with heavy forest.

Westward the precipitation falls off materially, and this combined with a much higher evaporation, results in conditions unfavorable for tree growth; and these conditions become still more marked in the elevated plains adjacent to the Rocky Mountains. In the cooler northern regions of Montana and Western Canada, the prairie reaches to the foot of the mountains; further south the western plains are arid, and may be described as steppes, rather than true prairie.

The absence of any mountains between the Rockies and the Appalachians, exposes all of the eastern United States to the great air movements originating in the Canadian Northwest. The effect of the "cold waves," starting in the far northwest, are felt as far south as the Gulf States.

Topography plays a minor rôle in the climate of eastern North America, the two most important factors being latitude, and proximity to the coast, or the effects of large inland bodies of water like the Great Lakes.

In the western mountain area, however, topography exercises a very great effect on the climate, largely controlling both temperature and precipitation. The direction of the mountain ranges, as well as their height, strongly influences the amount of precipitation, and also the temperatures of the adjacent regions. This is very plainly shown in many places on the Pacific Coast. Where the mountain ranges are parallel with the coast, as in central California, the moisture is mainly precipitated on the windward (west) side, and inland the climate is much drier. This difference in the rainfall within a short distance may be very great. Thus in the canyons of the Santa Cruz mountains within 25 miles or less of Stanford University, the rainfall may average more than 60 inches annually, and a forest of giant redwoods clothes the mountain sides; while at the University, in the valley to the east of the mountains, the rainfall rarely reaches 20 inches, and the open valley supports only scattered tree growth.

The inland valleys, too, shut off from the cool ocean breezes, have very high temperatures compared with the cool coastal summer climate. While San Francisco during July and August rarely sees the thermometer reach 70°, the inland cities like Fresno may have maxima exceeding 110°.

EASTERN UNITED STATES AND CANADA

As in the Eurasian continent, there is not a very clear line of demarcation between the sub-arctic zone and the north temperate.

Along the Atlantic coast temperate conditions prevail as far north as New Brunswick and Nova Scotia, which in the parts adjacent to the sea enjoy a much milder climate than prevails elsewhere in eastern Canada, and a number of plants are found here which are not met with again until the coast of New Jersey is reached. It has been thought [1] that they are relics of an ancient coastal flora which once occupied the now submerged continental shelf. Perhaps the most interesting of these is a small fern, *Schizaea pusilla*, the only representative in the United States of a

[1] Fernald, M. L., "The Gray Herbarium Expedition to Nova Scotia," *Rhodora*, Vol. XXIII, May, 1921.

genus mainly confined to the tropics and to the temperate regions of the southern hemisphere.

The forests of New Brunswick and Nova Scotia [1] are of two types, one in which conifers predominate, and which approaches the sub-arctic forest, the other mainly composed of deciduous species. The latter occupies the best soils, and its most abundant trees are sugar maple and paper birch, with an admixture of red spruce and balsam fir, with occasionally white pine. In some areas beeches are the prevailing trees.

Recently, attention has been called to the occurrence in certain isolated areas in eastern Canada of many plants unknown elsewhere in eastern America, but which are identical with or closely related to species of the Rocky Mountains and Pacific Coast. These western species are especially abundant in the Gaspé Peninsula at the mouth of the St. Lawrence, and on the Long Range in Western Newfoundland.

Fernald [2] has shown that the areas occupied by these far-western plants have apparently entirely escaped glaciation and that these plants are probably relics of wide-spread pre-glacial species which were destroyed elsewhere in eastern America by the great ice-sheet which covered the rest of the country.

Throughout northern New England, e. g., Maine, Northern Vermont, and New Hampshire, the forest is much the same as in New Brunswick. Red spruce is the most abundant species, together with white pine and balsam fir. Beech and sugar maple also occur, but less abundantly than the conifers. In the more southerly areas of the coniferous forest, black spruce is more abundant, and white cedar (*Thuja occidentalis*) and hemlock occur, as well as various deciduous trees.

The conifers are more abundant at higher elevations, while at the base of the mountains, especially in the better soils, deciduous trees become dominant, and there is a transition to the hard-wood forests characteristic of southern New England. Sugar maple, beech, and yellow birch (*Betula lutea*) are the commonest trees, but oaks, elms, and other common New England species begin to appear.

[1] Harshberger, J. W., *Phytogeographic Survey of North America*. DIE VEGATATION DER ERDE, XIII, pp. 361–370, 1911.

[2] Fernald M. L., *Persistence of Plants in Unglaciated Areas of Boreal North America*, Mem. Amer. Acad. of Arts and Science, Vol. XV, No. 111, 1925.

The northern Maine coast and the adjacent islands have a distinctly northern, almost sub-arctic flora, the forest being predominantly coniferous with a small admixture of such deciduous trees as birches and poplars, and an undergrowth of such boreal plants as Linnaea, dwarf cornel (*Cornus Canadensis*), gold-thread (Coptis), and bush maples.

FIG. 17.—Arbor vitae swamp, Douglas Lake, Michigan. *Photo., Dr. F. C. Gates.*

The coast is a very rugged one, with rocky headlands and reefs, sand dunes and extensive beaches, and in places with sandy moorlands and swamps. In the low forest near the coast in Massachusetts, pitch pine (*Pinus rigida*) is common, and red cedar (*Juniperus Virginiana*), with oaks, maples, and other deciduous trees.

The sandy moorlands harbor many interesting and beautiful plants. On Nantucket Island where this moorland is developed on a large scale three species of heaths are found, the common heather (*Calluna vulgaris*) and two species of true heaths (Erica), the latter unknown elsewhere in America, and perhaps introduced from Europe.

Characteristic plants of the moors and forest belt of the New England coast, are several others of the heath family, e. g., bearberry (*Arctostaphylos uva-ursi*), Kalmia, huckleberries, trailing arbutus (*Epigaea repens*), Azalea and wintergreen (*Gaultheria procumbens*). Roses, huckleberries, wax-berry (*Myrica Carolinensis*), wild plums and cherries, service-berry (Amelanchier) Spiraea, and sumac, are among the common shrubs of the New England coast. In some of the swamps north of Boston, the sweet-bay (*Magnolia glauca*) occurs, its northern limit. A number of beautiful orchids, as well as many other showy herbaceous flowers occur in this district. Of the orchids, the most beautiful is the pink lady's slipper, or "moccasin-flower," *Cypripedium acaule.*

The northern New England coast, owing to its rocky formations, and great differences in tide levels, offers exceptional opportunities for the study of the rich marine flora, much of which is exposed at low tide. The vertical rock faces show an interesting succession of forms, the light green sea-lettuce (Ulva), appearing near the high tide mark; below this, but exposed for much of the time are several bladder kelps (*Fucus spp.*) and the curious *Ascophyllum nodosum*, whose long whip-like fronds form a dense curtain along the base of the rocks, and partly conceal the bladder kelps. With these large sea-weeds are associated many smaller species of red and brown algae.

Below the low-water mark is a region with a great development of the large kelps, Laminariaceae, in which several species of Laminaria predominate. Other characteristic species are *Alaria esculenta* and *Agarum Turneri*. The more delicate red algae are found mostly at still greater depths.[1]

Throughout most of New England the American elm (*Ulmus Americana*), is a very characteristic tree, reaching perhaps its finest development in the Connecticut valley. Red and white oaks, white pine, walnut and hickory are abundant, and until it was completely exterminated by the blight, the chestnut (*Castanea dentata*) was one of the commonest trees of New England.

In southern Connecticut, near the shores of Long Island Sound, the tulip-tree and sweet gum (Liquidambar) are found, but these trees belong more to the regions further south.

From the St. Lawrence to the Lower Lakes, including western New York, southern Michigan and Ontario, is a forest region which has few or no coniferous trees throughout much of its extent, although in some districts hemlock and white pine occur. Further north, in northern Michigan, Wisconsin and Minnesota the forest is predominantly coniferous, but there is a considerable mixture of deciduous trees. The most important tree of this northern forest is the white pine (*Pinus strobus*), which has been largely exterminated by the lumberman. The white

---

[1] For a fuller account of these algae, see Harshberger, *loc. cit.*, pp. 383-4.

pine was dominant on gravelly and rocky soils, but also occurred in the mixed forest. Where are good, well drained soils, basswood, sugar maple, beech, elm, and canoe-birch are characteristic trees, with which are associated white pine, hemlock, spruce and balsam. The wetter areas may be swamps with a dense growth of tamarack (*Larix Americana*) or white cedar (*Thuja occidentalis*). In the drier soils, about the southern margin of

FIG. 18.—American elm (*Ulmus Americana*), banks of Unadilla River, New York. *Photo., E. L. Crandall.*

Lake Superior, the Norway pine (*P. resinosa*) is a common and picturesque tree.

In Michigan the mixed forest of the north passes into sandy barrens in which the Jack-pine (*P. Banksiana*), predominates, but there are also open groves of oaks, "oak openings," with stretches of intervening grass-lands, or small prairies. The latter formation is well shown in southwestern Michigan.

The forest of southeastern Michigan is a deciduous one, made up of much the same trees as that of New England.

In the neighborhood of Detroit, in clay soils, the commonest tree is probably the American elm; but sugar, silver, and red maples, walnut, hickory, ash, and several oaks, are also characteristic. In lighter soils, beeches, sassafras and pepperidge (Nyssa) and occasionally chestnut, may also be noted. Less abundant are hackberry (Celtis), honey-locust (Gleditschia), and of the smaller trees and large shrubs, are several species of thorns (Crataegus), the flowering dogwood, crab-apple (*Malus coronaria*), wild plums and cherries. The only conifer is a small cedar (Juniperus) occasionally seen on the banks of the Detroit river.

West of the Great Lakes, in Illinois, Wisconsin and Minnesota, this type of forest occurs, but much diminished in extent, and in the number of species. Its western limit has been placed at the valley of the Red River of the North, and marks the westward and northward limits of a good many tree-species.

Woody climbers are not especially abundant in this forest, but wild grapes of several species sometimes attain a great size, and the Virginia creeper and poison ivy (*Rhus toxicodendron*), may climb high up into the trees. Less conspicuous are the bittersweet (*Celastrus scandens*), moon-seed (*Menispermum Canadense*), Clematis, and several species of Smilax.

Many showy shrubs form the undergrowth of the more open forest, or along its edges. Elder, Viburnum, Spiraea, raspberries and blackberries, currants and gooseberries, roses and others are represented by several species, and the woods, fields and marshes show a wealth of beautiful herbaceous plants.

In the early spring, before the leaves of the trees unfold, many delicate and beautiful herbaceous plants cover the floor of the forest with a carpet of dainty bloom. Spring-beauty (Claytonia), blood-root (Sanguinaria), Dicentra, adder-tongue (Erythronium), cress (Cardamine, Dentaria), Hepatica, Anemone, buttercups, Trillium, crane's bill (Geranium), Phlox, violets, mandrake (Podophyllum), are a few of these woodland flowers.

Somewhat later, in the more open places, masses of blue lupins (*Lupinus perennis*), pink phlox, orange milkweed, shooting stars (Dodecatheon), tiger lilies, continue the floral display, and still later the host of showy Compositae, sunflowers, Rudbeckia, Eupatorium, asters and golden-rods, etc., offer the most brilliant floral display of the year.

The lower lake region is characterized by extensive marshes along the shallower shores of the lakes and the connecting rivers. These are developed on a large scale along the Detroit River, and the small streams emptying into it. The marshes have a rich and very interesting vegetation. Great beds of rushes (Scirpus) and cat-tails (Typha), and many species of sedges and grasses, among the latter the wild rice (*Zizania aquatica*) which in the late summer is very conspicuous with its graceful plumes. The open spaces of the marsh harbor a rich assortment of algae, stone-worts (Characeae), and many pond weeds (Potomogeton, Vallisneria, Elodea,

FIG. 19.—Small glacial lake, Cheboygan County, Michigan. *Photo., Dr. F. C. Gates.*

etc.), while beds of white and yellow water-lilies, and occasionally the great yellow lotus (Nelumbo), cover the surface of the water with their big leaves and showy flowers; and white arrow-head (Sagittaria) and blue pickerel-weed (Pontederia), abound about the margins of the shallow water.

Many showy herbaceous plants and shrubs grow around the edge of the marsh and advancing from year to year on the soil built up by the silt and their own decaying tissues, sometimes extend the land into the marsh with surprising rapidity. Elder, willows, button bush (Cephalanthus), wild roses, are among the common members of this community, and with these are such herbaceous plants, as the pink milkweed, purple Eupatorium, loosestrife (Lythrum), horse mint (Monarda), asters, golden-rods, thistles and many others.

Occasionally the big pink hollyhock flowers of the marsh mallow (*Hibiscus moscheutos*) are seen, a flower belonging properly to the salt marshes of the Jersey coast. Among the maritime plants that have made their way to the shores of the Great Lakes, are the sea-rocket (*Cakile maritima*) and the beach pea (*Lathyrus maritimus*).

The northern forest area abounds in glacial lakes of all sizes. The smaller lakes and ponds sometimes have been completely

FIG. 20.—Deciduous forest, early spring, Rock Creek Park, Washington, D. C. Oaks predominant; red-bud (*Cercis Canadensis*), and flowering dogwood, as undergrowth.

filled by the invasion of peat mosses (Sphagnum), and other bog plants, and form swamps of greater or less extent, in which white cedar or tamarack often form dense growths. These bogs are the home of many very beautiful plants, some of the finest orchids, like the great pink lady's slipper (*Cypripedium spectabile*) and the exquisite Arethusa, Pogonia and Calopogon. Cranberries, Andromeda and other heath-like plants inhabit these bogs, as well as the curious insectivorous sundews (Drosera) and pitcher plant (Sarracenia). With the reclamation of these swamplands, many of the choicest North American plants must disappear.

Eastward of the Mississippi, between 30° and 40° latitude, is the richest forest of temperate North America, and originally this region was almost entirely an unbroken forest, composed mostly of a great variety of deciduous trees. Along the east coast from New Jersey to Florida and also along the northern shore of the Gulf of Mexico is the coastal plain, in which are extensive pine-barrens occupying the sandy soils. Pines of several species are the predominant trees. Except for these coniferous forests, and those of the higher altitudes of the Appalachians, the forest of the eastern United States is made up mostly of deciduous species. This forest reaches its finest development on the lower slopes of the southern Appalachians in North Carolina and Tennessee, and in the rich river valleys of the Ohio and the lower Mississippi. Oaks of many species and often trees of great size are conspicuous, including the white, red, and scarlet oaks, as well as many other less familiar species. Ashes, elms, chestnut, several birches, maples, beech and bass-wood, are the same as those of the more northern forest area; but in addition to these, all of which are represented in the European forests by related species, there are a number of characteristic extra-European genera, most of which have allies in eastern Asia. First in importance is the tulip-tree, *Liriodendron tulipifera*, probably the tallest deciduous tree of the American forest, sometimes being nearly 200 feet in height, and with a straight lofty trunk which is said to occasionally be nearly ten feet in diameter. From New York southward, the sweet gum (*Liquidambar styraciflua*) is a common and very beautiful tree of large size, especially in rich alluvial soils. Pepperidge (Nyssa), persimmon (Diospyros) and sassafras are also characteristic, and in the southern areas the common locust (*Robinia pseudacacia*) as well as several other species occur. The sycamore (*Platanus occidentalis*), which is common throughout the eastern states, along streams, is one of the largest of American trees.

Among the most striking of the trees of the middle and southern states are several species of Magnolia. The great evergreen magnolia (*M. grandiflora*), is decidedly a southern tree, but two species,

PLATE VIII.—Mixed hardwood forest, Mt. Pisgah, National Forest, North Carolina. *Photo., courtesy of U. S. Forest Service.*

97

the cucumber tree (*M. acuminata*) and sweet bay (*M. glauca*) of the coastal swamps, extend as far north as New York. The southern species, like *M. grandiflora* and *M. macrophylla*, are very tropical looking with their big leaves and giant flowers.

The larger trees form a close forest with a dense canopy of foliage during the summer months. Below this upper tier of trees are a number of smaller trees and shrubs which can thrive in the shade of the larger trees. Among these are the flowering dogwood (*Cornus florida*), red-bud (*Cercis Canadensis*), witch hazel (*Hamamelis Virginica*), species of Viburnum, Euonymus, Azalea, and others. In more open localities, as about the margin of the forest, or in clearings, are many species of thorns (Crataegus) a genus which is extraordinarily developed in eastern America.

Crab-apples, wild plums and cherries, roses, spiraea, brambles, currants and goose-berries, honeysuckle, sumac of several species, are a few of the shrubs wide-spread throughout the whole area.

This magnificent mixed forest may be seen in great perfection in the southern Appalachian region. The variety of trees is very great, and the trees are tall and symmetrical. There is a small admixture of conifers, white pine and hemlock being common in places.

A feature of this region is the remarkable development of showy Ericaceae. Even as far north as New England, the beautiful mountain laurel (*Kalmia latifolia*) is common, and in its southern range it may become a small tree. The great rhododendron (*R. maximum*), also reaches New England, but is much more abundant further south. Few floral displays can equal the North Carolina mountains in May and June, when the thickets of laurel are covered with rosy bloom, and the flame-azalea lights up the mountain side with masses of orange and crimson. The big rhododendron is very common, and on the higher mountains are extensive thickets of the splendid purple *R. Catawbiense*, a gorgeous sight when in flower. Another characteristic member of the same family is the sorrel tree (Oxydendron).

The young foliage of the deciduous forest exhibits a great variety of color. The unfolding oak leaves show exquisite tints of pink, gold and pale green, contrasting with the vivid red of the scarlet maple, and bright green of the tulip-tree. The effect is as varied and beautiful, if not so gorgeous, as the tints which make these

PLATE IX.—Virgin beech-forest, Mt. Pisgah National Forest, North Carolina. *Photo., courtesy of U. S. Forest Service.*

99

same forests a blaze of color in the autumn. Where the snowy flowers of the dogwood, and the rosy pink of the red-bud light up the forest just as the leaves begin to unfold, the picture is complete.

South of the Carolinas and Tennessee the forests begin to assume a more tropical aspect, with an infusion of broad-leaved evergreens, like magnolia, live oaks, holly and laurel (Persea), and in the coastal region, palmettos, the northernmost representatives of the tropical family of palms.

There is a decided increase, too, in the number of woody climbers or lianas; Bignonia, trumpet creeper (Tecoma), Wistaria, yellow jasmine (Gelsemium) passion flowers and some others, are added to the grapes, Clematis, Virginia creeper, and other northern climbers.

THE COASTAL PLAIN

Eastward from the Appalachian mountain system, from New Jersey southward, is the Atlantic coastal plain, narrow in its northern portion, but widening at the south, and becoming very broad in the Carolinas and Georgia, where it passes into the coastal region of the Gulf of Mexico. This whole region is geologically comparatively recent, and much of it raised but little above sea-level.

North of Chesapeake Bay, it is a narrow, more or less interrupted strip of barren strand. A few plants, such as the dwarf pricklypear, characteristic of this region, occur at points further north, as in Nantucket and Martha's Vineyard, and relics of this coastal flora are also found in New Brunswick and Nova Scotia, indicating a former connection with the coastal plain further south, severed by the subsidence of the continental shelf.

The extensive beaches of Long Island and New Jersey belong to this formation and support a characteristic strand flora, much like that found along the Massachusetts coast in similar localities, such as huckleberries, wax-myrtles and others, and the stunted trees are also many of the same species. In places the drifting sand is gradually burying the forest on the land side.[1]

The Jersey pine-barrens have been very thoroughly studied. The pitch pine (*Pinus rigida*) is the predominant species, and

[1] Harshberger, *loc. cit.*, pp. 413–423.

covers large areas, in an open formation, associated with scrub-oaks of several species together with such shrubs, as huckleberries, Andromeda, Azalea, Leucothöe, bear-berry and trailing arbutus, all members of the heath family, as well as many others, among them the sweet fern (Comptonia) and many herbaceous plants, some of which are almost entirely confined to it.

Cedar swamps in which southern white cedar (*Chamaecyparis thuyoides*) is predominant, are a common feature of the region, and harbor many rare and interesting plants. Of the small trees and shrubs may be mentioned red maple, *Magnolia glauca*, *Azalea viscosa*, black alder (*Ilex verticillata*) and the fragrant white alder (*Clethra alnifolia*).

The rare fern *Schizaea pusilla*, occurs in this region, and cranberries, sundews and pitcher plants abound in the bogs, as well as the royal fern (*Osmunda regalis*) and cinnamon fern (*O. cinnamomea*).

The whole coast south of New Jersey is destitute of rocky formations, and the conditions are much less favorable to the growth of algae than along the rocky New England shore. The water is much warmer, and the algae are often of tropical or sub-tropical types, e. g., Dictyota, Padina, Sargassum, etc. Marshes abound along the tidal rivers, with a mixture of fresh and salt water types of vegetation.

From Virginia southward, the northern pitch pine is replaced by other species, *Pinus taeda* being the common species in Virginia. While the vegetation of the pine-barrens, is on the whole much the same as in New Jersey, distinctly southern species become increasingly abundant; locust, trumpet creeper (Tecoma), yellow jasmine (Gelsemium), occur in Virginia, and in North Carolina the southern elements become still more conspicuous. Among the characteristic species is the red bay (*Persea borbonia*) belonging to the laurel family; live oaks and dwarf palmettos, and in South Carolina the tall palmetto (*Sabal palmetto*) are common. A famous denizen of the pine-barrens of the Carolinas, is the remarkable Venus's flytrap (*Dionaea muscipula*) unknown elsewhere. In this same region are also several species of pitcher plants (Sarracenia).

The pine forests of Virginia and the Carolinas are very extensive and reach far inland, and are of great value. Near Washington

the common species is *P. rigida*, further south the long-leaved
pine, *P. palustris*, occurs, but *P. taeda* and *P. rigida*, occur throughout the region. These pine forests may have no other trees,
or there may be an undergrowth of smaller trees, especially
oaks.

In South Carolina, as in Florida, there are level sandy stretches
of great extent, with a dense growth of the dwarf saw-palmetto
(*Serenoa serrulata*) interspersed with stunted pines, including the

FIG. 21.—Cypress swamp, Wakulla Springs, Florida. *Taxodium distichum*, with
Tillandsia. *Photo., Professor H. Kurz.*

West Indian *P. Caribaea*. In Georgia are extensive pure stands of
the long-leaved pine (*Pinus palustris*), highly prized for its timber.
In the wet districts are often extensive "cane-brakes," in which
the principal element is the reed-grass, *Arundinaria macrosperma*.
The coastal plain of the Gulf States much resembles the southern
Atlantic coast and the long-leaved pine is the prevailing species.
This formation reaches its western limit in Texas, and part of it
may be seen along the Southern Pacific railway, before reaching
the swamp-lands near New Orleans.

As one passes from the dry prairies of the interior of Texas, scattered pines begin to appear and finally form an open forest. This gradually is replaced by a mixed hard-wood forest as the moister coastal region is approached, and cypress swamps become frequent, in which one sees the fantastic cypresses bearded with the "Spanish moss" (Tillandsia).

These cypress swamps are among the most striking plant associations of the country. They occur as far north as Virginia, near the coast, and extend up the Mississippi Valley into southern Missouri and Illinois.

The bald cypress (*Taxodium distichum*), is a large tree, often growing permanently in water, but also in rich moist ground which is not submerged. Where the base of the trunk is submerged, there are developed on the roots, the "knees," conical outgrowths which appear above the water, and serve for aërating the roots. The young trees are very symmetrical in form, like most conifers, but the older trees develop a very irregular and fantastically branched crown rising above the other trees of the association. In the wetter portions of the cypress association the principal species are the sour gum (*Nyssa aquatica*) and an ash (*Fraxinus platycarpa*), but oaks, maples, hickories, and some others also occur.

In the Gulf region, dense growths of the dwarf palmetto (*Sabal Adansonii*) are common, and the branches of the cypress are heavily draped with the dismal blackish streamers of Tillandsia.

About the margins of the swamp are some showy herbaceous aquatics. Passing through this region in early April, the writer noted two handsome species of Iris (*I. hexagona*, and *I. cuprea*), a white spider-lily (Hymenocallis), showy species of Phlox, Senecio, Oenothera and Lobelia, and magnificent masses of the royal fern (*Osmunda regalis*) as well as several other ferns.

In the river valleys of eastern Texas there is a hard-wood forest, which in places is dense and with trees of large size; but westward with the lessening rainfall, the forest disappears and the prairie becomes dominant. Eastern Texas marks the westward limit of the southern deciduous forest as well as the pine forest of the coastal plain.

The transition from the heavily wooded eastern states, to the prairie states along and beyond the Mississippi, is a gradual one. In southeastern Michigan, northwest Indiana, and much of Illi-

FIG. 22.—Alluvial swamp, about six miles west of Tuscaloosa, Alabama.   *Photo.*,
Dr. R. M. Harper.

nois, there is a mingling of forest and prairie floras. In alluvial soils there may be a well developed forest of the usual type, but with fewer species than further east. In the lighter soils, forests when present are much more open, and the predominant trees are oaks of relatively small size. These "oak openings" are familiar features of the transition regions of northern Illinois and Wisconsin. In the sandy soil at the foot of Lake Michigan, there are white pines growing on the dunes, among the oaks, and in the lower ground the pepperidge (*Nyssa sylvatica*), is also a

Fig. 23.—Woodland and prairie near Chicago; Sumac invading grass-land. *Photo.,*
Dr. A. G. Vestal.

feature of the formation. For the most part, however, the forest is a strictly deciduous one. With the oaks there are sometimes hickories amd walnuts. The trees of the oak openings are rather scattered with thin under-growth, except for grasses, and a variety of other herbaceous plants.

The soil of the typical oak openings is usually a sandy one, and not favorable for the growth of moisture-loving plants. Where there has been a sufficient accumulation of humus, a few woodland species become established, but they are few in number of species, and less luxuriant than those of the typical deciduous forest.

The following species of oaks occur in the oak openings, viz., *Quercus alba*, *Q. rubra*, *Q. coccinea*, *Q. velutina*, *Q. macrocarpa*, and *Q. Marylandica*. The common hickory is *Carya microcarpa*.

The forest of the northern transition region according to Harshberger [1] is of three kinds. On the ridges and hill-slopes oaks are the predominant trees, but with these are associated hickories (*Carya alba*), aspens, cotton-woods, ash (*Fraxinus sambucifolia*), hornbeams (Ostrya, Carpinus), canoe-birch, butternut (*Juglans cinerea*), and occasionally bass-wood (*Tilia Americana*). In the moister alluvial soils the silver maple, green ash, elm, bass-wood, black walnut, hickory and cotton-wood are found.

At the northern limit of the region, there are sandy areas where the white pine and yew occur, with birches and alders, this formation being decidedly boreal in character.

Further south, in Iowa, there occur in the alluvial formations a number of more southern species, like the honey-locust (Gleditschia), Sycamore (*Platanus occidentalis*), and mulberry (*Morus rubra*).

The grass-lands become more and more predominant westward, until the unbroken prairie is reached, which at the north extends unbroken to the foot of the Rockies.

Toward the south the grass-lands are less extensive, and in western Kansas and Nebraska the region is rather a dry steppe, than true prairie, and this is still more marked in western Texas and New Mexico, where the country is an arid steppe or desert, a northward extension of the dry plateau of Mexico.

With the diminution in rainfall toward the west, and the increased elevation, the close sod of the eastern prairie is replaced by an open formation of bunch grasses, among which occur many species of plants like the yuccas, and occasional cacti, characteristic of the arid regions further south.

The eastern prairie region has a fair rainfall, and the absence of trees has been the subject of some speculation, as conditions would seem to be favorable for their growth.[2] It has been conjectured that the prairies owe their origin to the burning of the forests by the Indians to furnish feed for the herds of buffalo, but the latter themselves may very well have played an important

[1] *Loc. cit.*, p. 521.

[2] Harshberger discusses this question at some length, see *loc. cit.*, p. 516.

rôle in the destruction, by close cropping of any young trees that may have attempted to get a foot-hold. Once established, however, the dense mat of grass offers very little opportunity for the growth of seedling trees.

Further west, the extreme weather conditions, dry and cold, are sufficient to account for the absence of tree growth on the western plains, which naturally would assume their present condition of arid prairie or steppe.

A study of the wet prairie near Chicago [1] indicates that it was

FIG. 24.—Sand prairie, valley of Illinois River. *Photo., Dr. A. G. Vestal.*

originally a swamp. While grasses are the predominant plants of this prairie, they are associated with a number of other characteristic forms, some of which have very attractive flowers. Where there are remnants of the original vegetation, as along the railway in places, one may see in spring, even near Chicago, masses of pink phlox, shooting star (Dodecatheon), the beautiful bird's-foot violets (*Viola pedata*), and the big leaves of the rosin-weed (Silphium), which later sends up its tall stems bearing big sunflower like blooms. In the late summer and autumn, golden-rods and asters abound, and the pink blazing-star (Liatris) is also

[1] Cowles, H. C., *Bot. Gazette*, XXXI, p. 145, 1901.

common, as well as a number of Leguminosae, e. g., *Amorpha can-escens*, Baptisia, Melilotus.

The prairie reaches its most typical development in western Iowa, eastern Kansas and Nebraska,[1] and the Dakotas. The grass flora comprises over 30 species, but there are many other herbaceous plants, of which the most abundant are various Compositae, sun-flowers, Coreopsis, iron-weed (Vernonia), asters and golden rods, worm-wood (Artemisia), and others. Anemones, larkspurs, phlox, verbena, oxalis, flax, blue-eyed grass (*Sisyrinchium*), milkweeds (Asclepias), are characteristic, as well as others including several genera of Leguminosae, e. g., Desmodium, Astragalus, Baptisia.

The only woody plants belonging properly to the prairie of this region are a dwarf willow (*Salix humilis*) and a rose (*Rosa Arkansana*).

Along the streams, willows and cotton-woods are found, but these do not invade the prairie. Of course much of the original prairie has been broken up, and is now covered with the great wheat and corn fields of the midwest.

The constitution of the prairie of Nebraska has been very thoroughly studied.[2] There are two types, depending on soil conditions. On loamy soils there is a close sod composed of several species of grasses, e. g., Sporobolus, Koeleria, Eatonia, Panicum; on heavy clay is the buffalo-grass formation, where "bunch grasses" form separate mats or large tufts, with bare ground between. The most important of the bunch grasses are the buffalo-grass (*Buchloë dactyloides*) and "grama-grass" (*Bouteloa oligostachya*). Buffalo-grass formation is typical of most of the western cattle ranges.

A good many secondary species of grasses, as well as various other plants may occupy the space between the prevailing bunch grasses. One of the common grasses, *Stipa comata*, at once attracts attention by its conspicuous silvery plumes. Occasionally a small yucca or cactus suggests the still drier plains further west.

Toward the north the true prairie reaches to the foot of the mountains which rise abruptly from the rolling prairie. This is

---

[1] Pound, Roscoe and Clements, F. E., *Botanical Gazette*, XXV, p. 384, 1898.
[2] Harshberger, *loc. cit.*, p. 526. See also Woodard, J., in *Botanical Gazette*, May, 1924.

well illustrated in Glacier National Park in Montana, where the rolling prairie of the Blackfeet Indian reservation meets the main range of the Rockies, This prairie is rich in showy flowers, and very beautiful in the late summer. Near the base of the mountains are dense groves of aspens and scrub cotton-woods, while scattered conifers,—pines and spruces—begin to appear.

The spring flora includes a number of pretty liliaceous species, fritillaries, adder-tongue (Erythronium), mariposa lilies (Calochortus) and the blue quamash (*Camassia esculenta*), formerly an important food plant of the Indians. Other spring flowers, like those of the eastern prairies are also met with, but it is in late July and August that the prairie flora is at its best.

The prairie is of the bunch-grass type, and the silky plumes of *Stipa comata*, are very conspicuous. The space between the grass tussocks is completely covered with an extraordinary profusion of showy flowers, reminding one of the flowery Swiss meadows.

This prairie is in the foot-hill region at an elevation of about 4,000 feet. Asters, golden-rods and several very beautiful species of Erigeron are perhaps the most abundant flowers, and another even showier composite is *Gaillardia aristata*, whose big yellow flowers with crimson discs are not infrequently seen in gardens.

Lupins, Astragalus, and several vetches are abundant, and yarrow (Achillaea), and several umbellifers furnish most of the white flowers. Bluebells (*Campanula rotundifolia*), one of the most widespread of northern plants, are extremely abundant and a showy mint (Monarda) was conspicuous, and here and there were masses of the beautiful pink blossoms of a dwarf rose (*R. Arkansana*).

At the edge of the prairie, and along the banks of the streams, there is a luxuriant growth of tall herbaceous plants with showy flowers, the most abundant being the pink fire-weed (Epilobium) which occurs in immense quantities, and with it is often associated a very showy Senecio, with golden yellow flowers. The huge umbels of the cow-parsnip (Heracleum) are conspicuous in the low ground, and in places the ground is scarlet with the Indian paint-brush (Castilleja), of which there are a number of extremely beautiful species in the mountains near by.

Southward the prairie-region diminishes in breadth, and the western plains gradually assume the character of dry steppes, or semi-deserts merging into the arid Mexican plateau.

The southern prairies are drier than those of the north, the
region having very hot summers, and there is a considerable
development of annual species such as characterize the desert
and semi-desert regions of the far western states.

FLORIDA

The only part of the United States which can be called tropical
is the southern part of Florida and the "keys" south of it. The
climate is a hot humid one,
and the vegetation is to a
great extent West Indian in
composition.

The eastern part of the
Florida peninsula is mostly a
sandy plain with coral rock
near the surface. The gritty
soil is covered with a thin
growth of coarse grass, and
toward the south, the saw-
palmetto (*Serenoa serrulata*),
is very abundant as an undergrowth for the pines which
form an open forest. The
principal species is the West
Indian *P. Caribaea*.

A common plant of these
southern pine-barrens is a small
c y c a d (*Zamia Floridana*),
which with a second species
growing in moister situations
are the only cycads found in
the United States.

FIG. 25.—Open pine forest (*Pinus Caribaea*); undergrowth of saw palmetto,
Miami, Florida.

Inland is the extensive region of the "Everglades,"
formerly impenetrable swamps covered with a dense growth of
saw-grass (*Cladium effusum*). Here and there are streams which
lead into the interior of this great swamp. Sometimes there are
areas of more elevated land covered with pine woods, and there

PLATE X.—Interior of "hammock" near Manatee, Florida. To the right, cabbage palmetto; at left, tree covered with "Spanish moss." *Photo., Mr. T. R. Robinson.*

111

are also cypress swamps. This region is now being drained on an extensive scale, the land being exceedingly productive.

Along the coast of southern Florida are extensive mangrove formations, the principal species being the wide-spread *Rhizophora mangle*.

Elsewhere extensive sandy beaches are encountered, with a characteristic strand flora. There is a mixture of typical northern species, like the sea-rocket (Cakile) and various grasses, and tropical forms like the saw-palmetto, and the beach morning

Fig. 26.—Mangrove formation, Miami, Florida.

glory (*Ipomoea pes-caprae*), the latter a denizen of pretty much every tropical beach, the world over. Small Cacti, a Yucca and an Agave hint at Mexican relationships.

While much of southern Florida is occupied by pine-barrens and the saw-grass swamps of the Everglades, there are numerous areas of greater or less extent distinguished by good soil, which support heavy growths of broad-leaved trees. These patches of forest are known locally as "hammocks," and the vegetation is mainly composed of species common to the West Indies, or closely related ones,—in short, the flora of the hammocks is a distinctly tropical one.

With the live oaks, which usually are found in the hammocks, are associated species of figs (Ficus), mahogany, custard apples, laurels (Persea), Terminalia, Eugenia, Guayacum, Chrysophyllum, Sideroxylon, Mimusops and other trees and shrubs unknown elsewhere in the United States. The tropical character of the flora of south Florida is shown by the number of trees and shrubs of the madder family (Rubiaceae), a feature of most tropical countries. In the temperate regions, most Rubiaceae are herbaceous.

Various Araceae, Crinum and Hymenocallis of the Amaryllidaceae, Canna, and Thalia (Marantaceae), are all suggestive of the West Indies, and in the humid atmosphere of the hammocks, the trees are laden with epiphytic ferns, orchids and Bromeliads, presenting a pretty tropical picture. Florida has many species of orchids, some of which like Vanilla and Epidendrum are distinctly tropical types, and very handsome. Peperomia, a distinctly tropical genus of the pepper family has two species in southern Florida.

No feature of the flora of south Florida is more distinctly tropical than the palms, of which there are over a dozen species. Except for the palmettoes, which reach the Gulf states and Carolinas, all the palms of the eastern United States are confined to southern Florida.

The coconut thrives along the shore as it does in most tropical countries, and in addition are some dozen other species of palms most of which are confined to this region. The finest palm of Florida is the royal palm (*Oreodoxa regia*), also a native of Cuba.

Most of the conifers of Florida are pines, except in the swamps where the cypress occurs. An exception is the rare and interesting *Torreya taxifolia*, a member of the yew family, known only from a very limited habitat in middle Florida. The only other American species *T. Californica* is confined to central California.

The fern flora of Florida is not particularly rich, but in the south includes a number of tropical genera and species. Among these may be mentioned Vittaria, Ceratopteris, *Acrostichum aureum*, several species of Polypodium, and the remarkable *Ophioglossum* (*Cheiroglossa*) *palmatum*. The latter, as well as a good many others, grow as epiphytes in the hammocks. Several species of Selaginella, *Psilotum triquetrum* and *Lycopodium cernuum*, are also suggestive of the tropics.

CHAPTER V

THE NORTH TEMPERATE ZONE—*Concluded*

THE ROCKY MOUNTAINS AND PACIFIC SLOPE

The main range of the Rocky mountains extends from New Mexico to northwestern Montana, and thence into the Canadian northwest.

There are two pretty well marked regions which differ a good deal in character. The highest summits are in the southern part of the range, several peaks in Colorado, e. g., Pike's Peak, Long's Peak, exceeding 14,000 feet, but the mountains are far less abrupt than further north. In northern Montana and Canada, the main range is very much broken up, with very steep slopes and sharp peaks, but none of the latter attain the altitude of those further south.

The national parks in Colorado, Wyoming and Montana, make the Rocky Mountains very accessible, so that the floras of these interesting regions can be easily studied.

The country near Denver, and in Estes Park, illustrates very well the more salient features of the southern or Park region of the eastern Rockies.

As one approaches the mountains in Colorado, the prairies of Kansas and Nebraska merge into a semi-arid region of bunch-grasses interspersed with xerophytic types reminiscent of the true deserts of the south and west. This plain has an elevation of about 5,000 feet, and in places, the foot-hills form sloping table-lands or "mesas," which are often traversed by streams descending from the mountains.

The western edge of the mesa is both more sheltered and better watered than the eastern side, which slopes into the dry grass-land of the great plains. The vegetation of the western edge of the mesa is of a somewhat mixed type. There is sufficient moisture to permit the growth of a few conifers and aspens, and a number of shrubs and herbaceous species occur which require more moisture than those of the open plains. There is also an infusion of high mountain species, which mingle with those belonging to the dry prairie.

A feature of the Colorado mountains are the "parks," broad, grassy, nearly level valleys lying between high mountains. Estes Park is familiar to tourists, and is a good example of this formation.

These parks are fairly level valleys having an elevation of 6,000 to 10,000 feet. The grassy meadows are rich in beautiful flowers, most of which are true sub-alpine types and quite distinct from the plains flora.

The Rocky mountain flora while having a good deal in common with the alpine floras of Europe, differs in many details. The gentians, campanulas and primroses, are much less in evidence, while on the other hand, American genera, e. g., Castilleia, Pentstemon, Mimulus, as well as Aster and Solidago and some other Compositae, are very abundant, both as to species and individuals, and these are mostly absent from the European mountains, or in the case of the Compositae, much less developed. One of the finest of the mountain flowers is the great blue and white columbine (*Aquilegia coerulea*) the state flower of Colorado.

Above the parks the mountain sides are in many places clothed with a fairly heavy forest mostly of conifers. On Pike's Peak the timber line ascends to 11,500 feet. The forest is composed of several species. The yellow pine (*Pinus ponderosa*, var. *scopulorum*) is abundant above 6,000 feet, usually associated with Douglas fir (Pseudotsuga), these being the most widely distributed of the western conifers with the possible exception of the lodgepole pine (*P. Murrayana*). Over large areas the Engelmann spruce (*Picea Engelmanni*) is the predominant tree, and is widespread in the Rockies, but scarcely reaches the Pacific coast. This species ascends to the timber line, occasionally over 12,000 feet. In the higher altitudes, the yellow pine gives place to the limber-pine (*P. flexilis*), which reaches its best development further north. The alpine fir (*Abies lasiocarpa*) also reaches timber line, and lower down the Pacific white fir (*Abies concolor*) is met with, but never reaches the dimensions attained in the Pacific forest. On the dry slopes low bushes of juniper are common, as elsewhere in the western mountains.

Nowhere do the deciduous trees play an important rôle. Except for thickets of aspens the deciduous trees are confined to the canyons and river banks of the lower elevations. Birches, willows and cotton-woods may be found in such localities, and several species of oaks occur in Colorado, but are never trees of large size, and usually merely shrubs, forming part of the "chaparral" or scrub on the dry hillsides.

North of the high mountains of Colorado is an elevated plateau which is traversed by the Union Pacific railway in Wyoming. At the continental divide, about 8,000 feet elevation, the country is an undulating dry prairie or steppe with almost no trees, and in general scanty vegetation.

The Yellowstone Park is approached over much the same type of country, and is also a relatively level area with no high mountains in the immediate vicinity. The hills are covered with a forest of lodge-pole pine, but the trees are small. In the early summer there are a good many attractive flowers growing in the woods and on the grassy slopes. One of the most abundant is a large yellow adder-tongue (*Erythronium grandiflorum*). Other characteristic flowers are some fine larkspurs and fringed gentians, and a small orange fritillary (*Fritillaria pudica*).

The barren soil of the peculiar thermal formations is mostly bare, but it is interesting to note that some species, usually found on the seashore, or salt marshes (*Salicornia herbacea, Rumex maritima*), have established themselves on the hot alkaline geyser formations.

The main range of the Rockies, in northwest Montana and Canada, is extremely rugged, broken up into separate mountain masses with steep slopes and sharp peaks. Owing to the latitude there is much more snow than in the southern Rockies, and glaciers are common, especially in the Canadian mountains, and the snow line is much lower.

The main range traverses Glacier Park in northwest Montana, and affords a most interesting study in plant distribution.

The prairie flora to the east has already been referred to, and an analysis of its constituents shows a mixture of eastern and western species, the former rather predominating.

The eastern slopes of the mountains are exposed to the extremely severe weather conditions of eastern Montana, intense cold, great summer heat, and scanty rainfall; hence the vegetation of the exposed areas is decidedly xerophytic.

There are several lakes, more or less protected by the surrounding mountains, and about these, and in sheltered canyons, there is a

FIG. 27.—Coniferous forest, Glacier National Park, Montana. Left, western hemlock; right, western white pine.

fairly luxuriant forest in which Douglas fir and Engelmann spruce predominate. Both of these trees descend to a much lower elevation than in Colorado, and the same is true of the limber-pine which becomes a fair sized tree, while usually it is a high mountain species of low and spreading habit. Some of the drier areas are occupied by nearly pure stands of lodge-pole pine, and low junipers grow on the exposed hillsides, where there is often a dense scrub or chaparral composed of a variety of shrubs. These include two species of buffalo-berry (*Shepherdia*), raspberries, currants, sumac, huckleberries, plums, and others.

Crossing the divide to the west side of the range, one finds within less than twenty miles a remarkable difference in the forest vegetation, due to a marked change in climate. The west side

FIG. 28.—Forest, Glacier National Park. At right, center, cotton-wood (*Populus trichocarpa*).

of the range evidently intercepts a large share of the moisture brought by the west winds from the Pacific, and the rainfall is consequently very much greater than on the eastern side of the mountains. Moreover the winter cold is much tempered by the westerly winds.

The forest about Lake McDonald at the western base of the

range in Glacier Park is a very heavy one, and composed of a remarkable variety of conifers, which attain a much greater size than those of the eastern slope.

The most abundant tree is the western larch (*Larix occidentalis*), a graceful tree, sometimes exceeding 150 feet in height. This tree is deciduous, like its relative the eastern tamarack. With this are the Douglas fir and Engelmann spruce, and at higher elevations the alpine fir. Besides these, however, are species belonging to the humid Pacific coast forest, the grand fir (*Abies grandis*), giant arborvitae (*Thuja plicata*), and western hemlock. The western yew (*Taxus brevifolia*) is common, but does not become a tree. For the number of species of conifers growing together, this forest has few if any equals.

The peaty soil supports an interesting assemblage of boreal shade-loving plants. The twin-flower (Linnaea) forms extensive carpets in places, and the Indian-pipe (*Monotropa uniflora*) lifts its clusters of dead-white stems and flowers from the dank mould.

FIG. 29.—Forest interior, giant arborvitae; Lake McDonald, Glacier National Park.

Pipsissewa (Chimaphila), and several species of Pyrola; the dwarf Cornel, and several orchids, e. g., coral-root (Corallorrhiza), rattlesnake plantain (Goodyera); *Clintonia uniflora, Berberis repens, Aralia nudicaulis.*

Where the shade is less dense, as along the banks of the small streams, and in clearings, a number of characteristic species are noted. Elder, cow-parsnip (Heracleum), and maples make fine masses of foliage in the low ground, and with these are associated the handsome leaves and large white flowers of the thimble-berry (*Rubus Nutkanus*), and the "devil's club" (*Echinopanax horridus*), a handsome but horribly spiny shrub, an emigrant from the Pacific coast. Ferns are not uncommon, and the lady fern (*Asplenium filix-foemina*) is especially abundant and luxuriant in the low ground; also a variety of shrubs, snowberry (Symphoricarpus), Spiraea, Viburnum, twin-berry (*Lonicera involucrata*).

While deciduous trees are greatly in a minority, the forest is not so exclusively coniferous as that of the drier parts of the mountains. The canoe-birch is not uncommon, and becomes a tree of considerable size, while the balsam poplar (*Populus trichocarpa*) is a lofty tree with tall straight trunk, rivalling the conifers in height. A small maple (*Acer. glabrum*) is also common.

Showy flowers are less abundant than in the drier and more open country of the eastern side of the mountains; but at higher elevations there are many beautiful alpine and sub-alpine species.

The alpine meadows of the northern Rocky Mountains have a profusion of extremely beautiful flowers, and there are many interesting and attractive rock-species also, like the Pentstemons, *Epilobium latifolium*, various saxifrages, stone-crops, etc.

The meadows early in the season are adorned with the large yellow adder-tongue, which soon ripens its fruit and is followed by a great variety of attractive flowers. Yellow arnica, white valerian, blue gentians; and lupins and magnificent scarlet, crimson and pink Castilleia abound, as well as many other pretty and interesting species. In the wetter ground a beautiful pink Mimulus (*M. Lewisii*), is abundant, as well as yellow Senecio, larkspurs, forget-me-nots, asters, Erigeron, and a pale yellow columbine, quite different from the blue Colorado species. The curious little "elephant's head" (*Pedicularis Groenlandica*) is not uncommon, and the pretty grass of Parnassus (Parnassia) is abundant in moist places. A very conspicuous plant of the sub-alpine region is the green false-hellebore (*Veratrum viride*), whose big plaited leaves, and tall racemes of greenish flowers, are extremely common.

Among the rock-plants is the mountain avens (*Dryas octopetala*), a species common to the arctic and alpine regions of both hemispheres. Other wide spread species are *Silene acaulis*, Iceland poppy, and the little primrose, *Primula farinosa*. With these are associated such distinctly American genera as Pentstemon and Phlox.

Northwestward, the western Rocky Mountains unite with the northern Cordillera in Idaho, Washington and British Columbia; and this accounts for the strong infusion of Pacific coast species in the Rockies of Idaho and northern Montana. These are mostly

Fig. 30.—Alpine vegetation, Glacier National Park; left, Alpine fir; right, false-hellebore (*Veratrum viride*).

absent from the southern Rocky Mountains, where the drier and hotter climate is less suited to these northern moisture-loving species.

West of the main continental divide is the extensive plateau region, the Great Basin, comprising most of Utah and Nevada, and parts of Idaho, Oregon and Washington. This is a region of arid steppes and broken mountain ranges, with light precipitation, this being specially marked in the southern areas.

The arid climate of the Great Basin is due largely to its almost complete encirclement by lofty mountains. The western Cordillera forms an effective barrier against the moist Pacific winds, and the southern portion is open to the hot winds from the Mexican plateau. Except for the Columbia and its tributaries, which traverse the northern parts of the basin, there are no streams of importance within the area, and these are often lost in the desert sands, or as in the case of the Jordan, flow into saline lakes.

Parts of the region, like that adjacent to the Great Salt Lake, are deserts of the most pronounced type, quite destitute of vegetation; or the arid, often alkaline soils support only a thin growth of such plants as sage-brush (Artemisia), and grease-wood (Sarcobatus) and similar shrubs capable of enduring long periods of drought.

This region is traversed by the Union Pacific railway, and between Cheyenne and Reno one has an opportunity of seeing the most characteristic portions of this Great American desert.

FIG. 31.—Sub-alpine meadow, Glacier National Park.

From an elevation of over 8,000 feet at the continental divide there is a descent of about 4,000 feet into Utah and Nevada.

The bunch-grass prairie of Wyoming passes gradually into a dry steppe with thinly scattered bunch-grasses interspersed with sage-brush and other xerophytic growths. The rocky hillsides support a few scrubby junipers and firs, and various low shrubs and herbaceous plants in the sheltered hollows among the rocks; but these mostly disappear in the lower parts of the basin. Where there are streams, the banks are lined with willows and cotton-woods, as well as a number of deciduous shrubs, currants, elder, roses, spiraea, etc., and herbaceous plants, like asters, golden-rod, willow-herb, and others.

Along the railway in Utah and Nevada as far as one can see, is a monotonous landscape of barren plains and low hills sometimes almost destitute of vegetation, but usually covered with a dull-green mantle of sage-brush which is the predominant plant of this region. Between the clumps of sage-brush, there are often scattered tufts of grass, and sometimes after spring rains, various flowers appear for a brief season. Among these may be mentioned the "sego lily" of Utah, a pretty lily of the genus Calochortus; evening primrose, lupins, and various other showy annuals.

When the soil is strongly alkaline, grease-wood (*Sarcobatus vermicularis*) takes the place of the common sage-brush, and with it occur other plants characteristic of alkaline soils, e. g., Atriplex, Bigelovia, Suaeda and others.

This dreary landscape continues almost to the foot of the Sierras, where the effect of the coastal moisture begins to make itself manifest.

This arid region extends northward into Oregon and Washington, where desert conditions are less extreme, and the northern portion of the Great Basin is traversed by the Columbia which breaks through the Cascade mountains and reaches the sea. A considerable portion of the Columbia basin lies in this arid region, and although much of it is very dry, there is a true forest growth in many places, and even at the lower elevations the yellow pine may form open forests. Only a small area in eastern Washington is comparable to the deserts of Nevada and Utah.

The desert of the Great Basin has a much more monotonous vegetation than the regions to the south. The Cacti, Yuccas, and other striking forms of the deserts of Arizona and southern California, are almost entirely absent. These are of Mexican origin, and apparently not fitted for the severe winters of the northern desert.

Of course, even in a true desert region, the sheltered valleys, watered by mountain streams, may develop a relatively luxuriant vegetation, and if sufficiently open are available for cultivation. Before reaching Ogden, the railway passes through the canyon of the Webber River, which furnishes water for irrigation, and where the floor of the valley expands there are prosperous looking ranches with luxuriant fields of alfalfa and other crops, and fine orchards. The contrast between the forest growth of some of these sheltered canyons, and the barren desert without, is quite extraordinary.

As the lower slopes of the Sierra and the Cascades are reached, the effect of the increasing moisture is seen in the greater number of trees as one ascends toward the summit of the ranges. Although the eastern slopes of the Sierra are much drier than those of the Pacific side, nevertheless there is an abundant growth of fine trees in which the yellow pine predominates.

This intermediate region is well shown near Lake Tahoe,

Fig. 32.—Desert vegetation, Utah. Sage-brush (*Artemisia sp.*), *Chrysothamnus sp. Photo., Mr. Fred Buss.*

which lies at about 6,000 feet elevation on the boundary between Nevada and California. About the eastern shore, the yellow pine is the commonest tree, and sage-brush and other xerophytic plants occupy the ground between the trees. On the western side, especially at the northern end of the lake, the effect of an extremely heavy snow-fall is seen in a forest of mixed conifers, in which the white fir (*Abies concolor*), is the commonest species, with sugar pine (*P. Lambertiana*), yellow pine, and incense cedar (*Li-*

bocedrus decurrens). In moister ground the tamarack (*Pinus Murrayana*) occurs.

The drier ground is covered with chaparral, in which the characteristic western shrubs Manzanita and Ceanothus are conspicuous. Alpine meadows like those of the Northern Rockies are common, and in general the vegetation is much like that of the western Rockies at similar altitudes.

THE PACIFIC COAST

Climatic conditions on the Pacific Coast are very different from those elsewhere in North America, where for the most part

Fig. 33.—Coniferous forest, Lake Tahoe, California. Left, incense cedar, yellow pine; right, white fir.

the climate is a pronounced continental one, with great extremes of heat and cold.

The whole coast, from Sitka to San Diego enjoys a remarkably equable climate, insular in type, rather than continental. The two great factors concerned are the lofty range of the Great Cordillera, protecting the coastal strip from the great temperature fluctuations of the interior, and secondly the proximity of the ocean whose surface waters maintain a nearly constant temperature, which has a very great influence on that of the coast, especially as the prevailing winds are from the sea.

The effect of the ocean temperature is especially marked on the immediate coast. San Francisco, lat. 38°, about the same as Washington, has a mean annual temperature of 55°F, with only ten degrees difference between the warmest and coldest months, viz., 60°–50°. In Washington, the difference is more than four times as great. The moderating effect of the ocean is particularly noticeable at the north. Sitka, seventeen degrees north of New York, has almost exactly the same temperature ($+1$°C) for its coldest month.

Away from the immediate coast the temperature is greatly influenced by topography. Where the cool ocean winds in summer are intercepted by mountain ranges, as in central and southern California, arid regions like parts of the San Joaquin Valley and the Mojave desert show the highest summer temperatures of any part of the United States. For example at Needles, on the California bank of the Colorado River in the Mojave desert, there are few days in summer when the thermometer does not reach 100°F, and 120° and even more are sometimes registered. This same region, in winter, is subject to sharp frost.

The distribution of rain on the Pacific Coast is also very different from that of eastern North America. The rainiest regions are at the north, where some of the stations have annual means of over 100 inches, and exceed any points in the eastern United States. Southward the rainfall diminishes rapidly until at the Mexican boundary it is ten inches or less.

Like the temperature, the rainfall is also strongly controlled by topography, especially by the trend of the mountains, and there may be a great difference in precipitation within a short distance, due to topography. At Stanford University which lies to the east of the outer coast range, the annual rainfall averages less than 20 inches, but at some stations, e. g., Boulder Creek, about twenty-five miles away in an air-line, it is more than three times as much.

Of course these great differences in temperature and moisture exercise a great influence upon the vegetation. For example, the Santa Clara Valley in the vicinity of Stanford University, is an open grassy savanna, with scattered oak trees, and only on the northern slopes of the hills do the trees form an approach to a forest. In the mountains, however, in the regions of heaviest rainfall, is a magnificent forest of giant redwoods, with an undergrowth of almost tropical luxuriance.

Throughout the southern part of the Pacific Coast, including all of coastal California, the winter is a period of active vegetation. The rains are confined to the cooler part of the year, the summer being quite rainless in most of California; and as far north as British Columbia the rains are small in amount compared with the autumn and winter precipitation. Thus in lowland California,

FIG. 34.—Santa Clara Valley, near Stanford University. White oak, with mistletoe (*Phoradendron flavescens*).

at least, the growth periods are reversed when compared with eastern North America.

During the long dry summer the native vegetation is largely dormant, but with the autumn rains, in October and November, a host of annual grasses and herbaceous flowers sprout, and the perennial herbs, especially the numerous bulbous and tuberous species, start into growth, continuing to grow through the rainy winter, flowering in spring, ripening their fruits and dying down after the spring rains have ceased.

As in all climates with mild winters, there is a preponderance of evergreen trees and shrubs. Not only are coniferous trees developed to a remarkable degree, but a great variety of broad-leaved evergreens are found, especially in the southern part of the area. Evergreen oaks, laurels, huckleberries, barberries, and other less familiar genera, abound in the Californian flora.

The mild climate and a very heavy rainfall result in a luxuriant forest as far north as about 60° in coastal Alaska, corresponding in latitude to northern Labrador and the southern tip of Greenland, regions of arctic cold and destitute of any forest vegetation.

A feature of the Pacific coast is an extraordinary development of the giant kelps, these huge brown sea-weeds growing in profusion on the rocky shores from Alaska to the Mexican boundary, being especially abundant in Central California.

The best known of the giant kelps is the great bladder-kelp (*Macrocystis pyrifera*), which also is found in the colder waters of the southern hemisphere. Other kelps reaching a great size are species of Alaria, Egregia, Nereocystis and Pelagophycus. The two latter may reach a length of 100 feet or more, and grow in deep water, the huge leaves being buoyed up by a single globular float, which in Pelagophycus is as large as a coconut.

The majority of these kelps are peculiar to the Pacific Coast of North America, and constitute one of the most remarkable features of the Pacific Coast vegetation.[1]

The typical coastal flora of southern Alaska is well developed about Sitka. The forest is very dense, made up mostly of two species, the Sitka spruce (*Picea Sitchensis*) and a hemlock (*Tsuga Mertensiana*). A third species, the Alaska cedar (*Chamaecyparis Nootkatensis*), has been largely exterminated, as its wood is especially prized for making the great dugout canoes, and for wood carvings.

While the trees of this forest do not attain the great size found further south, still they are fine large trees, the spruces often attaining a height of over 100 feet, with a diameter, occasionally, of 6 to 8 feet. The forest floor is covered with a dense carpet of mosses, which also cover every stump and fallen log. Among the mosses grow the usual low evergreen species of the northern forests, e. g., Pyrola, Linnaea, dwarf cornel, various species of Lycopodium, and ferns, etc. The abundant and constant mois-

[1] The algae of the Alaska coast are decribed at some length by Harshberger, *loc. cit.*, p. 587.

ture is especially favorable for seed-germination, and myriads of tiny spruces and hemlocks are found on every log and stump, growing in the moss. As the logs decay very slowly, it is common to see a young tree perched on a stump several feet above the ground, sending down its roots until they reach the earth. When the log or stump finally decays and disappears, the tree is supported by a cone of stilt-like roots often five or six feet high.

In every clearing is an impenetrable jungle of shrubs and young trees, among which the spiny devil's club (Echinopanax) is only too abundant. It is, however, a remarkably handsome plant, with its large palmate leaves and spikes of showy red berries. This, with the huge leaves of the Aroid, Lysichiton, known locally as "skunk-cabbage," gives quite a tropical aspect to the edge of the jungle. The salmon-berry (*Rubus spectabilis*) with pretty pink flowers, and showy red and yellow fruit, is a common and characteristic shrub. Red-berried elder, huckleberries, mountain ash, roses and spiraea, are also abundant in the woodland thickets, and in low ground are extensive growths of the giant horse-tail (*Equisetum telmateia*).

Deciduous trees, willows, poplars, alders and small maples, are mostly restricted to the banks of the numerous streams.

Sphagnum bogs abound near Sitka and contain the usual northern bog-species: sundews, cranberries, *Kalmia glauca*, various bog orchids, buck-bean (Menyanthes), etc., with numerous grasses and sedges, including species of cotton-grass (Eriophorum). The pools in the Sphagnum bogs are very rich in small algae, e. g., desmids, diatoms, and a great variety of other unicellular species.

British Columbia and Puget Sound

The general character of the coastal vegetation of British Columbia and Puget Sound, is much the same as that of southeast Alaska, but with the warmer climate, the number of species increases and the trees reach enormous size. About Puget Sound, the Douglas fir (*Pseudotsuga Douglasii*),[1] is the most abundant species, and is the most important timber-tree of the Pacific Coast. Originally forests of this species everywhere lined the

[1] *P. taxifolia.*

coast, but the accessible areas have been mostly stripped of timber, with the development of the cities and agricultural districts. These forests, where they still exist, are very dense, and the trees attain a great height, occasionally upwards of 300 feet.

The trees of the Alaska coast forest also occur, and the Sitka or "tideland" spruce attains its greatest development here, as does the giant arbor-vitae (*Thuja plicata*) known usually as "cedar." Of the deciduous trees of this region, the big-leaved maple (*Acer macrophyllum*) and the handsome flowering dogwood (*Cornus Nuttallii*) are conspicuous. These with the smaller vine-leaved maple (*A. circinnatum*), color brilliantly in the autumn and make fine masses of color in the evergreen forest. From Washington south, the fine western rhododendron (*R. Californicum*) is abundant, as well as the shrubs found in the more northern forest. Another characteristic shrub is the salal (*Gaultheria shallon*), related to the little wintergreen of the Atlantic states.

In the neighborhood of Tacoma are some open prairies where are oaks (*Quercus Garryana*) in scattered groves; but as a rule, oaks are not abundant in this region.

While the forest has been largely cut away from the lowlands, one can get an idea of the primaeval forest from the pieces of forest land that have been reserved for parks. Thus Stanley Park at Vancouver has enormous specimens of tideland spruce, cedar, and Douglas fir, and shows what the coastal forests were before the advent of the white man.

The western slopes of the Cascades are covered with dense forest in which the Douglas fir is much the most abundant tree, and often forms pure stands of great extent.

The great volcanic peaks which rise from the Cascades illustrate very beautifully the change in vegetation as one ascends from sea-level to the regions of perpetual snow and ice. The snow-line is about 6500 feet elevation.

The finest of all these mountains, Mt. Rainier, is easily accessible, and shows perfectly the different zones of vegetation. Moreover, as it is a National Park, the forest is largely intact.

At the base the forest is mostly Douglas fir. Above this the Douglas fir is associated with white pine (*P. monticola*), hemlock, and two fine firs, *Abies grandis*, and *A. amabilis.* Above 3,500 feet, the Douglas fir is replaced by the noble fir (*A. nobilis*), and at timber line, the Alpine fir (*A. lasiocarpa*), and white-barked pine (*P. albicaulis*) are found.

The ground flora of the forest is very much the same as that in the northern Rockies, and the same is true of many of the species making up the luxuriant thickets of shrubs in the more open places. The vine-leaved maple, already referred to, is

Fig. 35.—Avalanche lilies (*Erythronium montanum*), Mt. Ranier.

one of the commonest and most beautiful. It closely resembles some of the Japanese maples, and like them in the fall assumes gorgeous hues of crimson and scarlet.

The alpine flora of Mt. Rainier is perhaps unrivalled in America. As the snow melts, the alpine meadows are adorned with a great profusion of beautiful flowers. Beds of big snow-white "avalanche lilies" (*Erythronium montanum*) spring up close to the snow-banks, and dense masses of brilliant crimson Castilleia, blue lupins, and pink heather (Bryanthus), make superb expanses of vivid color, and with these are many others, many of them wide-spread alpine species. The unusual profusion of flowers on Mt. Ranier is probably due to the abundant moisture from the great snow fields and glaciers which cover the mountain for a distance of nearly 8,000 feet.

The eastern slopes of the Cascades are much drier, and the plateau traversed by the Columbia and its tributaries is arid, and belongs rather to the Great Basin than to the Pacific Coast.

The southern Cascades have a much less luxuriant vegetation than in the Puget Sound region, and this becomes very marked as the California boundary is reached. The northern conifers become less numerous, and the yellow and sugar pines, and white fir are more in evidence, and indicate an approach to the drier climate of the Sierra Nevada.

Along the coast, however, the dense wet forest belt is continued into northern California, but the characteristic trees of the northern forests are to a great extent replaced by the redwood (*Sequoia sempervirens*), which in some places forms pure stands of great extent, and throughout the great redwood belt, reaching from southern Oregon to central California, is the predominant species.

Associated with the redwood, throughout most of its range, is the tan-bark oak (*Pasania densiflora*) the only American representative of a genus otherwise restricted to Himalayan and Indo-Malayan regions. Another beautiful tree of the redwood region, but not confined to it, is the madroño (*Arbutus Menziesii*), with broad evergreen leaves suggesting a magnolia. This reaches its greatest dimensions in central California.

Owing to the great diversity of topography and climate, California surpasses any other equal area in the United States in the richness of its flora. Not only is the number of species very great but a suprisingly large number are peculiar to the state, and often of very limited range.

Covering 10 degrees of latitude (42° to 32°) and with a coast-line nearly a thousand miles long there is naturally considerable range of climate due to latitude; but this is very much less marked, as regards temperature, than is the case on the Atlantic coast, due to the uniform temperature of the Pacific.

While the temperature in California is relatively little affected by latitude, this is not true of the precipitation. Eureka, near the northern end of the state has more than four times as much rain as San Diego; while some stations in northwest California may have

PLATE XI.—Redwood forest, Humboldt County, California. *Photo., courtesy of Save the Redwoods League.*

more than a hundred inches annually. On the other hand, some places in the desert of southern California are almost rainless.

Topography plays an extremely important rôle in determining the climate of different parts of California. The principal mountains are parallel with the coast. In central California there are three, the outer and inner Coast Ranges, and the Sierra Nevada forming the eastern boundary of the state. At the north the Siskiyous separate California from Oregon, and connect with the southern Cascades. In central California the Tehachapi Mountains connect the Coast Ranges and the southern Sierra, and in southern California are more or less isolated lofty mountains, the San Bernardino and San Jacinto ranges.

These mountain ranges exercise an immense effect on the climate of the adjacent regions. Thus while the western slopes of the outer Coast Range receive a heavy rainfall, so that the northern redwood forest is probably the heaviest stand of timber in the world, the valleys to the east are too dry to support anything but a scattered growth of oaks, and are often quite treeless.

In the southern part of the state, where the precipitation at best is scanty, the moisture-laden winds from the ocean are quite unable to reach the interior valleys and plateaus, and these are more or less complete deserts, like the Mojave desert, Death Valley, and the Colorado desert.

In central California, the great central valley, made up of the Sacramento and San Joaquin, has a very light rainfall except in the upper Sacramento Valley. For the most part the rainfall is insufficient for ordinary farming, but under irrigation these valleys are extremely productive, and a great quantity of grain, including rice, and fruit of all kinds, make this great valley the most important agricultural region of California.

There may be great differences in temperature and precipitation due to local conditions. For example, San Francisco, situated on a peninsula exposed to the full effects of the ocean wind and fog, has a remarkably cold summer climate, the mid-summer maximum usually being below 70°F. In the central valley, at this season, intense heat prevails, while in the deserts of southern California are the hottest regions in the United States. Even in the immediate vicinity of San Francisco places lying inside the Coast Range,

e. g., Stanford University, usually have summer maxima ten to twenty degrees higher than the city.

While the west side of the Coast Ranges intercepts much of the moisture from the ocean winds, so that the valleys are comparatively dry, the mountains are not of sufficient elevation to shut off the Sierra from the moisture laden winds, and the west side of the Sierra above about 4,000 feet has a very heavy precipitation, mostly in the form of snow, which allows the development of a forest of giant trees.

The main range has an average elevation of about 10,000 feet, the highest peak, Mt. Whitney (14,502 ft.) being the highest point in the United States, outside Alaska. This great barrier effectually protects California from the extreme climate of the Great Basin. Owing to the southerly position, the snow fields are much less developed than in the Cascades, and except on Mt. Shasta in northern California, glaciers are practically absent. There is, however, a very heavy snow-fall, the melting snow providing the necessary moisture for the great forests that clothe much of the western slopes of the Sierra, and feeding the numerous glacial lakes of the high mountains, and the streams that flow from them.

It is interesting to note that Mt. Whitney, the highest point in the United States, overlooks Death Valley, also in California, the lowest spot, over 300 feet below sea-level.

The coast of California is very varied in character, and this is reflected in the great variety of the coastal vegetation. Through much of the state, the outer Coast Range runs close to the sea, and as at the Golden Gate, high cliffs rise sheer from the water, and bold rocky headlands are a feature of much of the coast, especially in central California. Low clay bluffs are sometimes met with and elsewhere broad sandy beaches and dunes. At San Francisco and near Monterey, dunes are developed on a great scale. Salt marshes occur in such sheltered places as parts of San Francisco Bay, but are comparatively rare.

The rocky shores with extensive reefs and tide-pools, harbor an extraordinary variety of algae and the whole Pacific Coast from Alaska to Mexico is extremely rich in both red and brown species. In the deeper and quieter water are delicate red algae in great variety; but the species growing on the rocky ledges and reefs, exposed to the tremendous Pacific surf, are usually tough and leathery in texture, fitted to withstand the buffeting of the heavy waves. Some of these large red species, like the spiny Gigartina and Iridea, the latter reflecting peacock-hues in the shallow pools, are very conspicuous.

The most striking marine plants of this coast, however, are the big brown sea-weeds, or kelps, which reach extraordinary size,

and show great diversity of form. Some of them, like Fucus, are entirely exposed at low tide, and drape the rocks as they do on the northern Atlantic coast; others are rooted in water far below tide mark, and their leaf-like fronds float near the surface, often buoyed up by air-bladders. The tough stems are anchored by strong root-like hold-fasts in water many fathoms deep.

Of these giant kelps, the great bladder-kelp (Macrocystis) is abundant from Alaska to Santa Barbara, and great beds of this kelp, off shore, act as a quite efficient breakwater. Another very large species, *Nereocystis Lutkeana*, sometimes attains a length of over 100 feet. The big leaves are attached to a single air-bladder

FIG. 36.—Sea-palms (*Postelsia palmaeformis*). *Photo., Miss E. M. Bartlett.*

the size of a baseball, the stem tapering gradually to the slender solid stem. This huge plant is the growth of a single season. Much like Nereocystis is the "bull-kelp" (Pelagophycus) of southern California, in which the float is the size of a coconut, and the big leaves are attached to two great antler-like branches.

Another kelp peculiar to the Pacific coast is the sea-palm (*Postelsia palmaeformis*), a stout upright plant about two feet high growing on rocks exposed to the full force of the breakers. It resembles a small palm tree, and the flexible trunk is perfectly adapted to withstand the pounding of the surf, being so firmly anchored to the rocks that it can be removed only by chopping it loose.

The flora of the sand-dunes is a very varied and attractive one, and may be seen in perfection on the shores of the Monterey peninsula. Especially conspicuous are the masses of bush-

FIG. 37.—Sand-dunes, Monterey Peninsula, California. The trees are Monterey pine.

lupins, with yellow, white and purple flowers, making a fine show of color when in bloom. Other characteristic shrubs are species of Ceanothus, "wild lilac," and "Cascara" (Rhamnus), as well as willows, and several Compositae. Sometimes the Monterey pine (*Pinus radiata*) and live oak (*Quercus agrifolia*) are found on the inshore dunes, where they form dense low thickets.

Besides grasses and sedges, there are a number of showy herbaceous plants, among which the yellow and pink umbels of the "sand-verbenas" (Abronia) are conspicuous.

Where there are bluffs back of the dunes, upon them are found a number of striking flowers, which may also invade the dunes. A large Mesembryanthemum (*M. aequilaterale*) is very common, and Castilleia with flowers varying from cream to scarlet are among the common and very showy species. A large aster-like Erigeron is also very abundant.

The steep cliffs above the Golden Gate show a similar flora, and there are also many others: buttercups, Iris, Eschscholtzia, Sanicula, evergreen strawberries (*Fragaria Chilensis*), cow-parsnip (Heracleum), Fritillaria, etc. Several ferns and horse-tails are also common in places.

A feature of the coastal flora of California is the occurrence of several endemic conifers of very limited range. The Monterey pine, and cypress (*Cupressus macrocarpa*) are practically confined to a few miles of coast on the Monterey peninsula, and in southern California, the Torrey and Parry pines are even less abundant.

In places there is a "mesa" extending from the base of the outer Coast Range to the sea, with bluffs of moderate height along the shore. These mesas in central California owing to the cool summer, and frequent fogs, may be covered with a permanent turf, and in the spring are decked with a great variety of pretty flowers.

About Monterey the hills are covered with a forest of the Monterey pine, which also occupies much of the lowland adjacent to the shore, where it mingles with the cypress, which occurs only close to the shore, often clinging to the very edge of the rocky headlands.

In the loose sandy soil between the pines is a more or less dense chaparral formation in which Ceanothus and manzanita (Arc-tostaphylus) are perhaps the commonest shrubs, but with these are a number of others, including several species of currants, goose-berries, cascara and others.

The outer coast ranges, from the Oregon boundary to Santa Cruz, are characterized by the redwood formation. The redwood reaches the greatest development in its northern range, Humboldt and Del Norte counties. The Humboldt forest is sometimes a pure stand of redwood, where the huge trees, sometimes more than 300 feet high, grow so closely together that on account of the dense shade, there is very little undergrowth except ferns, and a few low evergreen shrubs.

So far as known, the redwood exceeds all other trees in height, an authentic measurement being 342 feet. Occasionally trunks 15 to 20 feet in diameter are met with.

The redwood formation reaches its maximum development along the Eel River, south of Eureka, about latitude 40°. In places there is a pure stand of these enormous trees, many of them more than 300 feet in height, and probably the heaviest stand of timber in existence.

Between Eureka and the Oregon line, a region of extremely heavy rainfall, the redwood is replaced gradually by the tideland spruce, hemlock, and a fir, *Abies grandis*. This forest has a dense undergrowth of almost tropical luxuriance. The ground

FIG. 38.—Grove of Monterey cypress; Monterey Peninsula.

is carpeted with ferns, and there is an abundant growth of rhododendrons, evergreen barberries and huckleberries, dogwood, and alders, and a variety of other shrubs and small trees.

In the southern redwood belt the Douglas fir is common, as far south as the Santa Cruz Mountains.

The main body of redwood is confined to the coastal mountains north of San Francisco; but there are fine redwood forests in the Santa Cruz mountains, and smaller growths in the sheltered coastal canyons of the Santa Lucia mountains south of Monterey.

The range of the redwood is controlled by the summer coastal fogs. Only where these reach does the redwood naturally flourish, apparently requiring the protection of the fog-blanket against the hot sun of the rainless summer. In the mixed redwood forest of central California there are several characteristic broad-leaved evergreen trees. The tan-bark oak and madroño have already been mentioned and in addition to these are the mountain live oak (*Quercus chrysolepis*), an evergreen chestnut (Castanopsis), and the beautiful bay-tree (Umbellularia). Black oak (*Quercus Kelloggii*) and the big-leaved maple, are the most important deciduous trees, but along the streams are large alders, cotton-woods, willows, and the box-elder (*Acer Negundo*).

A dwarf yew (*Taxus brevifolia*) and the "nutmeg" (*Torreya Californica*), also of the yew family, are sometimes found in the redwood forest. Torreya has its only other American representative in Florida.

Of the attractive shrubs of the redwood forest, the most beautiful are the pink rhododendron (*R. Californicum*), and the azalea (*R. occidentale*). The former is mainly confined to the north, and is restricted to the coastal region, while the azalea has a wider distribution. Evergreen huckleberries and barberries are abundant, and the big white-flowered thimble-berry (*Rubus Nutkanus*), pink-flowered currants, blackberries, Spiraea, and roses, are characteristic.

Among the common woodland flowers are Trillium, Erythronium, Fritillaria, Clintonia, violets and cress (Cardamine, Dentaria), Smilacina, Aquilegia, Cynoglossum, Delphinium and many others. Ferns are abundant, but there is no great variety. *Adiantum pedatum, Woodwardia Chamissoi, Aspidium munitum*, are perhaps the most striking.

Central California is a meeting place for the northern and southern floras. This is very well shown in the region about Stanford University in the Santa Clara Valley, about thirty miles south of San Francisco. To the west are the Santa Cruz mountains, the highest points rising about 3,000 feet above the valley. The sheltered valleys, which are accessible to the sea-fogs, have a fine growth of redwoods, some of great size, and with them are the usual associates, Douglas fir, tan-bark oak, madroño, laurel, etc.

These mountains, all through the summer, get the ocean fogs which drift into the redwood canyons, but rarely reach the valley floor, except occasionally as "high fog."

These cool, moist coast mountains harbor many plants evidently of northern origin, such as violets, trilliums, lilies, anemones, Erythronium, roses, elders, and many others. While these genera are wide-spread boreal ones, the species are mostly peculiar.

On the valley side of the mountains the character of the vegetation is very different. While redwood is still found in places, the forest is mainly an open one in which oaks predominate, partly the deciduous black oak (*Quercus Kelloggii*), partly live oaks. Madroño, bay, and buckeye (*Aesculus Californica*), also occur, as well as other trees and shrubs.

The dry slopes are covered with chaparral made up of a variety of shrubs and small trees, mostly evergreen, but including a good many deciduous species. Several species of Ceanothus, with white or blue flowers are abundant and very ornamental, and known locally as "wild lilac." Manzanita (Arctostaphylos) is also represented by several species. These two genera are remarkably developed in Pacific North America. Several species of scrub oaks, buckeye, Garrya, "poison oak" (*Rhus diversiloba*), "Yerba santa" (Eriodictyon), Adenostoma, bush-poppy (Dendromecon), several species of Ribes, as well as the more familiar roses, blackberries, and elder, are common constituents of the chaparral.

The valley itself is open, and except on the north slopes of the foot-hills, is scantily wooded. Groves of picturesque, spreading oaks, however, give the landscape a park-like aspect that is very attractive. The commonest oaks are the live oak (*Q. agrifolia*) and the white oak (*Q. lobata*). The latter under favorable conditions reaches a gigantic size, hardly rivalled by any other species. Less common in dry soil, is the blue oak (*Q. Douglasii*).

In general, both the woody plants and the herbaceous vegetation of the valley, are of southern rather than northern affinities, and are related more or less closely to the flora of the northern Mexican plateau, which really comprises southern California and Arizona.

The coastal mountains of southern California are much drier than those of the north, and except in the canyons are largely bare of trees, the southern Californian forests being mainly restricted to the higher elevations of the interior mountains. Along the coast and in the interior valleys, the rainfall is scanty, and much of the country is too dry for tree-growth, and some of it is genuine desert.

Inside the coast ranges are many valleys, great and small, by far the most important being the great central valley drained by the Sacramento and San Joaquin rivers which unite and discharge into the Bay of San Francisco. This great valley is a vast plain some 400 miles long, and over 50 miles wide in places. Much of this is treeless, recalling the mid-western prairies, and is a region of great fertility, which under irrigation has become very productive. Numerous smaller valleys, also highly fertile, occur in both northern and southern California.

The valleys and foot-hills are largely covered with annual grasses, which die at the beginning of the long dry summer, this being the period when much of the native vegetation is dormant. As soon as the first heavy rains come, usually in October or November, the grass-seeds quickly germinate, as well as those of many other annuals, native and introduced, and the landscape changes from brown to vivid green, to last through the winter and spring.

The annual grasses which are so abundant in the valleys of California, are mostly species introduced from southern Europe. The most conspicuous of these is the wild oat (*Avena fatua*), which is very common, and furnishes valuable forage. The native grasses are mostly perennial bunch-grasses, e. g., *Stipa spp.*, *Danthonia spp.*, *Bouteloua spp.*

There is a great variety of showy annuals which in favorable seasons cover the hillsides and meadows with masses of splendid color. Many of these are familiar in cultivation, e. g., Nemophila, Gilia, Eschscholtzia, Phacelia, Lupinus, Godetia, Clarkia, etc., but there are many others, especially such showy Compositae as Layia, Baeria, and others like Orthocarpus, which are not so well known. Perhaps the showiest of all, and almost the commonest, is the California poppy, *Eschscholtzia Californica*, which forms solid masses of blazing orange sometimes acres in extent, and often associated with patches of brilliant blue lupins, almost as showy, and produced in equal profusion.

With the annuals are associated a number of perennials, largely tuberous or bulbous species. Buttercups, mallows (Sidalcea), a large yellow composite (Wyethia), various Umbelliferae, and especially a variety of liliaceous species, as well as species of Iris and Sisyrynchium.

Ten species of true lilies are found in California, including some of the finest of the genus. These are mostly mountain species, or in the coastal region growing in the moist canyons, or forest. The Humboldt and Washington lilies of the Sierra Nevada, and the redwood lily (*Lilium rubescens*) are especially beautiful.

In the northern part of the state are several fine species of Erythronium, a genus which reaches its finest development in the northern Pacific States.

Especially beautiful are the many species of Calochortus, "Mariposas," "butterfly-tulips," the majority of which are confined to

Fig. 39.—Death Valley. *Photo., Dr. W. S. Cooper.*

California. Another common and attractive genus is Brodiaea (now split up into several genera), with umbels of white, blue, or yellow flowers. Allium, Chlorogalum and Zygadenus are other common genera of Liliaceae. Of the Iridaceae, the genus Iris has a number of common and handsome species, and the showy *Sisyrinchium bellum* is one of the most abundant spring flowers in central California.

A feature of the Californian flora is the great number of species within some genera, as well as the large number of endemic genera, sometimes monotypic. Of the former, Trifolium, Lupinus, Calochortus, Mimulus, Pentstemon, may be cited; of the latter, Platystemon, Romneya, Bloomeria, Brevoortia, Limnanthes,

Pickeringia, Chamaebatia, Adenostoma, Bolandra, Carpenteria, Eucharidium, Hemizonia, and many others.

The inner valleys of southern California are as a rule arid, and often actual deserts. South of the Tehachipi Mountains, which form the southern boundary of the great central valley, lies the Mojave desert, which is a plateau of 3,000 to 4,000 feet elevation toward the west, but descending on the east to the Colorado River. To the southeast lies Death Valley, a region of intense heat which lies more than 300 feet below sea-level and is the lowest point in the United States.

In the more elevated portion of the Mojave desert, which is traversed by the railway, the traveller's attention is at once attracted by the fantastic tree-yuccas (*Yucca brevifolia*), scattered over the landscape. With these are found in places scrub junipers and some other shrubs. Cacti are scarce, in marked contrast to the Colorado desert to the south, which is separated from the Mojave by the San Bernardino mountains.

In the Mojave the predominant shrub is the creosote-bush (*Larrea Mexicana*), also a feature of the Colorado desert. With it are associated a number of other characteristic species, e. g., *Franseria dumosa*, species of Atriplex, Opuntia, Ephedra, Euphorbia, Lepidium, Gilia, Eschscholtzia and others.

Along the Mexican boundary in southeastern California and Arizona, is the Colorado Desert, a region with a vegetation distinctly Mexican in type, which will be discussed more in detail later.

While the floor of the great valley is largely destitute of trees, especially in the southern areas, the banks of the rivers and smaller streams are more or less heavily wooded. Sometimes, as along parts of the Sacramento, extensive bottom lands are developed, which support a quite heavy forest of large cotton-woods, and elsewhere along the streams are willows and alders.

Sometimes the western sycamore (*Platanus racemosa*) is found along the stream-banks, especially toward the south, and the box-elder (*Acer Negundo*) is a common and wide-spread species. Less common is the Californian walnut (*Juglans Californica*). Roses, blackberries, poison oak (Rhus), dogwood, button-bush (Cephalanthus) are the commonest shrubs of the stream-side thickets.

Marshes are not especially characteristic of the Californian coast, but in the delta lands of the Sacramento and San Joaquin, are extensive tracts of marsh-land, through which the railway between San Francisco and Sacramento passes. These "Tule marshes" are largely almost pure associations of bulrushes (*Scirpus*

Fig. 40.   A   B
A. Coniferous forest, Mt. Shasta region.   B. Azalea (*A. occidentalis*).

spp.). together with cat-tails and other characteristic marsh plants in the more open places.

The accumulation of vegetable matter builds up islands of peaty humus soil, which support many plants, some quite characteristic of the marsh region. When drained, the delta lands are extremely productive, and of great value.

Extending from the Oregon line to southern California, the lofty range of the Sierra Nevada forms California's eastern boundary. The range is less definite at the north, merging into the Cascades of southern Oregon. Southward from Mt. Shasta it is more clearly defined and forms the eastern boundary of the great central valley. The mountains rise rapidly from the level valley floor, and as one ascends, a marked change is noted in the vegetation.

Along the upper Sacramento, and in the vicinity of Mr. Shasta, the Douglas fir is the commonest tree, and the general type of the moist forest is much like that of Oregon and Washington. The flowering dogwood and vine-leaved maple are common and along the Sacramento river one sees bushes of syringa (Philadelphus), and Calycanthus. This region is the home of the Californian pitcher plant (Darlingtonia).

The foot-hills of most of the great valley are grass covered, and with an open growth of oaks, buckeye, and various shrubs, often forming chaparral formations of greater or less extent. The chaparral shrubs are much the same as on the coast ranges, e. g., Manzanita, Ceanothus, Rhus, Ribes, Rhamnus, Eriodictyon, etc.

The first conifers to appear are "digger-pines" (*Pinus Sabiniana*), curious thin-leaved, gray open-branched trees, characteristic of the dry belt which in parts of the range occupies the slopes above the lower foot-hills.

At about 2,500 feet the yellow pine (*P. ponderosa*) begins, and at about 4,000 feet in the middle Sierra, one enters the magnificent belt of mixed coniferous forest, which is perhaps without a rival anywhere in the world.

Below this zone, and sometimes extending into it on dry and exposed slopes, are extensive chaparral formations made up of a good many species. Manzanita (*Arctostaphylos spp.*), Ceanothus, scrub oaks and chinquapin (Castanopsis) are the most abundant chaparral shrubs, but there are a good many others mixed with these. Among the less common but very showy shrubs may be mentioned *Fremontia Californica* (Sterculiaceae), with big yellow flowers, and the rare *Carpenteria Californica* with very handsome white flowers. This chaparral covers great expanses of the dry mountain slopes and is often quite impenetrable, the tough interlacing branches making an impassable thicket.

At about 4,000 feet, the main forest zone begins. This is well shown in the Yosemite valley. At this elevation the yellow pine is the most abundant tree, and reaches its finest development. Some of the trees exceed 200 feet in height with a diameter of five to six feet, or even more.

Higher up, especially where there is abundant moisture, the yellow pine is less in evidence, and at about 6,000 feet, the white

A   B
FIG. 41.—Yellow Pine (*Pinus ponderosa*).   B. Shasta Springs,
      A. Yosemite Valley.   Northern California.

fir (*Abies concolor*) is the commonest species in the regions where the giant Sequoia (*S. gigantea*) is found. The latter, unlike the coast redwood is never predominant in the forest, but occurs in small groups, or singly, in a forest made up mostly of other trees. These in the most important grove, the Giant Forest, are principally white fir, and sugar pine; but in the drier and more exposed

places, yellow pine and incense cedar (*Libocedrus decurrens*), also
are found, and above 6,000 feet, the red fir (*Abies magnifica*).
These are all trees of the first rank and this coniferous forest is
quite unrivalled.

Next in size to the sequoias, is the great sugar pine, the largest
of all pines, and a notable tree from southern Oregon southward.

A   B
Fig. 42.—Sugar Pine (*Pinus Lambertiana*.)
A. Yosemite.   B. Shasta Springs.

In habit it resembles the eastern white pine, but greatly exceeds
it in size. The cones, also, are notable, as the longest of any coniferous tree.

This great forest depends for its water supply mainly upon the
very heavy snow-fall, as little or no rain falls during the summer.
As the snow melts many attractive herbaceous plants appear,

and the woods and moist meadows are adorned throughout the summer with a great variety of beautiful flowers, many of them related to those of the Rocky Mountains, but a large number are peculiar to California. Among the latter is the curious "snow-plant" (*Sarcodes sanguinea*) related to the Indian-pipe of the eastern states, but sometimes a foot high, and with a large raceme of blood-red flowers.

In the lower forest zone, there is an undergrowth of deciduous trees, oaks, maples, and the showy flowering dogwood (*Cornus Nuttallii*). There are also many showy shrubs, like the syringa (*Philadelphus Lewisii*) and the azalea, which is extremely abundant and beautiful in the Yosemite.

Most of the deciduous trees disappear at the higher elevations, and the forest is exclusively coniferous, and certain Rocky Mountain species, e. g., lodge-pole pine, western white pine (*Pinus monticola*) are associated with the Pacific coast species. At timber line, the alpine white pine (*P. albicaulis*), and a large juniper (*Juniperus occidentalis*), are found.

FIG. 43.—False hellebore (*Veratrum Californicum*). Lake Tahoe.

On the rocks and in drier soil are many showy flowers: blue Pentstemons, forget-me-nots (Lappula), and lupins; scarlet Gilias, pink Spraguea, yellow Wyethia, looking like dwarf sun-flowers, little pink and yellow Mimulus and others. In the wet moist meadows are masses of blue Camassia and pink shooting-star (Dodecatheon), white marsh marigold (Caltha) and white violets, and somewhat later white orchids (*Habenaria leucostachys*), blue monkshood and larkspur, gentians, mimulus, scarlet Castilleia, and the small tiger-lily, *L. parvum.* The tall false hellebore (*Veratrum Californicum*) is a very striking and common plant, and in the late summer the meadows are gay with asters, golden-rod, Gaillardia, and others reminiscent of the northern prairies.

FIG. 44.—*Ceanothus sp.*, a characteristic chaparral shrub, Mt. Shasta region.

The true alpine flora of the Sierras is much less developed than on the snow-clad peaks of the Cascades and Rockies; but there are a good many of the same, or closely related species, of Primula, Phlox, Silene, Gentiana, etc.

The flora of the Shasta region of northern California resembles to some extent that of the Cascades, rather than the Sierra. While both yellow and sugar pines occur, the commonest tree is the Douglas fir, which is found also in the Sierra forest, but in much smaller numbers. Where moisture is abundant the beautiful Lawson cypress (*Chamaecyperis Lawsoniana*) also occurs near Mt. Shasta, and deciduous trees, oaks, maples and dogwood, are much in evidence. On springy hillsides, which are a feature of this region, are many flowers which recall the northern woods.

Columbine, bleeding-heart (Dicentra), monkshood, spring-beauty (Claytonia) and tiger-lilies (*L. pardalinum*), grow in the wet mossy ground, with ferns of several species. Thimble-berry (*Rubus Nutkanus*), and cow-parsnip, with its huge leaves and great umbels of white flowers are prominent in this plant formation.

In this region is found the remarkable Californian pitcher plant (*Darlingtonia Californica*), reminding one of the tall Sarracenias of the Gulf states. A number of orchids, Cypripedium, Epipactis, Cephalanthera and others are also characteristic of

A   B

Fig. 45.—A. Californian pitcher plant (*Darlingtonia Californica*), Shasta region, California; B. Giant saxifrage (*Saxifraga peltata*), Upper Sacramento River; Azalea in background.

this region. In general the Californian flora is not rich in orchids.

Many boreal plants, e. g., Linnaea, Clintonia, Pyrola, etc., are common in the woods of this district.

The Colorado Desert

Southeastern California and southern Arizona, the regions adjacent to the Colorado River, are very arid, much of the country being a true desert. Part of this region, like the Imperial valley, is below sea-level, and a region of intense summer heat. The less

arid portions of this desert develop an extremely interesting
vegetation, in which Cacti play an important rôle and comprise
numerous species, ranging in size from the low-spreading prickly-
pears and little melon-cacti, to the giant Suarro (*Cereus giganteus*),

FIG. 46.—"Ocatilla" (*Fouquiera splendens*), Colorado desert.
Photo., Dr. W. S. Cooper.

whose huge fluted columns are sometimes 30 to 40 feet high, and
the most conspicuous objects in the desert landscape.

Creosote-bush (Larrea), Palo-verde (Parkinsonia), and the extraordinary Ocatilla (*Fouqueira splendens*) are also characteristic
of this region. The latter consists of a cluster of unbranched
slender stems, 8 to 10 feet long, bearing small bright green leaves
at times, but mostly quite bare. In the spring each wand is tipped
with a cluster of bright red flowers.

In seasons of heavy spring rains, the ground is covered for a
brief period with a carpet of showy flowers, but these soon disappear with the intense dry heat of the desert summer.

In the vicinity of the Colorado desert are found the only native
Californian palms. Rising abruptly from the desert to a height
of 10,000 feet, the San Jacinto mountains have at their base
canyons opening on the desert. Some of these are watered by
streams which lose themselves in the desert sands, but the floor
of the canyons is permanently moist.

Entering one of these canyons from the sandy desert outside, is like being transported to the tropics, for instead of cactus and creosote-bush, there are groves of tall fan-palms growing luxuriantly in the moist bottom of the canyon, an extraordinary con-

FIG. 47.—California fan-palm (*Washingtonia filifera*), Stanford University. *Photo., Dr. L. L. Burlingame.*

trast to the desert vegetation, only a few rods away. This palm, *Washingtonia filifera*, is very common in cultivation in California, and other countries of similar climate.

Southern California, Arizona, New Mexico and western Texas,

originally Mexican politically, belong botanically to the northern Mexican botanical province. The flora of this region is a typical

Fig. 48.—Desert vegetation, Arizona. *Nolina sp., Yucca sp.*
Photo., Dr. W. S. Cooper.

Fig. 49.—Mountain forest, Arizona. *Photo., Dr. W. S. Cooper.*

xerophytic one, and is very rich in species, mostly belonging to strictly American genera; indeed as a whole, this flora is perhaps the most exclusively American of any region. First in importance

Plate XII.—Vegetation, Pima Canyon, Santa Catalina Mts., Arizona, elevation 3,000 feet. Giant cactus (*Cereus giganteus*), *Ferocactus Wislizenii* (center), *Acacia Greggii* (right). Photo., Dr. Forrest Shreve.

155

are the Cacti, which reach their maximum development in Mexico, as do most of the genera found in the states adjacent to Mexico. About Tucson, in southern Arizona, the desert flora is a rich one, embracing many species of Cacti, Fouquiera, Agave, Ephedra, Larrea, mesquit (Prosopis), and others. Most of the species of Yucca belong to this north Mexican region, as well as the species of Agave, of which the century plant is sufficiently familiar. It has been thought [1] that these peculiarly American forms originated in northern Mexico, and have migrated from this centre both north and south.

Of the more than 1,000 species of Cacti the greater number are Mexican, and the same is true of Agave. Of the latter, 140 species are found in Mexico, while only 24 are known elsewhere.

The Mexican plateau region differs from that of the Pacific Slope in a different distribution of rain, having a marked rainy season in summer. This has an evident effect on the distribution of certain plants. The Cacti, especially, are adapted to utilizing the summer showers, and are rare, or wanting in those parts of California where summer rains are absent. This difference in rainfall is probably largely responsible for the absence or scantiness, of certain Arizona species in southern California.

South of the dry Mexican plateau the rainfall is heavier, and the mountains are clothed with forests much like those of the adjacent United States. Evergreen oaks, pines, and other northern trees, are the principal constituents of the north Mexican mountain forests.

[1] Harshberger, *loc. cit.*, pp. 298–300.

CHAPTER VI

THE PALAEOTROPICS

AFRICA AND CONTINENTAL ASIA

As we have already seen, the tropical floras of the two hemispheres differ far more from each other, than do those of the boreal zones.

In the eastern hemisphere (Palaeotropics), there are two distinct floras, the African and Indo-Malayan, which occupy widely separated regions, and are very different from each other. The American tropics (Neotropics), form a single geographical unit, and the flora is much more homogeneous.

TROPICAL AFRICA

Much the greater part of Africa lies within the tropics, the Tropic of Cancer passing through the centre of the Sahara, while the Tropic of Capricorn lies only about 12° north of the Cape of Good Hope. In spite of the latitude, however, only a relatively small part of Africa exhibits the climatic conditions usually associated with the tropics.

The topography of the great African continent is peculiar. For the most part there is a gradual rise from the coast, sometimes in broad terraces, to a great central plateau, with relatively little land at sea-level. This is less marked in the equatorial regions of the West Coast where there is a development of the rank forest growth characteristic of the wet tropics, not shown to any great extent elsewhere in Africa.

While the greater part of the continent consists of table lands, the elevation of these is moderate (1,000—2,000 metres), and the high mountains, like Kilimanjaro and the great Kamerun, are generally more or less isolated masses rising from the much lower table land.

This elevation of the general mass of the continent of course involves a decided lowering of the mean temperature of the plateau

157

compared with that at sea-level, so that the climate is for the most part sub-tropical rather than tropical. Of course at the coast the temperatures are very high, indeed some of the stations in the Sahara and on the coast of the Red Sea, are probably the hottest places anywhere. A mean annual temperature of 30°C (86°F) is recorded for some stations in the Sahara.

Precipitation in tropical Africa shows a very great range, which of course has a corresponding effect on the development of vegetation. In much of the northern area, including the Sahara and the Egyptian deserts, the rainfall is extremely scanty, or even practically *nil*. On the other hand, the West Coast equatorial belt is one of the rainiest regions known. One station in Kamarun [1] is reported to have an annual average of 9,374 mm. (about 350 in.).

There is, therefore, every type of vegetation between that of the absolute deserts of Upper Egypt and the Sahara, and the steaming mangrove swamps and jungles of the Guinea coast, Congo basin and Kamerun.

Much of the interior is occupied by grass-lands, supporting the immense herds of herbivorous animals which are such a marked feature of the African fauna. These grass-lands are often of the savanna type, i. e., there are trees and shrubs growing singly or in open forests, and also often serving as food for giraffes, elephants, and other animals.

The transition from the open grass-land, or prairie, to the true forest may be a gradual one, the savanna being an intermediate phase.

In northeast Africa the mountainous region of Abyssinia rises abruptly from the shores of the Red Sea, and descends on the west to the humid region which includes the great lakes in which the Nile takes its rise. The Abyssinian mountains are in more or less direct connection with those of South Africa by means of the central African highlands, and this is of great importance in a study of the African vegetation, as there has been undoubtedly a large amount of interchange between Abyssinia and South Africa.

Unlike North America, the African continent supports a large indigenous population, who are agriculturists and herdsmen. There is no question that the vegetation of Africa has been very much affected by their activities. It is more than

[1] Engler, A., DIE VEGETATION DER ERDE, Vol. IX, p. 907.

likely that the extent of forested country has been greatly diminished by their primitive agricultural methods: cutting and burning the forest, and setting fire to the grass-lands, which have no doubt much extended their original area.

EQUATORIAL WEST AFRICA

In the excessively wet coastal regions of western equatorial Africa, and in the basins of the great rivers which discharge their waters into the Atlantic, there is developed a great rain-forest of the most pronounced type.

An enormous amount of silt is discharged by the West African rivers, and along the coast as far as the tidal influence extends up the rivers and estuaries, there is a vast extent of mangrove swamps. These are rapidly advancing, owing to the constant deposit of mud, but as they advance the inner portions are gradually shut off from the tidal water, and by degrees the mangrove formation is replaced by a belt of vegetation which gradually merges into the typical rain-forest of the solid land.

The outer margin of the swamp is composed entirely of the same species of mangrove (*Rhizophora mangle*), as that on the American side of the Atlantic, and is quite distinct from the species on the shores of the Indian Ocean. Further inland the "white mangrove" (*Avicennia nitida*) occurs, and this species also occurs in tropical America, but not in the eastern tropics. Two species of Combretaceae, *Laguncularia racemosa* and *Conocarpus erectus*, form low thickets beyond the mangrove formation, and the handsome fern, *Acrostichum aureum*, common in similar situations everywhere in the tropics, grows between the mangroves.[1]

Between the mangrove formation and the rain-forest is a strip of land partly reclaimed from the swamp, but with strongly saline soil in which a number of characteristic shrubs and small trees grow. Among these, Engler mentions *Scaevola lobelia*, *Caesalpinia bonducella*, *Flagellaria Indica*, a climber, as is also the curious leafless *Cassytha filiformis*, which much resembles dodder in appearance, but belongs to the laurel family. These plants also grow on sand-dunes along the coast.

[1] Engler, *loc. cit.*, p. 938.

From the Niger delta to the Congo, the mangrove swamps are developed on an enormous scale.

The West African rain-forest reaches its greatest development in Kamerun, where rich volcanic soils combine with an equatorial climate to produce a maximum luxuriance of vegetation; but the whole coastal region from the Niger to the Congo has a very heavy forest.

The country rises rapidly back of the coast, and the forest is largely restricted to the regions bordering the great rivers which descend from the interior, while much of the inland country is open grass-land or savanna.

Back of the coastal belt of mangroves is a strip of "alluvial forest," composed of a variety of trees, shrubs, and climbing plants, but having only trees of moderate size.

Almost the first tree to invade the new land, is a screw-pine (*Pandanus candelabrum*). The screw-pines are all palaeotropic, and are very characteristic of the strand floras, although by no means restricted to the coastal regions. Their curious stilt-like roots and spirally set sword-shaped leaves are a familiar sight in the tropics of the old world, and they are not uncommon in cultivation.

Several species of palms are characteristic of the alluvial forest. Among these are a wild date (*Phoenix spinosa*) and the wine-palm (*Raphia vinifera*), as well as rattan-palms, climbing species, whose thorny stems and leaves are a terror to the explorer. With these are associated species of low-growing trees and shrubs, belonging to many families, but with Leguminosae most abundant. Climbing plants of many sorts abound, as they do everywhere where light is sufficient.

Characteristic of the whole coastal zone is the oil-palm (*Elaeis Guieneensis*), which grows wild, but is also extensively planted. This yields the palm-oil, such an important article of commerce. The oil-palm is a very handsome tree, often seen in cultivation in tropical countries. It has enormous feathery leaves, and the persistent leaf-bases, and rough stem offer a very favorable attachment for orchids, ferns and other epiphytes.

The alluvial, or border forest, passes gradually into the high rain-forest in which the variety of trees is very great, and many of them attain gigantic size. The trees are very tall, and the

interior of the forest is so densely shaded that very little undergrowth is developed, and such species as occur are able to exist
with a minimum of light.

This forest interior has been very graphically described by
Miss Kingsley.[1] The giant, smooth gray or red trunks form
huge pillars, sometimes a hundred feet high, or more, before
branching to form the roof of this great temple. There are few
epiphytic growths, except high up in the crowns of the trees,
and the huge lianas which swing from tree to tree are quite bare
until they reach the light above the dense canopy of foliage.

The most important of these lianas are several species of Lan-
dolphia (Apocynaceae) which yield most of the West African
rubber.

Where light is admitted, as when trees are blown down by
tornadoes, which often devastate these regions, or in clearings
made by the lumberman, or along the banks of the rivers, the
forest presents a very different aspect. In such situations there
is an amazing luxuriance of vegetation, the lofty trees being clothed
from top to bottom with epiphytes and a great variety of lianas.

Some of these vines, e. g., *Quisqualis indica, Clerodendron
splendens, Solanum sp.*, as well as certain trees, have showy
flowers, which in their season relieve the monotony of the uniform
green of the rain-forest.

The number of species of trees in this great forest is very large,
and only a few of the more characteristic ones can be mentioned.[2]

As in most tropical forests, the Leguminosae are abundant, and
some of them reach enormous size. Giant figs are also a feature
of the forest. The latter often begin life as epiphytes perched on
a branch, or in a crotch of some tall tree, near the light. The
young fig sends its roots downward, and these completely encircle
the parent tree, which is finally strangled, leaving the fig with
its crown supported by a huge hollow trunk formed of the coales-
cent roots. These "strangling figs" occur in the rain-forests of
both hemispheres.

Some of the giant trees of West Africa are of great value for
their timber. These include several species of mahogany and

---

[1] Mary H. Kingsley, *Travels in West Africa*, pp. 261–262, 1897.
[2] For a very full account of the vegetation of this region see Engler, *loc. cit.*,
Vol. I, Pt. II.

ebony, the latter related to our persimmon. Among the notable trees are species of silk-cotton (*Ceiba, Bombax*), trees of the largest size, with enormous buttresses supporting the huge trunks. Other trees belong to the nutmeg family (Myristicaceae), and the Euphorbiaceae have numerous representatives.

Some of the trees exceed 200 feet in height, and among them are species with showy flowers, which, however, are quite invisible to the wanderer in the forest floor beneath. Among the best known of these is *Spathodea campanulata*, related to our Catalpa and trumpet creeper, whose big orange-scarlet bell-shaped flowers are very handsome. This tree is quite common in cultivation throughout the tropics.

Where the light is sufficient there is a heavy undergrowth of herbaceous plants. Some of the Araceae, and Scitamineae (gingers, Cannas, bananas, etc.) are especially conspicuous and the ponds and shallow river margins show a profusion of aquatics: sedges, water-lilies, pond-weeds, etc. Some of the climbing Araceae are very conspicuous, as they are in nearly all wet tropical regions.

The Scitamineae include several species of true bananas (Musa), distributed over tropical Africa, in addition to the many cultivated varieties of plantains and bananas. The gingers (Zingiber, Costus, etc.), are extremely abundant in the wet districts, and *Canna indica* is a common weed, as it is in many countries where it has been introduced from America.

Of the sedges, the famous papyrus (*Cyperus Papyrus*) is abundant in many other parts of tropical Africa, as well as in the Nile district.

Compared with the equatorial regions of America and Indo-Malaya, the West African forest flora is relatively limited in extent and poor in species, especially in such very characteristic types as the palms and orchids, both of which attain their maximum development in the American and eastern tropics. This is true also of the Araceae.

A remarkable result of the more recent studies in the flora of equatorial West Africa is the demonstration of unmistakable relationships with tropical America. Engler [1] gives a long list of genera and species peculiar to West Africa and America, or predominant in these regions. Examples of these are the two

[1] *Loc. cit.*, pp. 984-986.

common mangroves, the wine-palm, and a species of oil-palm (Elaeis), as well as many others. Engler concludes that there must have been more or less complete land connections between South America and Africa, at some earlier period.

Much of the more elevated portions of tropical Africa is occupied by grass-land and open forest or savanna, with a sub-tropical rather than tropical climate. The grass flora is a very rich one and is a very important constituent of the African vegetation, much of the "veldt" in the Transvaal and Rhodesia looking quite like the prairies of the western Mississippi valley and Great Plains. These grasses comprise many such wide-spread genera as Andropogon, Panicum, Paspalum, Agrostis, etc., but tropical Africa possesses a considerable number of genera, either strictly endemic or mainly African. Examples of these are Beckera, Perotis, Schmidtea, Chaetobromus.[1]

In addition to the numerous grasses of the open plains and savannas, there are giant grasses like the common reed (*Phragmites vulgaris*) and various bamboos; and the wild sugar cane (*Saccharum spontaneum*) is common in many places. A good many grasses, like the bamboos and many smaller species, are found in the wet forest, and such forest grasses usually have soft and relatively broad leaves.

TROPICAL EAST AFRICA

The equatorial portion of the East coast offers a marked contrast to the opposite side of the continent. Nowhere, at sea-level, is the rain-forest developed, and only back of the coast, at the base of the mountains which intercept the rains which pass over the immediate coast, is a rain-forest encountered. It is much less luxuriant than the west coast forest both because of the limited extent of the area of heavy precipitation, and because a large part of the forest has been cleared for agriculture.

As one sails along the East African coast the shore for the most part shows a sandy beach. Mangrove swamps are found where rivers discharge, as at Beira in Portuguese East Africa and other points along the coast, and in places, back of the shore are hills clothed with forest; but the trees are mostly deciduous, and in

---

[1] Engler, *loc. cit.*, p. 992.

October, when the writer made this trip, being the dry season, they were mostly bare with only a few evergreen species like some of the figs.

The most remarkable tree of this region, but wide-spread in central Africa, is the Baobab (*Adansonia digitata*). These trees, with their huge ungainly trunks, and wide-spread naked limbs were much the most conspicuous trees of this east coast. The leaves

FIG. 50.—Coast, tropical East Africa. Coconut palms, baobab.

of the baobab are somewhat like those of the horse-chestnut, and the flowers, and later the big fruits, hang vertically from long slender stalks.

The mangrove formations are relatively limited in extent, and not comparable with the immense coastal swamps of West Africa. They are also inferior in the size of the trees. The eastern mangrove, *Rhizophora mucronata*, is a much smaller tree than *R. mangle* of the west coast.

From the excessively wet coastal districts of equatorial West Africa, there is a rapid falling off in precipitation both north and south. The delta region of the Congo, is much drier than the Kamerun coast, and in much of Portuguese West Africa, and the former German West Africa, desert conditions prevail, even at the coast. North of the Gulf of Guinea, there is a similar diminution in rainfall until in Senegal, and especially in the western Sahara, desert conditions are encountered.

The coastal region of Angola (Portuguese West Africa), from the

Fig. 51.—Baobab, Mombasa, British East Africa.

Congo southward, is a dry plain with characteristic xerophytic vegetation, scattered shrubs and stunted trees, with an occasional baobab. The commonest tree is *Sterculia tomentosa*. With these are found Aloes, the curious cactus-like Euphorbias, so characteristic of South Africa, and *Sansevieria cylindrica*, a liliaceous plant with stiff, rush-like leaves.

The vegetation changes, however, as soon as the hilly country, some 30–40 miles from the coast, is reached. Here there is a forest growth of both deciduous and evergreen species.[1]

[1] Engler, *loc. cit.*, pp. 623–24.

At higher altitudes in the mountains there is a marked increase in rainfall, and in the valleys and more sheltered situations, a true rain-forest is developed.

Further south the coast is very arid, and finally true desert conditions prevail.

The most remarkable plant of this district is the extraordinary Tumboa (Welwitschia) which has no near relatives elsewhere. It belongs to the small order Gnetales, which in some respects is intermediate between the true gymnosperms (conifers and cycads), and the higher flowering plants. Welwitschia has a short woody trunk which sends a long tap-root deep into the ground, and bears two great persistent, strap-shaped leaves, generally split into ribbons, which are all the plant ever develops. This desert coast region is continuous with the great Kalahari desert of South Africa.

THE GREAT KAMERUN

The high volcanic peaks of equatorial Africa show, as might be expected, great changes in vegetation as one ascends. The great peak of Kamerun (13,370 ft.) has been carefully studied, and will serve as an example.[1]

At the base of the mountain, where the land has not been cleared, is a lofty rain-forest of the most pronounced type. Where the cultivated land has been abandoned, a second growth forest of a very different character soon occupies the clearings. This second growth forest contains many species which are unable to grow in the dense shade of the primitive rain-forest. Areas of meadowland and savanna also develop in the cleared spots, and in more open places are many attractive herbaceous plants, some having handsome flowers, like Crinum, with big lily-like blossoms, or balsams (Impatiens) with attractive flowers of various colors. Ferns and some of the numerous gingers, are noticeable for their fine foliage, and some of the latter, also, have showy flowers.

A very characteristic grass of this region is the elephant-grass (*Pennisetum purpureum*) which is ordinarily some ten feet in height, but may exceed this. This very valuable forage grass often covers extensive areas, and only permits a scattered growth

[1] Engler, *loc. cit.*, p. 758.

PLATE XIII.—*Welwitschia mirabilis.* The upper figure shows the character of the habitat; the lower a nearer view of the staminate plant. About 40 km. east of Swakopmund, West Africa. *Photo., Dr. W. A. Cannon.*

167

of trees, among which are the oil-palm, Kigelia, and the showy Spathodea.

Above the lower forest zone, is a belt of second growth forest, with many oil- and wine-palms, and at a still higher elevation is a mixed forest, of deciduous and evergreen species. Of the latter, figs are perhaps the most characteristic, and of the deciduous trees, *Erythrina excelsa* is the most notable. Erythrina is a genus of leguminous trees with representatives in nearly all tropical regions. Most of them have extremely showy scarlet flowers, which often appear while the tree is bare of leaves. *E. excelsa*, as its name indicates, is a very tall tree, and blooms in December. It is a common tree and overtops all its neighbors.

Among the many shrubs and smaller trees is a composite, *Vernonia amygdalina*, a near relative of the iron-weed of the eastern United States, but becoming a small tree. Among the many climbers, species of Clematis, morning glories (Ipomoea) vines (Cissus) related to the grape, and some others, are not entirely unfamiliar.

The high forest extends in places to an elevation of about 3,000 feet, but for the most part the forest at this elevation is composed of lower trees in great variety, and contains also many species of shrubs, climbers, and herbaceous plants. In the gorges especially, ferns become an important element in the vegetation, among them a tree fern (*Alsophila Kamarunensis*), and *Marattia fraxinea*, a fern with very big fronds. There is a profusion of terrestrial herbaceous plants, orchids, Begonias, Coleus, balsams, and a graceful club-moss (*Selaginella nitens*). Liverworts and mosses play a more important rôle than at lower elevations, the trunks of trees being sometimes quite overgrown with them, as well as with ferns, and several species of epiphytic orchids, e. g., Angraecum, Saccolobium, are abundant.

As at lower elevations, the clearings may support a heavy growth of elephant-grass, and there are many striking herbaceous plants in the more open parts of the forest. Among these may be mentioned Begonias, Clerodendron, several orchids, Coleus, and the foxglove-like flowers of *Streptocarpus elongatus*.

Above 1,500 metres, wild coffee trees (*Coffea brevipes*) are found, and the vegetation begins to show an infusion of northern genera, Viola, Thalictrum, and others.

The high forest stops at about 6,000 feet, a remarkably low point when compared with high mountains in much colder regions, as in the Rocky Mountains and Sierra Nevada in America, or the Himalayas.

Above the forest zone, the mountain is covered with a grass-formation, interspersed up to 2,500 metres, with patches of stunted trees, which are covered with a heavy growth of epiphytes.

The summit of the mountain has a flora which includes many familiar types of temperate climes, such as St. John's wort (Hypericum), buttercups, foreget-me-not, hound's tongue (Cynoglossum), milfoil (Achillaea), Stachys, Veronica, Galium, plantain, etc.[1]

EAST CENTRAL AFRICA

The region near the headwaters of the Blue and White Nile is an elevated rugged plateau of steppe character. It is largely open grass-land but there are also savannas and dry forest in places. The baobab and several species of Acacia are wide-spread in this region, and two characteristic palms, the Indian fan-palm (*Borassus flabelliformis*) and the dom-palm (*Hyphaene Thebaica*), are common, especially in the narrow forest areas along the rivers.

This plateau region is enclosed by mountains which connect with the highlands of Abyssinia, and are the source of most of the water that feeds the Nile.

The White Nile, especially, and its tributaries are in many places bordered by extensive swamps, formed by the flood waters. These marshes contain many characteristic aquatics, among which the famous papyrus is especially conspicuous. Between the clumps of papyrus, reeds, rushes, and other tall marsh plants, are solid patches of "sudd," dense turfy masses of shorter grasses and other plants, which completely hide the surface of the water, giving the appearance of solid ground. Detached masses of sudd, floating in the open water, are often a serious hindrance to navigation.

Along the banks of the rivers, is a belt of forest, in which groves of palms are the most conspicuous feature, but back

[1] For details of the flora of the Great Kamerun, see Engler, *loc. cit.*

of this the land is either a grassy savanna with scattered trees, or a steppe covered with dry thorny, and in winter, leafless scrub; or sometimes, low open forest.

Rising to the east and north are the highlands of Abyssinia, 1,800–2,500 metres in height, and consequently temperate in climate. The lower portions of the western slopes, rising from the Nile steppe, have dry open woods with tall grasses between the trees, one of the commonest trees being the tamarind (*Tamarindus Indicus*), which in general appearance is not unlike the American honey-locust (Gleditschia). Acacias of several species, figs, including the sycamore fig (*Ficus Sycamora*) and a variety of other trees and shrubs occur. Most of these shed their leaves in the dry season, and often flower before the new foliage appears, very much as do so many trees of northern climates.

In the highlands there is no marked dry season, and the differences in the vegetation are due largely to soil and exposure. Where volcanic soils occur, there is a luxuriant evergreen forest in which species of Ficus are conspicuous, and in general the trees and shrubs are related to those of the drier lowlands. A date-palm (*Phoenix reclinata*) is common, and among the characteristic genera, are the following: Rhus, Pittosporum, Catha, Sparmannia, Dombeya, Croton, Acacia.

The more luxuriant vegetation of these moister uplands is also indicated by the increasing number of climbing plants, e. g., Asparagus, Dioscorea, Clematis, Rubus, Phaseolus, Convolvulus, etc.

As in other tropical high mountains, there is a large floral element related to that of the temperate zone. In the Abyssinian highlands one meets with many species of such familiar genera as Gladiolus, Geranium, Pelargonium, Polygala, Hypericum, Primula, Campanula, Dianthus, Lobelia, and many others, especially members of the families Labiatae, Scrophulariaceae and Solanaceae.

Some of these are closely related to, or even identical with European species, but many are unmistakably allied to species of the Cape region of Africa. In the latter category are many beautiful Iridaceae, e. g., Gladiolus, Moraea, Acidanthera; also many ground orchids (Habenaria, Plantanthera, Satyrium, Disa); Haemanthus, Crinum, Aloe, Mesembryanthemum, Protea, Gerbera, etc., are also characteristic.

The Abyssinian highlands have but two gymnospermous trees, a juniper (*Juniperus procera*), which is abundant in some localities, and becomes a large tree, furnishing valuable timber; the second, *Podocarpus gracilior*, a member of the Yew family, represents a genus characteristic of South Africa and others regions of the southern hemisphere.[1]

Eastward is the abrupt descent to the shores of the Red Sea. At the higher elevations, the temperate, well watered regions have an abundant vegetation; but as the descent is made to the intensely hot arid Red Sea shores, the plants assume more and more the xerophytic character common to so much of the tropical African flora. Cactus-like Euphorbias, Aloes, thorny Acacias, jujube (Zizyphus), together with various bunch-grasses and thorny shrubs, are the principal features.

In places along the coast are mangrove swamps and saline flats, where salt-bushes and other salt-resistant plants grow, while on the coral rock are succulents of various kinds and the whole vegetation proclaims the intense heat and aridity of this inhospitable region.

Southward from the equator to the Tropic of Capricorn, except for the Congo basin, the general type of country is very uniform, a plateau with moderate or scanty rainfall, and much barren soil.

The predominant type of vegetation is the savanna, the amount of tree growth depending much on soil and moisture. This region is subject to a more or less pronounced dry season, during which many trees and shrubs are either quite leafless or with a few dry leaves clinging to the bare branches. Such a savanna country in the dry season presents quite as dreary a picture as the bare winter forests of northern climes.

This savanna, "bosch-veldt" in the vernacular, may be seen well developed in the vicinity of the Victoria Falls of the Zambesi.

In 1905, the writer visited South Africa with the British Association for the Advancement of Science, and in September made the trip from Bulawayo, in Rhodesia, to the Falls.

Bulawayo lies in the Matabele plateau between 4,000 and 5,000 feet elevation, and the climate is much like that of northern Mexico. About Bulawayo Mexican plants are said to be very much

[1] For details of the Abyssinian Flora, see Engler, *loc. cit.*, pp. 84-127.

at home, and the writer noted a common Mexican bush-poppy (Hunnemannia) growing with remarkable luxuriance.

In September the end of the dry season was approaching, and a number of showy trees and shrubs were coming into flower. Especially notable were the pendent racemes of yellow flowers of *Cassia fistula*, the "golden shower," of Honolulu, and the rosy flowers of the related *Bauhinia sp.* and scarlet flowered Erythrina.

North of Bulawayo, where one takes the train for the Victoria Falls, lies the rugged range of granite hills, the Matoppos, where rests the body of Cecil Rhodes. From these barren granite rocks one looks over a vast expanse of "bosch-veldt," the trees growing fairly close together in some parts, elsewhere more scattered. Between are bunch-grasses, especially species of Andropogon, and *Aristida stipoides*, the latter a very tall and striking species.

Although the climate is rather warm temperate than tropical, nevertheless many species are of equatorial origin, and are widespread over the great central African plateau.

Among the largest trees were several species of Ficus, among them a variety of the sycamore fig, sometimes 25 to 30 feet high. Other trees or large shrubs are species of Dombeya (Sterculiaceae) with white or pink flowers which are occasionally cultivated in California; Terminalia, Erythrina, Pterocarpus, Combretum, Cassia, Strychnos, and others. Leguminosae are particularly abundant. On some of the trees were growing parasites of the mistletoe family, Loranthus and Viscum, and an epiphytic orchid (*Ansellia Africana*).

Shrubby plants in great variety grow between the trees, some belonging to familiar types like sumacs and mallows; other characteristic genera are Colpoon (Santalaceae), Turraea (Meliaceae), Clerodendron (Verbenaceae), Euclea (Ebenaceae), *Coffea Engleri* (Rubiaceae).

Among the rocks of the Matoppos, stunted trees and shrubs find a foot-hold. One of these, the "Natal plum" (*Carissa edulis*), is sometimes cultivated in Florida and Southern California.

These rocky situations offer a congenial habitat for numerous succulents: Euphorbias, Aloes and a curious leafless plant (Sarcostemma) of the milkweed family. Several xerophytic ferns, (Cheilanthes, Pellaea), and a club-moss (*Selagenella Dregei*), grow in the rock crevices.

On the open veldt leguminous trees predominate. Acacias, so abundant in all the drier parts of Africa, are represented by many species, usually small thorny trees with umbrella crowns. One of the commonest is *A. giraffae*, "Kameel-dorn," in the vernacular, the favorite food of the giraffe. *A. horrida* as its name implies, is a particularly thorny species. *Peltophorum Africanum, Copaifera sp.*, several species of Rhus, Combretum, *Terminalia sericea*, Strychnos, Dombeya, Burkea, Albizzia, Bauhinia, are all characteristic of the open veldt.

Fig. 52.—Savanna vegetation, Victoria Falls, Rhodesia.

As one travels northward from Bulawayo, the land descends to the Zambesi, the Victoria Falls being less than 1,000 metres above sea-level. The lower elevation, as well as lower latitude, makes the flora of the region more tropical in aspect than that of the higher plateau to the south.

The vegetation is more luxuriant and the variety of trees and shrubs greater. Near the Falls the baobab is seen, and the trees in general are taller, and may form open forests of considerable extent. In September, these trees were mostly leafless, and the country covered with dry grass and leafless trees, presented anything but a picture of tropical luxuriance. The exception to this impression was the occasional presence of a Cassia or Bauhinia, covered with golden or rosy flowers.

A very common low shrub of the more open country is *Protea mellifera*, a member of the Proteaceae, a family particularly abundant in the Cape region, but poorly represented in tropical Africa.

While the country as a whole between Bulawayo and the Zambesi was very dry and dead-looking, where moisture was present, as along the banks of the infrequent streams, groves of palms (*Hyphaene sp.*), gave quite a tropical look to the landscape.

In the dry forest, trees 40–50 feet high are found, mostly Leguminosae, with spreading crowns. The commonest of these are *Baikiaea plurijuga* and *Copaifera coleosperma*. The latter has bifid leaves like those of Bauhinia. Between the trees is a heavy growth of the tall grass, *Aristida stipoides*. Much of the country is more of the nature of a steppe, in which the baobab is a conspicuous feature, and the candelabra-Euphorbias, and Aloes, recall the Cacti and Agaves of Arizona and Mexico.

A great contrast to the prevailing xerophytic vegetation of this region is seen in those places near the river which get a sufficiency of moisture.

Thus on Livingstone Island, at the brink of the Falls, there is a vegetation of quite tropical luxuriance: palms, figs, orchids, and in the river, clumps of papyrus and other aquatics, offered a strong contrast to the parched dead landscape of the surrounding country. Such delicate moisture-loving plants as bladder-weed (Utricularia) and a pretty Lobelia, as well as other delicate herbs were common, and on rocks in the river, were specimens of a curious aquatic, Podostemon.

In a narrow ravine near the Falls, known as "Palmkloof" were many graceful date-palms (*Phoenix reclinata*), evergreen figs, and other large trees, with numerous climbing plants and ferns, all testifying to the presence of ample moisture.

Still more striking is the so-called rain-forest at the edge of the great gorge directly opposite the cataract, and constantly drenched with clouds of spray sent up from the narrow gorge into which the river plunges. The margin of the gorge, within reach of the shower of spray, is clothed with a dense growth of trees, with ferns, orchids and other characteristic rain-forest species beneath, recalling the great equatorial rain-forests, although the number of species is much restricted by the limited extent of this "rain-forest," as well as by latitude and elevation, which result in a much lower average temperature than in the equatorial coastal belt.

The most important trees of the Zambesi rain-forest are two species of Syzygium, a handsome evergreen tree of the myrtle family, which has few African representatives. These were low spreading trees, and with them were associated three species of Ficus, which were much taller, 50–60 feet, and over these were growing several stout woody climbers, with cable-like stems. The ground was carpeted with maidenhair, and other ferns, and

FIG. 53.—"Rain-forest," Victoria Falls of the Zambesi, Rhodesia.

among them were growing several orchids, as well as various other herbaceous plants.

This bit of rain-forest is especially interesting as it was originally described by Livingstone when he discovered the great Victoria Falls. While it presents a decidedly tropical aspect, still one misses some of the plants which would be found at similar altitudes nearer the equator. Thus there are no tree-ferns, or the conspicuous wild gingers, bananas, arums and rattans which one associates with the upland rain-forest of the equatorial regions. This, however, is probably a matter of isolation as much as temperature, since many of these tropical growths would probably flourish if transported to the Zambesi rain-forest.

THE ASIATIC TROPICS

Unlike Africa, much the greater part of Asia is extratropical; but the southeastern part of the continent, Indo-China and Malaya, shows a far more extensive and luxuriant tropical vegetation than any part of Africa except the relatively small equatorial region of the West Coast. The latter region, moreover, is much poorer in species than the Indo-Malayan flora, whose only rival is equatorial America.

In western Asia, southern Arabia is the only region lying within the tropics, and this, in climate and vegetation is closely related to the regions on the African side of the Red Sea. Much of tropical India is also arid or semi-arid, and it is only in limited areas, like parts of the west coast, and the regions about the Bay of Bengal, that the vegetation exhibits the luxuriant development of the wet tropics, although owing to the mild climate of the southern slopes of the Himalaya, the vegetation is largely composed of tropical species which extend far into the temperate zone where there is a mixture of tropical and boreal types.

The tropical Asiatic forest attains its highest development in the Malayan region, where equatorial conditions of heat and moisture combine to produce a maximum growth of the rank, exuberant, rain-forest vegetation.

In the Malay Peninsula and the great islands of the Malay archipelago, Borneo, Sumatra, Java, New Guinea, and the southern Philippines, most of the lowland country has a hot-house climate with almost constant temperatures, and very heavy and uniform rainfall. When, in addition, rich volcanic or alluvial soils prevail, as in western Java and parts of Sumatra, the luxuriance and variety of the vegetation is unsurpassed in any part of the world.

ARABIA

Arabia, north of the Tropic of Cancer, is in topography and climate like the deserts of North Africa, and the vegetation is much the same. The portion which lies within the tropics shows much variety of elevation, and a corresponding range in precipitation and the resultant vegetation.

From the almost rainless, intensely hot coastal belt along the Red Sea and Indian Ocean, the southwest point of Arabia rises very much like the corresponding shores of Africa on the west side of the Red Sea, to an elevation of about 9,000 feet.

As in Abyssinia, the higher mountains intercept the moisture-laden winds from the Indian Ocean, and the upper and intermediate elevations receive a fairly abundant rainfall, so that a luxuriant vegetation of sub-tropical and warm temperate type flourishes. Very little moisture passes inland and the elevated plateau soon merges into the desert which covers much the greater part of Arabia. The rainfall at the higher elevations is supplemented by frequent clouds and mists, and heavy dews play their part in conserving moisture. Conditions are especially favorable in the deep valleys and gorges eroded by the mountain streams.

The vegetation of the mountains much resembles that of the Abyssinian highlands, but there is also a large endemic element more nearly allied to true Asiastic species, and related to the desert vegetation to the east.

Of the indigenous plants, the original coffee (*Coffea arabica*), is the most notable. The Arabian town of Mocha is inseparably associated with this famous product of Arabia. As we have seen, other species of coffee occur in various parts of Africa, and one of them, the Liberian coffee, is extensively cultivated in regions where the Arabian coffee does not thrive.

With the sub-tropical vegetation related to the Abyssinian flora, there are a good many Mediterranean species, so that the flora as a whole is an extensive one. This portion of Arabia was formerly much more densely populated than at present, and the centre of an important trade in gums, balsams, spices, etc., which abound in the hot semi-arid regions of medium elevation.

"Araby the blest," "Arabia felix" of the ancients has sadly declined from those days when it was the source of the prized balsams and spices. The Arabian balsam was the product of trees of two genera Boswellea and Balsamodendron. Species of Acacia, as in Africa, are common, and from some of them the gum-arabic of commerce is derived.

India

Only about half of the total area of India lies actually within the tropics, and in the northwestern part, and much of the Himalayan districts, sub-tropical rather than tropical conditions prevail.

Immediately south of the great barrier of the Himalaya lies the extensive alluvial plain extending from the Arabian Sea to the Bay of Bengal and comprising much of the land watered by the Indus and Ganges.

The great plain of the Indus is extremely arid, sometimes absolutely rainless for a year or more. It is partly alluvial, partly occupied by saline swamps, but a large part is a sandy or rocky desert. Eastward the precipitation increases rapidly, and the central, and especially the eastern portions of the Gangetic plain, have a heavy rainfall. This is greatest about the head of the Bay of Bengal, and the Ganges delta, where annual precipitation exceeding 100 inches is not unusual.

The central and eastern plains, which get the regular monsoon rains, are extremely productive, and the most densely populated portion of India.

Most of the tropical part of India is comprised in the great central plateau, enclosed by low ranges of mountains near the coast, and a range to the north separating it from the Gangetic plain. The two coastal ranges, the Western and Eastern Ghats, converge southward, and are partially connected by transverse hills. The great enclosed central plain is the Deccan, a plateau of about 3,000 feet elevation. The northern portion of the Deccan is semi-arid, as the moisture of the southwest monsoon is mostly intercepted by the Western Ghats. To the south, conditions are better, but nowhere in the interior of India are conditions such that a tropical rain-forest can develop.

The western coast (Malabar), receives the full benefit of the southwest monsoon, and has an abundant rainfall, resulting in evergreen forests of true tropical luxuriance.

The conditions northeast of the Bay of Bengal are such that in Assam and the Kasi hills, there is an excessively heavy rainfall. One station, Cheripunji, has an annual precipitation of nearly 500 inches, exceeding this in some years, giving it the reputation of the rainiest spot in the world. This region, however, lies outside the tropics, and the vegetation, although extremely luxuriant, is to a great extent sub-tropical, rather than tropical. Separating the Indus and Ganges plain from the plateau of the Deccan is a series of hills or low mountains of which the highest, Mt. Abu, rises above the Punjab plain to an altitude of 5,650 feet. Famous for the beautiful Jain temples, Mt. Abu is often visited by tourists in northern India.

The Western Ghats rise from the western coast in a series of terraces. The highest point is 4,700 feet above the sea. From the eastern edge of the Ghats, the plateau slopes gradually to the less elevated Eastern Ghats, the two border ranges uniting at the south in the Nilgiri Hills, with an extreme elevation of 8,700 feet. The enclosed Deccan plateau, with an elevation of from 1,000 to 3,000 feet, is occupied by the Central Provinces.

The southern point of the Peninsula has mountains along the coast, continuing the Western Ghats; but the eastern side is nearly level with only isolated ranges of low hills.

Separated from the extreme southern point of the Indian Peninsula, by only about 50 miles, is the Island of Ceylon.

THE INDUS PLAIN

The northwestern plains of India traversed by the Indus, are a continuation of the great desert stretching from Egypt through Arabia and Mesopotamia. Excessively hot in summer, with relatively cold winter, the whole region is too arid for agriculture, except where irrigation is available. Some parts of this region are practically rainless.

The scanty vegetation is very uniform throughout, and in northwest India the vegetation is much the same as in the desert regions to the west. Thorny Acacias (*A. Arabica*), a poplar (*Populus Euphratica*) and wild figs grow along the streams, tamarisk and jujube (*Zizyphus sp.*), a leafless caper (*Capparis aphylla*), and various shrubby Leguminosae are the most important elements of the flora.

The northwest provinces get very little rain from the southwest monsoon, which is deflected to the east by the mountains to the south. This whole region is dependent upon the Indus, which furnishes water for irrigation, but apparently the flow of the river has diminished since ancient times.

The original flora of the great alluvial plains of the Punjab and Bengal has long since disappeared before the intense cultivation of the land for ages by the dense population, and the whole region is practically destitute of any indigenous forest formations. Only

PLATE XIV.—Vegetation near Mt. Abu, northwest India. At the right, on the rocks, a bushy Euphorbia.

180

in the most barren regions, impossible of cultivation, can one find any wild vegetation, and the desperate poverty of much of this over-populated region leaves scarcely a trace of any tree, shrub, or weed that can be used for fuel.

Journeying in Rajputana, from Mt. Abu to Jaipur, the principal city of the Province, one passes through a less densely populated country, an open dry region, with rugged hills and scattered stunted trees. Acacias, the showy "Dhak" (*Butea frondosa,*) with brilliant scarlet flowers, "Neem" (*Azaderachta indica*) with ash-like leaves, and wild date-palms (*Phoenix sylvestris*). In the rocky places one sees cactus-like Euphorbias, like those of Africa, and other xerophytes.

THE GANGETIC PLAIN. BENGAL

The eastern portion of the great plain of the Ganges, is a region of exuberant fertility, and very densely populated. Rice is the staple food-crop, but most tropical fruits, bananas, mangoes, papaya, etc, thrive. Indigo, cotton and jute are important crops and the opium poppy is grown on a large scale. Bamboos, palms of several species, and many ornamental trees and shrubs are extensively planted.

As one approaches Calcutta from the sea, the scenery along the river banks is very attractive, the villages and plantations, with their luxuriant vegetation, testifying to the fertility of the country. The famous botanical gardens, on the bank of the river a few miles below the city, will at once attract the attention of the botanist. These gardens are interesting not only for their rich collections of plants, native and exotic, but for a hundred years or more they have been the centre of botanical research for British India, and are intimately associated with the labors of many distinguished British botanists.

A very large collection of trees is a feature of the garden and includes magnificent avenues of mahogany, "almond" (*Terminalia catappa*), royal palms, and other striking species of which the palm collections comprise many both native and exotic.

The pride of these gardens is an immense banyan (*Ficus Bengalensis*), said to be about 135 years old in 1900, five years before the writer saw it. It had a main trunk 51 feet in circumference, and over 450 smaller root-trunks, while the crown was 938 feet in circumference.

The vegetation about Calcutta is luxuriant, including several species of palms, screw-pines, bamboos, bananas, and many other characteristic tropical growths. The graceful betel-nut (*Areca Catechu*) and the coco-palm are extensively planted, as well as the native toddy-palm (*Borassus flabelliformis*), with great fan-leaves. The wild date-palm (*Phoenix sylvestris*) is very common, as it is elsewhere in India.

Besides the banyan, another species of Ficus is common in

Fig. 54.—Banyan (*Ficus Bengalensis*), Botanical Gardens, Calcutta.

India, the "Pipul" (*F. religiosa*), with heart-shaped leaves suggesting a cotton-wood poplar.

Approaching Calcutta from the sea one sails up the Hugli River through the swamp region known as the "sunderbans."

The mangrove swamps of the Indo-Malayan regions are much like those of East Africa, but developed on a much more extensive scale, and with a greater number of species. As in Africa the outside is composed of *Rhizophora mucronata*, the predominant species throughout the Malayan and Australasian regions. Other mangroves occupy the inner portion of the swamp, e. g., *Brughiera spp.*, *Avicennia officinalis*, and a number of other characteristic genera, e. g., Sonneratia, Acanthus, Carapa, and the Nipa-palm.[1]

[1] Schimper, A. F. W., *Plant-geography*, p. 395.

At high tide the mangroves appear to rest on the surface of the water, but with the ebbing tide the shiny black mud banks are exposed, showing the fantastic tangle of stilt-roots. These aërial roots are important aërating organs for the roots buried in the mud; the white mangrove (Avicennia), sends up myriads of slender aërial roots or "pneumatophores" for the same purpose.

The seaward extension of the mangrove formation may be rapid. The seed germinates while still attached to the parent tree, and the seedling develops into an elongated, rod-like body, ending in a stout root. The young plant, detached from the branch, falls like a plummet, the root penetrating deep into the mud, thus firmly anchoring the seedling mangrove, which quickly forms a bush of considerable size.

Back of the swamp, as noted for West Africa, there is built up a strip of drier soil which gradually adds to the mainland.

The great delta area of the Ganges back of the mangroves is largely a region of fresh water marshes and wet forest, supporting a great variety of hygrophilous plants, among them many palms.

The low vegetation, with brackish swamps, chiefly composed of dwarf palms and mangroves, does not give an impression of tropical luxuriance, and it is not until the sandy spits and marshy jungles of the delta are passed, that the full luxuriance of the tropical vegetation is seen. In the delta of the Ganges, as in other tidal swamps of the East, the Nipa-palm is a conspicuous feature.[1]

Directly north of Calcutta is the well-known mountain station Darjiling, commanding probably the finest mountain-panorama in the world, as it comprises a perfect view of the main range of the Himalaya, with the giant Kinchinjunga in the centre.

The journey from Calcutta to Darjiling is a most interesting one to the botanist. A line running from Calcutta to Darjiling has been proposed as a division between two quite dissimilar floras, that to the east being predominantly Malayan, while westward there is a marked infusion of African types.

Proceeding northward from Calcutta the rank luxuriance of the delta country is succeeded by the drier portion of the Gangetic plain and still further northward the "Terai" is reached, the

[1] Hooker, J. D., *Himalayan Journals*, pp. 1–2, 1855.

jungle belt skirting the foot of the great range of the Himalaya. This jungle is composed for the most part of stunted scrubby trees and shrubs, with coarse tall grass between. The commonest trees are species of Acacia, Dalbergia, Sterculia, and several others. This region is notoriously malarial, and the haunt of tigers and other big game.

The change in the vegetation as one ascends from Siliguri, at the base of the mountains to Darjiling, about 7,000 feet elevation, is very marked, and as the tiny train makes very slow progress along the steep and crooked track, one has ample time to study the character of the forest along the railway.

Up to an altitude of about 3,000 feet, the forest has a decidedly tropical aspect, although it lies beyond the northern tropic; but the southern slopes of the great mountains have abundant moisture, and an equable climate.

A lofty forest replaces the scrub of the Terai and includes some very large and valuable trees. Of these the most important is the "Sal" (*Shorea robusta*), a gregarious species, and a very important timber-tree belonging to the peculiarly Indo-Malayan family, Dipterocarpaceae. Other notable trees are the "cedar" (*Cedrela Toona*), a wide-spread species reaching to Northern Australia, and several species of Terminalia which like the cedar, shed their leaves in the dry season, as many other Indian trees do; *Gordonia Wallichii*, belonging to the Camellia family, and a genus also represented in the southern United States is a common tree of the sub-Himalayan forest, and several species of Ficus are also characteristic of this tropical zone.

The tropical character of this forest is most pronounced at the lower levels, especially in the deep, very wet lower valleys of the streams descending from the mountains. Palms, bananas, bamboos, screw-pines, huge Aroids, and other characteristic tropical types abound. Few of these extend above 3,000 feet, where there begins an intermingling of the temperate types characteristic of the upper Himalayan forest region. Thus a pine (*Pinus longifolia*) occurs as low as 1,500 feet, although most of the vegetation at this elevation is tropical.

The abundant moisture, especially in the sheltered valleys and gorges, favors a luxuriant growth of climbing plants and epiphytes.

As in most tropical forests, the Leguminosae are among the commonest of the lianas. Among these are species of Mucuna, Pueraria, Bauhinia, Entada, while the Vine family, is represented by a number of species of Vitis; Peppers, Ipomoeas, Bignonias, and big-leaved Araceae form great cables looped from tree to tree, or clamber up the trunks and branches of the lower trees and shrubs. Rattan-palms of several species are characteristic, and some of these reach into the temperate zone up to 7,000 feet.

The screw-pines (Pandanus), with leaves 8 to 10 feet long, and bamboos of several sorts, are striking features of the vegetation. The bamboos are especially abundant in the Himalayan forest, and many species extend into the temperate zone. Some of these are gigantic, sometimes a hundred feet high.

Ferns are abundant, and include some fine tree-ferns (*Alsophila sp.*) as well as many epiphytes, and epiphytic orchids are common, some of them of great beauty.

Above 3,000 feet the tropical forest shows an increasing number of temperate species which become predominant above 4,000 feet [1] and from this elevation to Darjiling (7,000 ft.), the flora has much in common with the temperate floras of Eurasia and North America, especially the Atlantic States.

ASSAM AND UPPER BURMA

Northeastward from Bengal, and continuous with the tropical Himalayan forest belt is Assam, which includes the valley and delta of the Brahmaputra, and a series of mountain ranges with their intervening valleys. It is a region of excessively heavy rainfall, and the rain-forest of the valleys and lower hills is an eastward extension of the lower Himalayan forest zone, and reaches further eastward into Burma and Indo-China.

This forest, however, while made up largely of Indo-Malayan tropical genera, also, especially at higher elevations, as in the Himalayas, has many species of northern rather than tropical affinities, such as oaks, chestnuts, camellias, and others. The whole of this region lies within the monsoon belt, i. e., it has a more or less pronounced dry season, and a considerable number of deciduous trees.

[1] Hooker, *loc. cit.*, pp. 95–100.

THE WESTERN GHATS

The Western Ghats descend by a series of terraces to the coast, and these slopes, and the coastal strip below, get the full benefit of the southwest monsoon, and the dry season is much less pronounced than in the interior of the country. The whole coast line, as far north as Bombay, is clothed with luxuriant evergreen forest, and presents a marked.contrast to the barren shores of northwest India.

These evergreen forests have much in common with the rainforests of eastern Bengal and Assam, but many of the Malayan species are wanting and there is an admixture of African types. The tropical character of the vegetation becomes still more pronounced toward the south, where the flora is much like that of Ceylon.

Descending on the east to the Deccan plateau, much drier conditions prevail. This is especially marked close to the eastern slope of the mountains, as the rains pass over the crest and fall some distance inland.

Between Bombay and Poona, on the eastern side of the Western Ghats, the lowlands are very productive, rice and other tropical crops growing luxuriantly, and a profusion of palms of several species, evergreen figs, bamboos, and other luxuriant vegetation, forming a characteristic tropical landscape.

Further south the interior country is much drier, and where the forest still remains, as in the gorges on the flanks of the mountains, the trees are mostly deciduous in the dry season. Some of these trees are of great value as timber, among them being the "sal," already referred to, and the very important teak (*Tectona grandis*). The open country is too dry for a true forest, but there are many species of shrubs and small trees, many of which are also common to the dry northwestern provinces.

Passing from the rich evergreen forests of the seaward side of the Western Ghats, and descending to the dry plain of the Deccan, there is a transition first through a moist deciduous forest to a dry open forest which gradually passes into the thorny scrub of the Deccan.

On the eastern shore of the Peninusla which gets rain from the northwest monsoon from the Bay of Bengal, there is nearly evergreen forest, but much less luxuriant than that of the west coast, and denominated by Brandis [1] "semi-evergreen scrub." Among the constituents of this formation may be mentioned species of Flacourtia, Pterospermum, Erythroxylon, Carissa, Ehretia. Where moisture is more abundant, as in some of the hill-country, and parts of Madras, this formation becomes a true evergreen forest.

The province of Madras, occupying the southeastern part of the Peninsula is open to the sea and much better watered than the Deccan. It is a fertile region, and travelling through in December, the writer noted luxuriant crops of rice and cotton, the latter in full bloom. Tobacco and millet are both important crops.

A very different flora is found in the Nilgiri Hills where the Eastern and Western Ghats join. In the higher elevations, which exceed 7,000 feet, a temperate flora occurs much like that of the eastern Himalaya and the mountains of Assam and north Burma. Such common northern genera as Rubus, Viburnum, Rhamnus, Hypericum, etc., occur, many of them the same species as those of the mountains of northeast India.

Ceylon

Ceylon, an island of more than 25,000 square miles area, owing to its proximity to the equator has a uniformly hot climate, without the extremes that prevail in much of continental India. In the humid coastal areas, such as Colombo, the annual range is very small.

The rainfall varies much in the different parts of the island, and is largely controlled by the trend of the principal mountain mass which rises to over 8,000 feet in the southwest. This range is an effective barrier to the passage of the rain-clouds brought by the southwest monsoon in the late spring, and most of the moisture is precipitated on the seaward side of the mountains, while the northeastern plains get very little rain at this time. In the autumn, the northwest monsoon brings much more general, but less heavy rainfall.

The flora of Ceylon, in its main features, is much like that of

[1] For details of the vegetation of the forest regions of India, see Brandis, D., *Indian Trees*, London, 1906.

PLATE XV.—Screw-pine (*Pandanus sp.*), Botanical Garden, Peradeniya, Ceylon.

southern India, but there is a pretty large proportion of peculiar species.

Little forest remains in the lowlands, except in swampy regions unfit for cultivation, and such as remains is not particularly luxuriant. In the drier districts are many of the same species of trees and shrubs as in southern India, e. g., species of Acacia, Cassia, Eugenia, and others, but in the more humid districts, like those about Colombo, little is left of the original vegetation, and most of the available ground is occupied by various crops,— rice, sugar, coconuts, and the usual fruit trees: bread-fruit, bananas, papaya, mangoes, etc. Coconuts form one of the most important products of Ceylon, and are planted in enormous numbers, forming almost uninterrupted groves along the shore for many miles.

Practically all the forest in the humid areas between 2,000 and 4,000 feet elevation has been destroyed for the purpose of planting tea. The coffee plantations of an earlier period were destroyed by the ravages of a fungus, and were replaced by tea, which is now the principal product of the island, being cultivated up to 6,000 feet elevation. Rubber is also cultivated to some extent but can hardly compete with the plantations of the Malay region.

Neither in soil nor climate is Ceylon equal to the great Malayan islands, and as the general character of the lowland vegetation of Ceylon is similar to that of the Malayan region, but is less luxuriant and varied, it will not be considered further.

Some efforts have been made at reafforestation in Ceylon, and teak has been planted with some success in the lowlands. The writer visited the Hanwella forest not far from Colombo, where there are teak plantations. The luxuriance of the vegetation gave evidence of an abundant rainfall, although it was the dry season (Feb.). There were many ferns, including a beautiful climbing species (*Lygodium sp.*) as well as a good many epiphytic ones, among them the curious giant adder-tongue, *Ophioglossum pendulum*, whose forked strap-shaped fronds hung down for nearly two yards in length. A number of epiphytic orchids were also noted. Of the terrestrial ferns, the most interesting was *Helminthostachys Zeylanica*, a relative of Ophioglossum, and widespread through the eastern tropics. There were a number of showy flowers noted, one a beautiful blue gentian (*Exacum sp.*)

PLATE XVI.—Giant bamboo (*Dendrocalamus giganteus*), Botanical Gardens,
Peradeniya.

and the fine *Ixora coccinea*, a shrub with clusters of tubular scarlet flowers.

At Peradeniya, about 1,700 feet elevation, is a fine botanical garden, with a large collection of tropical and sub-tropical plants, including the most notable native species. There are some remarkably fine clumps of the largest of all bamboos (*Dendrocalamus giganteus*) more than a hundred feet high. Here may also be seen fine specimens of the native Talipot-palm (*Corypha umbraculifera*), whose immense fan leaves are over four yards across. At maturity an enormous terminal panicle of flowers is developed, after which the tree dies. In the early spring many of the showiest trees come into flower. One of these, *Bombax Malabaricum*, is a very large tree with big carmine-red, mallow-like flowers, especially striking, as the tree is quite leafless when in bloom. The magnificent *Amherstia nobilis*, from Burma, was especially fine at Peradeniya, and the long pendent racemes of brilliant red flowers, looking like orchids, make it one of the finest of flowering trees.

The principal mountain mass of Ceylon rises to a plateau, 6,000–7,000 feet high, with some peaks a thousand feet higher. The climate of the plateau is temperate, and the vegetation is reminiscent of the Nilgiris of South India, or the temperate Himalaya. As the plateau is too high, in most places, for tea culture, it is still largely in a state of nature, and shows little admixture of introduced species.

This region is a combination of low evergreen forest and open grass-land, the latter known locally as "Patana." The line between patana and forest, is a very sharp one. The evergreen forest is composed of a good many genera, e. g., Eugenia, Calophyllum, Luytsia, Symplocos and others. A feature of this region is a magnificent tree-rhododendron (*R. arboreum*), also found in the Himalaya. It is a spreading tree of considerable size, the flowers a brilliant blood-red, presenting a splendid sight.

In the early spring, the young foliage of these evergreen forests shows a great variety of color, red, yellow, pink and purple, the effect being very beautiful.

The herbaceous plants are largely familiar boreal types. Thus at Horton Plains, the following genera were noted: Viola, Hypericum, Gnaphalium, Lobelia, Ranunculus, Gentiana, Gaultheria, Alchemilla, Fragaria, Plantago. Other less familiar were

PLATE XVII.—Talipot-palm (*Corypha umbraculifera*); at right, betel-palm (*Areca Catechu*). Botanical gardens, Peradeniya.

the blue-flowered Exacum, Hedyotis, Strobilanthus and Ceropegia (Asclepiadaceae).

Orchids are quite common, a beautiful white epiphytic species (*Coelogyne odoratissimum*) being especially abundant. Other orchids noted were species of Dendrobium, Satyrium, Oberonia, Listera.

Ferns are well represented, especially in the moist shady forest, but some species are characteristic of the open and drier places. On rocky banks, *Gleichenia dichotoma* (*linearis*), a cosmopolitan

FIG. 55.—Botanical Garden, Hakgala, Ceylon.

species, forms thickets, and associated with it is an equally widespread club-moss, *Lycopodium cernuum*. In the shady localities one may find some of the filmy ferns (Hymenophyllaceae), but these are not particularly abundant. In sheltered gullies are fine tree-ferns, the most abundant one being *Alsophila crinita*. In the moist grassy meadows an adder-tongue fern, *Ophioglossum reticulatum* is not uncommon, and occasionally a related fern, *Botrychium lanuginosum* is met with. The boggy meadows also harbor sundews (*Drosera spp.*), and bladder-weed (*Ultricularia sp.*), as well as several club-mosses, two of which, *Lycopodium clavatum* and *L. Carolinianum* are characteristic boreal species.

In the shady woods, the trees are draped with the gray streamers of the lichen, Usnea, and here are also found a variety of epiphytic mosses and liverworts, which also are plentiful on the ground and on rocks and fallen logs.

In the cool moist climate of the Ceylon highland, most of the common garden flowers come to great perfection. In the attractive garden at Hakgala, together with a great variety of orchids, peppers, tree-ferns, and other sub-tropical plants, there were beautiful begonias, geraniums, heliotrope, fuchsias, violets, roses, etc., growing with unusual luxuriance.

INDO-CHINA

The Indo-Chinese peninsula, comprising Burma, French Indo-China and Siam, has a flora, which includes elements belonging respectively to the Indian, Himalayan and Malayan regions.

To the north, radiating from the great Himalayan system which forms the southeastern boundary of Tibet, extends a series of mountain ranges between which lie the valleys of the great rivers, Irrawaddy, Salween, and Mekong, which water the lowlands of Burma and Siam.

In the northern mountain country the vegetation is a continuation of the temperate Himalayan flora, and includes many genera related to the floras of both Eurasia and North America. Pines, firs and other coniferous trees; oaks, maples, magnolias, rhododendrons, and many others, both herbaceous and woody plants, are familiar to European and American botanists. There are, however, mingled with these boreal plants, many which are related to the tropical Malayan flora, such as bamboos, palms, many orchids, figs and others.

In the lower country in Assam, Burma and southern China, the vegetation is predominantly Malayan, and further south, most of the boreal genera disappear, and the vegetation is almost entirely composed of strictly tropical types. Only in the higher mountains do we again encounter the northern plants.

There are three principal mountain systems extending southward from the Himalaya in the Indo-Chinese Peninsula. To the west is the Arakan system of Burma; in the centre the ranges, which extending southward, form the backbone of the Malay Peninsula; to the east the mountain system of Annam.

These north and south ranges exert a great influence upon the climate, as much of the moisture from the southwest monsoon over the Bay of Bengal is intercepted by the Arakan range, so that Burma has a much heavier rainfall than Siam.

In Burma, however, there is by no means a uniform climate. The northern mountain region, next to Assam, has practically no dry season; but over most of the country, as in central India, the

FIG. 56.—Great pagoda, Rangoon, Burma. The trees are toddy-palms (*Borassus flabelliformis*).

monsoons, especially the southwest monsoon, have a marked effect upon the climate.

The coastal region of Burma, including the deltas of the Irrawaddy and Salween, and the coast south of Rangoon, have a very heavy rainfall, and correspondingly luxuriant vegetation. The delta-lands below Rangoon, when reclaimed are extremely fertile. This is a region of immense rice ("paddy") fields, rice being the great food crop of the country; but all the characteristic tropical products abound. Oranges, bananas, mangoes, bread-fruit, Jack-fruit, and others less familiar, are associated with bamboos, palms of many kinds, cinnamon, tamarinds and many other trees, shrubs and herbs.

A common and beautiful palm of this region, and indeed everywhere throughout the Malayan tropics is *Areca Catechu* which
produces the "betel-nut," which mixed with lime and the leaf of
the betel-pepper, furnishes the Malayan equivalent for chewing
gum. The Areca-palm is one of the most beautiful of the palm
tribe, its perfectly smooth, slender shaft bearing aloft a plume of
graceful feathery leaves.

Where the delta lands have not been cleared and drained, they
comprise a labyrinth of swamps and low jungle like the sunder-
buns of the Ganges delta, on the opposite side of the Bay of
Bengal.

As one travels northward, through the valley of the Irrawaddy,
the country becomes much drier, and above Mandalay the country is largely a dry savanna, open grass-land, and scattered deciduous
trees, recalling the bush-veldt of South Africa. Where the forest
is better developed, the trees are mainly deciduous, and in places,
teak forests of considerable extent occur, and the timber is of
great commercial importance.

While the valleys show evidences of a marked dry season, the
higher mountains have a heavier, and more uniform rainfall and
especially in the gorges cut by the rivers, there is a typical rain-
forest with a profusion of beautiful trees, shrubs and herbaceous
plants. Upper Burma is especially rich in orchids, many of which,
like the exquisite blue *Vanda coerulea* are greatly prized in cultivation.

Siam and Annam, on account of the mountains lying between
them and the Bay of Bengal, lose much of the benefit of the
southwest monsoon rains, and on the whole are much drier
than Burma, as the northeast monsoon brings much less rain
than the southwest.

Much of the lower country is open savanna, and the forests,
even in the hill-country are much less luxuriant than those of
the coastal region and mountains of Burma.

While the greater part of the Indo-Chinese peninsula has a
pronounced monsoon climate, the long extension southward,
the Malay Peninsula, reaches the equatorial zone, and the wet
and dry seasons are much less marked.

Somewhere in Indo-China, may have been the birthplace
of the human race. The discovery of the famous Ape-man

(Pithecanthropos) in Java points to this part of the world as the place where man first appeared.

Long before western civilization began, India and China were highly civilized communities, and today contain a very large part of mankind. Southeastern Asia, with the adjacent islands, is one of the richest parts of the world, abounding in food-plants of many kinds, and man very early learned to cultivate and improve the most important of these. The great food staple of most of the Orient is rice, native to this region, and the many varieties of bananas and plantains are undoubtedly derived from some of the many wild species, and the same is true of sugar cane.

Many important tropical fruits, mangoes, durian, mangosteen, and others are natives of the Indo-Malayan tropics, and to China we are probably indebted for the orange and other Citrus-fruits, as well as the peach and perhaps the apricot.

This region, too, abounds in spices, pepper, cloves, nutmeg; and the palms, bamboos, rubber and gums yield various important commercial products.

It is not remarkable, that in a region so richly dowered by nature, primitive man should have found a congenial habitation, increased and multiplied.

THE ISLANDS OF THE INDIAN OCEAN

The islands in the Indian Ocean lying east of Africa, owing to their isolation, have developed very characteristic floras.

Much the most important is Madagascar, next to Papua and Borneo the largest island in the world. Separated from the mainland by two hundred and sixty miles, its 228,000 square miles show a great variety of conditions, and the vegetation is equally varied and includes many extremely interesting endemic species.

A mountain range occupies the centre of the island, averaging about 5,000 feet in height, with an extreme elevation of 8,675 feet. This central region, which is largely made up of fertile plains and valleys, has a warm temperate climate; but the coastal zone has a pronounced tropical climate, very humid on the east, which receives the full benefit of the moisture-laden ocean winds, but much drier on the lee-side of the island.

Much of the land on the windward side is covered with heavy rain-forest, but on the west side the vegetation is very much like those parts of British South Africa which lie in the same latitude. There is a marked dry season and the vegetation is more or less decidedly xerophytic. Aloes, Euphorbias, Acacias, and other characteristic South African types abound, and in some places Cacti, introduced from America, have become naturalized. The extreme southwest of Madagascar is very dry, and may be called a desert.

In the rain-forest and the moister portions of the mountains, ferns are very abundant, and orchids are also a marked feature of the vegetation. One of the most striking of the orchids is a species of Angraecum, sometimes seen in cultivation, which has a spur, or nectary, a foot long!

There are many striking species peculiar to Madagascar, some of which are not uncommon in cultivation. Of these may be mentioned the "Flamboyant" (*Poinciana regia*), perhaps the showiest tree in cultivation, with its masses of flaming scarlet flowers. The "traveller's tree" (*Ravenala Madagascariensis*) is sometimes grown in warmer countries, where its great fan of big banana-leaves at once attracts attention; and sometimes one sees in conservatories the curious lace-leaved water-plant, *Ouvinandra fenestralis*.

Other characteristic plants are a peculiar screw-pine (*Pandanus obeliscus*), a handsome crape-myrtle (*Lagerstroemia sp.*), a palm (*Raphia ruffia*), and several rubber-plants, species of Vahea.

Some of the trees—e. g., Weinmannia, Elaeocarpus, Casuarina— are reminiscent of the Malayan-Australian region; but the bulk of the vegetation, especially in the drier parts, is unmistakably African. In the cooler mountain districts there are many species either identical or closely related to those of the highlands of Abyssinia and the Cape region.[1]

East of Madagascar are the Mascarene Islands, which like most tropical mountainous islands are notable for the great profusion of ferns. Orchids are also very abundant, and there are a number of interesting palms. Some of the latter are closely related to those of the African mainland—but others are more nearly allied to those of Indo-Malaya, or even of America.[2]

[1] Drude *loc. cit.*, pp. 475–476.   [2] Ibid., p. 476.

THE SEYCHELLES

The Seychelle archipelago, six hundred miles northeast of Madagascar, comprises forty-five islands lying between 3° 38′ and 5° 45′ south latitude. The flora is a very distinct one and includes six endemic genera and sixty endemic species. Five of the endemic genera are palms, and one, *Northea Seychellana*, a tree belonging to the Sapotaceae, was named in honor of Miss Marianne North, who visited the islands in 1883–1884 and who has given an interesting account of her visit, which was especially for the purpose of painting the extraordinary palm, *Lodoicea Seychellarum*, which bears the huge double coconut, a well-known botanical curiosity.[1]

The forest is rich in palms, tree-ferns, and screw-pines; and there are a good many trees, one of which, *Wormia ferruginea*, an endemic species, is especially abundant in the higher mountain forests. Miss North found pitcher plants (Nepenthes) on the top of the higher mountains. A single species is also found in Madagascar, and these, as well as some other forms, show an affinity with the Malayan flora. The most striking flowers noted by Miss North were two fine orchids, *Angraecum eburneum* and *Vanilla Phalaenopsis*.

[1] Marianne North, *Recollections of a Happy Life*, Vol. II., London, 1893.

CHAPTER VII

THE PALAEOTROPICS—*Continued*

MALAYA AND POLYNESIA

The long Malay Peninsula, the southernmost point of Continental Asia, together with the chain of large islands, the Malay Archipelago, is rivalled in the richness of its flora only by equatorial America. The tip of the Peninsula almost touches the equator which bisects the great islands of Sumatra, Borneo and Celebes, with Java and the southern Philippines less than ten degrees away.

These regions enjoy a climate that varies but little in temperature throughout the year, and in much of the regions there is no marked dry season, while in many districts the rainfall is extremely heavy. Where, as in western Java, Sumatra and Borneo, the uniform high temperature and heavy rainfall are combined with rich alluvial or volcanic soils, there results a luxuriance of vegetation that can scarcely be rivalled anywhere, and these regions are a veritable botanist's paradise.

The Peninsula is traversed by a central mountain range, rising to a height of 7,000–8,000 feet, but for the most part much lower. This range is composed mainly of granite, but there are more or less extensive limestone deposits in some districts. These limestone formations sometimes contain extensive caves, which are interesting biologically, as they harbor a number of peculiar species of animals.

At the foot of the central mountain range is a coastal plain, wider along the east coast than on the west side. This coastal plain is (or was) heavily forested for the most part. Along the west coast are extensive mangrove formations and swamps, with very little sandy shore, while the eastern coast has many sandy beaches.

Until comparatively recent times, the vegetable resources of this region had been but slightly exploited, except for local consumption. The natives cultivated the usual tropical food-plants, especially the fruits, which include the choicest of all tropical fruits, the mangosteen and durian.

Some fifteen or twenty years ago, however, rubber plantations were established, and so profitable did they prove, that soon most of the accessible lowland forest was cleared and planted to Pará-rubber (*Hevea Brasiliensis*). So great has been the subsequent development of the industry, that already there is great over-production, and prices have fallen to a point which renders many plantations quite unprofitable.[1]

Ten years ago, the writer travelled through this region, and on all sides the forests were being felled, and the trees burned to get rid of them in order to make room for planting rubber. Only occasionally along the railway was it possible to see bits of the untouched forest. From these remnants, however, it was plain that the original forest was a very rich one, with a great variety of lofty trees, and extremely luxuriant growth of lianas and epiphytes, with an undergrowth containing many ferns, and other herbaceous growths. Among the latter wild bananas were conspicuous, as well as the somewhat similar members of the ginger family. Aroids, both terrestrial and climbing species, were abundant and conspicuous.

This is a typical rain-forest, and practically no deciduous species occur, such as are so characteristic of the monsoon forests of Burma and Indo-China.

Palms in great variety are characteristic of the true Malayan flora, and form a notable feature of the vegetation. Some are dwarf species, comparable to the scrub palmettoes of our southern states, and occur in the swamps and low ground. Others are lofty trees with crowns of giant fan-shaped, or more commonly pinnate leaves. The genera are mostly distinct from those of Africa and India. Among the common dwarf-palms are species of Areca and Pinanga, while in the mangrove swamps, the Nipa (*N. fruticans*), is very common. The latter is wide-spread through much of the Indo-Malayan region, and is extensively used for thatch and mats, as well as for its fruit.

[1] Since the above was written, the action of the British Government restricting the export of rubber from the East Indian plantations, has greatly increased the market price.

In low ground may be seen large clumps of the "Nibong" (*Oncosperma horrida*), a beautiful palm with slender trunk and graceful feathery leaves, but with an armor of formidable spines that effectually protects it.   One of the most beautiful of the Malayan palms is the "sealing-wax" palm (*Cyrtostachys Lacca*), whose smooth sheathing leaf-bases are a vivid vermilion scarlet.

A   B
FIG. 57.—Lowland vegetation, Malay Peninsula.
A. Palms (*Oncosperma sp.*).   B. Ferns (*Gleichenia linearis*).

Many species of palms, aside from the coconut which is everywhere cultivated, are very important both for food, and for many constructive purposes, e. g., cordage, thatch and timber.

The sugar-palm (*Arenga saccharifera*) is one of the most striking species, with immense pinnate leaves, 25 feet or more in length. Its sap yields an excellent sugar, but is commonly fermented to form palm-wine.   Another wine-palm is *Caryota urens*.   The genus Caryota has about ten species in the Indo-Malayan regions, stately palms with enormous bi-pinnate leaves unlike those of any other palms. Fan-palms are much less abundant, the commonest belonging to the genera Livistona and Licuala.

In the wet jungles of the coastal plain the climbing rattan-palms are extremely abundant, and comprise a large number of species belonging to several genera, of which much the most important is

FIG. 58.—Rattans, botanical gardens, Buitenzorg, Java.

Calamus. They form impenetrable thorny thickets and some of them reach an incredible length, looping from tree to tree for hundreds of feet, and probably exceeding in length any other member of the vegetable kingdom. The rattan of commerce is the stem stripped of its outer tissues, and this, with the bamboos, which also reach their maximum development in the Malayan regions, furnish the staple building materials for the Malayan dwellings, as well as for endless other uses.

Ferns are abundant in the lowland forest, among them some small tree-ferns; but, as elsewhere in the tropics, ferns are still better developed at higher altitudes, although certain types, like the climbing ferns (*Lygodium*), are perhaps more abundant in the lowland forest.

While showy flowers are not abundant in the rain-forest, occasionally there is a brilliant mass of color, when some great creeper or tree bursts into bloom. The writer recalls two especially striking examples of this seen on the railway journey between Penang and Kuala Lumpur. This was in December. The first was a giant creeper (*Bauhinia sp.*), which was not infrequent, and reached to the tops of the tall trees, where it burst into a blaze of brilliant orange. The other was a moderate sized tree, a species of crape-myrtle (*Lagerstroemia sp.*) almost hidden by the mass of lilac-purple flowers.

Morning glories (*Ipomoea spp.*), are common, and now and then on the railway embankment, a pretty pink ground-orchid (*Spathoglottis sp.*) was noted, as well as a number of other pretty, if not remarkably striking flowers, some, no doubt, introduced species.

An occasional screw-pine was noted in the forest, but these are much commoner in the Malayan region as strand-plants, than in the forest, although there are forest species also.

SINGAPORE

The island of Singapore, separated from the tip of the Peninsula by a narrow strait, is familiar to every visitor to the Far East, as it is the great centre for travel in the East Indies. It is at once apparent that we are in the heart of the tropics. Almost on the Line, the constant heat and high humidity are reflected in the rank luxuriance of the vegetation. The gardens are overflowing with a wealth of gorgeous flowering trees and shrubs, orchids, palms, and all the other choicest products of the equatorial zone. The markets are filled with the many fruits for which the Malayan tropics are famous. With the oranges, pineapples, and bananas, are the papayas and avocados of America, and the native mangosteen and durian, as well as many less known fruits and vegetables.

The mangosteen and durian, are often pronounced the finest of all fruits. The former (*Garcinia mangostana*), in shape and size resembling a small tomato, is a dark maroon in color, the deep-red thick rind enclosing about half a dozen segments, something like an orange, each segment composed of a snow-white juicy pulp of delicate and delicious flavor. The durian (*Durio zibethinus*) is a very different type of fruit, and on account of its powerful odor, rather suggesting a skunk, it must be admitted, many persons cannot be induced to taste it, and thus miss enjoying a fruit which is quite without a rival, and almost alone worth a trip to the Far East. The Malays are passionately fond of the durian, and in its season the heaps of the big spiny green fruits in the

A   B

FIG. 59.—A. A characteristic Malayan palm (*Caryota sp.*); B. Dipterocarp left in a rubber plantation near Quala Lumpur, Federated Malay States. In front of the tall tree is a young rubber tree (*Hevea Braziliensis*).

market make their presence evident far and wide. Wallace in his "Malay Archipelago" gives an admirable description of this delicious fruit, quite the best that has been written.

Among the other common fruits are several species of Nephelium, related to the Chinese lichi. The commonest is the "Rambutan," a fruit about the size of a large plum, with a shaggy crimson rind enclosing an oval mass of juicy white pulp with a single big seed.

Singapore is now pretty well cleared of forest except for some small tracts on Bukit Tima, the principal hill on the island, and a tract connected with the very interesting botanical garden. The forest contains some palms, mostly rattans, and a variety of trees, among which may be mentioned species of Melaleuca, Terminalia, Albizzia, Eugenia, Diospyros, Flacourtia, Calophyllum, and others, including an oak. Among the lianas, the most prominent, aside from the rattans, were species of Uncaria, Bauhinia, and Derris,—all Leguminosae.

The garden contains an extensive collection of plants, both native and exotic. The collection of palms comprises about 250 species, and there is an unusually fine collection of ferns and orchids. The pitcher plants (Nepenthes) especially characteristic of the region, are particularly interesting.

The mountain forests of the Peninsula are to a great extent still intact, and afford a most interesting study to the botanist. The writer made brief visits to two localities,

FIG. 60.—Tree-ferns (*Alsophila glauca*), Taiping Hills, Federated Malay States.

the Pahang Gap, northwest of Kuala Lumpur, and the Taiping Hills in the northern part of the Peninsula.

Up to about 3,000 feet the vegetation is decidedly tropical in composition. The trees are often very tall, sometimes 150–200 feet high, and the straight smooth trunks may be 5–6 feet in diameter, although usually less. As in India, the Dipterocarps are much in evidence; Shorea, Dipterocarpus, Balanocarpus, and others. Figs, wild bread-fruit (Artocarpus), and many Leguminosae, e. g., Afzelia, Pterocarpus, Pithecolobium, Albizzia, etc., as well as a variety of trees belonging to many families. Coniferous trees are not common, but an occasional large Kauri-pine (*Agathis loranthifolia*) is met with, and species of Podocarpus and Dacrydium members of the yew family occur. Rattans are everywhere abundant, and in the Pahang region, bamboos were particularly numerous, in some places extensive groves of tall bamboos occupying the ground to the exclusion of everything else. The number of bamboos in the Malayan region is very great, and among them are species like the giant bamboo (*Dendrocalamus giganteus*) over a hundred feet high, with stems nearly a foot through. The bamboo groves are extremely beautiful, with their graceful drooping plumes of leaves, especially when they line the banks of some clear mountain stream.

The vegetation of the Taiping Hills, is even more luxuriant than that of the Pahang Gap. At 3,000 feet elevation the forest was remarkable for the great profusion of lianas and epiphytes, indicating a very heavy rainfall, which was also shown by the rich development of ferns, mosses and liverworts. Many of the ferns were epiphytes, and included a number of delicate filmy ferns (Hymenophyllaceae). Of the terrestrial ferns, the genus Gleichenia was especially abundant, sometimes forming dense tangles of interlacing wiry leaf-stalks that are very difficult to get through. Fine tree-ferns are also common, the most abundant being *Alsophila glauca*. Another very conspicuous fern, is a species of Angiopteris, a genus wide-spread in the eastern tropics, the leaves sometimes exceeding 20 feet in length.

Palms are much more abundant in the Taiping forest than in that of the Pahang Gap, while on the other hand, bamboos are better developed in the latter region, due perhaps to the lesser rainfall, as the bamboos as a rule are not so characteristic of regions of excessive rainfall. Of the numerous palms, large and small, which abound in the Taiping Hills, a very tall Caryota was especially notable.

Other distinctly tropical types were the giant Aroids, some climbing up the trees, others with huge calla-like leaves rising stiffly from short upright trunks. Some of the Araceae of the Malayan region are gigantic. One of these, *Amorphophallus titanum*, of Sumatra, has an enormous much divided leaf borne aloft on a thick stalk 10–15 feet high. A number of similar but somewhat smaller species are frequent in the lowland forest. The big inflorescences of these huge Aroids usually have a very offensive odor and attract swarms of carrion-loving insects which presumably assist in pollination.

Wild bananas (*Musa Malaccensis, M. violacea*) are abundant, and much resemble the cultivated ones except that the fruit has many seeds, and but little edible pulp. Presumably some of these wild bananas are the ancestors of the cultivated varieties.

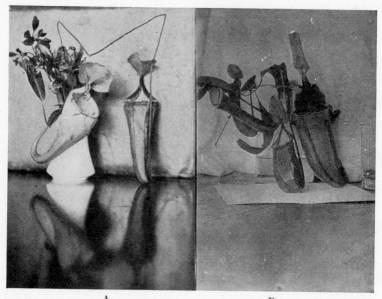

A   B
FIG. 61.—Pitcher plants (*Nepenthes spp.*).
A. From Malay Peninsula.   B. From Borneo.

Not very distantly related to these are the many forms of the ginger family, which are exceptionally abundant in the Malayan rain-forest. They are often very handsome plants, with fine foliage and showy flowers. Characteristic genera are Zingiber, Globba, Costus, Amomum, Alpinia, etc.

The epiphytic vegetation is a notable feature of the Taiping forest. As already mentioned this includes a large number of ferns, of which the big bird's-nest fern (*Asplenium nidus*) is the most conspicuous, and orchids are extremely abundant, mostly small inconspicuous species, but some of them of great beauty. Rhododendrons with white or scarlet flowers may be seen high up in the branches of the trees. The numerous epiphytic rhododendrons are a common and beautiful feature of the Malayan mountain forests. Sometimes growing as epiphytes, but more common on the ground, or climbing over the lower vegetation, are several species of pitcher plants (Nepenthes), whose centre of development is in the mountains of Malaya and Borneo. The graceful vases or urns, suspended from the leaf tendrils, are beautifully colored, and sometimes a foot or more in length. No plant structures are more remarkable than these curious organs. The climbing screw-pines (*Freycinetia*) are common and conspicuous, but Pandanus is much less in evidence.

The numerous species of Aeschynanthus (Gesneraceae), with very showy scarlet flowers something like a snapdragon, are among the most attractive of the epiphytes, but even more beautiful are species of Medinilla (Melastomaceae) whose great clusters of pink flowers subtended by big rosy bracts, at once attract attention. Some very handsome Begonias, too, occur as epiphytes in the wet mountain forests.

A visit was made to the summit of the main range, at Pahang Gap. At this elevation, about 4,000 feet, quite a different type of forest was encountered. The trees are much smaller and trunks and branches covered with a heavy growth of mosses, liverworts, and other epiphytes, mostly of rather small size. In this "moss-forest" were collected a number of interesting bryophytes, which found here a congenial habitat.

The exposed summit of the ridge was occupied largely by open boggy places, with stunted small trees and shrubs. In the bogs were masses of peat-mosses (Sphagnum) in which were growing rhododendrons and other members of the heath family; orchids, and other bog-plants, suggestive of the northern peat-bogs; but with these were strange ferns, and clambering over the bushes were magnificent Nepenthes with pitchers as big as a pint measure.

Of the ferns, several of the Gleichenias are wide-spread species, but two of the most conspicuous ferns, *Dipteris conjugata*, and *Matonia pectinata*, are less common, and the latter is restricted to rather limited areas on the mountains of the Peninsula and the larger islands of the Archipelago. Both are very handsome with large fan-shaped leaves borne on tall stalks. Matonia is especially interesting as it is almost the only survivor of a very old family, and for a long time was known only from a single locality, Mt. Ophir in Malacca.

While the Malay Peninsula is rich in ferns, and epiphytic mosses and liverworts, the ground liverworts are less abundant than might be expected from the general luxuriance of the vegetation. Whether or not this is due to the prevailing character of the soil, is a question. The rocks of the Peninsula are mostly granitic, and the coarse gritty soil resulting from the decomposition of these rocks does not seem to meet the needs of these plants. In the limestone region, there were species not found elsewhere, but nowhere in the Peninsula were they so abundant as in the volcanic regions of Java and Sumatra.

The Sunda Islands

The three great islands adjacent to the coast of the Malay Peninsula, Sumatra, Borneo, and Java, exhibit in the highest degree, the exuberant development of the equatorial Malayan vegetation. Both the plant and animal life indicate that these islands, at no very distant epoch, were united to the Asiatic mainland.

Borneo, the largest of these islands, separated from Singapore by about 400 miles of the shallow Java Sea, is still very incompletely known, as much of its nearly 300,000 square miles is an unexplored wilderness. The coastal regions of Sarawak in the west have been quite extensively explored botanically, as the country has been under British domination for nearly a century, and is comparatively easy of access.

Borneo is to a great extent mountainous, but there are large expanses of lowland swamp and forest in the coastal districts. There is a central range of mountains, attaining a maximum height of about 10,000 feet, and from this range, others diverge, with plateaus lying between the ranges. The main range is composed partly of ancient crystalline schists, and in British North Borneo, Kinabalu, the highest mountain in the island, is a granite mass, rising to 13,698 feet. Deposits of limestone are found in some localities, as well as volcanic formations; but there are none of the active volcanoes which are such a marked feature of Java and western Sumatra. Indeed the geology of Borneo is more like that of the Malay Peninsula, and there is also much in common in the vegetation between Borneo and the Peninsula.

As one approaches Sarawak from the west, the coast presents a very picturesque aspect, bold mountains coming down to the sea in places. Between two of these mountains, Mattang and Santu-bong, the Sarawak River, upon which is situated the principal town, Kuching, makes its way to the sea. Santubong is especially impressive, rising abruptly from the water to a height of 3,000 feet, its steep flanks clothed with primaeval forest.

The low banks of the delta are for the most part densely covered with mangroves, and the mud flats exposed at low-tide, are the haunt of crocodiles and other less formidable creatures, like the grotesque mud-fish, which climb about the exposed mangrove roots like lizards, while myriads of bright blue crabs scuttle about over the mud, and if the tide is low, cannot fail to attract attention.

Further up the river, the numerous narrow channels which traverse the mangrove formation, are lined with dense growths of the Nipa-palm, whose leaves are indispensable for thatch, or for the manufacture of the basket-work panels which form the sides of the native houses. Behind the Nipa zone, another beautiful palm, the "Nibong" (*Oncosperma filamentosa*) is common, and their slender stems and feathery crowns form a conspicuous and beautiful feature of the shore vegetation.

With the decreasing salinity of the water as the river is ascended, the mangroves gradually disappear and the solid river banks are covered with a dense growth of trees and shrubs in great variety. Back of the belt of shrubs and low trees there appear in places the tall trees of the high forest, the outposts of the prodigious forests which cover most of the wet lowlands of Borneo.

Wherever a native village appears on the river bank, coco-nuts, sago-palms, bananas, bread-fruit, and the other common cultivated trees are seen between the wild growths of the shore.

The trees and bushes of the jungle lining the river banks are smothered in a tangle of climbing plants and epiphytes in astonishing variety and profusion. Ferns, orchids, and other epiphytes cling to the trunks and branches of the trees, often almost entirely concealing them, evidence of the extreme humidity of the climate of these lowland forests.

Kuching, the capital of Sarawak, lies within a single degree of the equator, which almost bisects Borneo. With an annual rainfall of 160 inches, and an almost constant hot-house temperature, Sarawak has a true equatorial climate, and the vegetation exhibits a luxuriance that very few regions, even under the equator, can rival. All the common tropical products abound, and reach great perfection. Palms of many sorts, bananas, pineapples, bamboos, orchids, grow in rich profusion, and the gardens show a wonderful wealth of rare and beautiful trees and shrubs. The trunks of the palms and the trunks and branches of other trees are laden with epiphytes in bewildering profusion, while giant creepers, with flowers of every hue, are draped over every fence, or climb high into the trees.

While the forest has been cleared in the immediate vicinity of Kuching, one does not have to go far to see samples of the original forest, whose exploration is by no means easy, as the lowlands are largely swamps, or else overgrown with impenetrable thickets of rattans and other troublesome undergrowths.

Where the original forest has been removed, a second growth quickly springs up, composed of many species of trees, and a dense tangle of bushes, lianas, ferns, and a great variety of herbaceous species.

As might be expected in so humid a climate, ferns are much in evidence. Among the commonest are species of Gleichenia. We have already referred to the great development of Gleichenias in the Malay Peninsula, which in this respect, as well as some others, shows a marked resemblance to Borneo. The climbing ferns (*Lygodium spp.*) are also common and very beautiful.

One of the commonest and showiest shrubs of this region is *Wormia pulchella* (Dilleniaceae), whose big yellow flowers are seen everywhere. The genus Wormia is very abundant throughout Malaya, and at once attracts attention. The Acanthus family, and the Melastomaceae, the latter with pretty pink or purple flowers, are among the commonest of the more showy shrubs, and now and then one sees a scarlet Aeschynanthus climbing up the trunk of a tree or established as an epiphyte.

The pitcher plants (Nepenthes), are extraordinarily abundant in Borneo, and may be found at all elevations from sea-level to an altitude of 8,000 feet. Some are low-growing terrestrial species, but more commonly they are climbers or epiphytes. In most species, the pitchers are developed at the end of the tendril formed by a prolongation of the midrib of the leaf; but in the young plants, and also in some terrestrial species, the pitcher seems to represent the whole leaf, and the plant may consist of a rosette of these urn-shaped organs. There seems to be little doubt that the fluid in the pitcher contains definite enzymes similar in their action to pepsin, and capable of a true digestion of the insects and other small animals that may be captured. Whether or not, as has been stated, the Malays use this fluid as a corrective for indigestion, the writer will not venture an opinion. Young plants with pitchers no bigger than a thimble are common along the sides of ditches and on wet banks, while it is said the great *N. Rajah*, from Mt. Kinabalu, has pitchers, perhaps one might say jugs, holding two quarts. The Malay Peninsula, next to Borneo, probably has the greatest number of species, but they are found also throughout the whole Malay Archipelago, from northeastern Australia and New Guinea, to the Philippines, a single species also occurring in Ceylon.

Travelling in Sarawak depends very largely upon water-ways, as there are practically no roads, except in the immediate vicinity of the towns. If one leaves the streams, one must proceed on foot through the swamp and jungle, not always a pleasant operation, as the low ground is almost always more or less under water. Such excursions into the magnificent forests are not only fatiguing but include, incidentally, the discomfort of swarms of mosquitoes, and myriads of land-leeches, which are especially numerous and voracious in the Bornean forest.

Among the rare plants of Sarawak are several ferns. One of these, *Matonia sarmentosa*, is known only from one locality, the Bidi Caves, limestone caverns where it hangs down in long festoons only to be reached by long ladders used by the natives for collecting the edible birds' nests which are found in these same caves. Another fine species, the principal object of the writer's visit to Sarawak, is *Macroglossum Alidae*, one of the small order Marattiales. This, or a similar species has since been collected in Sumatra. It is a magnificent plant, with great palm-like leaves four yards long.

The two mountains guarding the delta of the Sarawak River, Mattang and Santubong, are fairly easy of access, and their floras are extremely interesting. Mattang, which for some reason is avoided by the natives, has never been denuded of forest, and affords an admirable opportunity of studying the primitive vegetation of the region.

The forest is a very rich one. Very tall trees, including many Dipterocarpaceae, like those of Indo-China and the Malay States, are bound together by great lianas, like huge cables, or with climbing Araceae and other creepers, clinging to their trunks, which with the branches are often smothered in a profusion of epiphytic growths of all kinds.

Below the tall trees are smaller ones, with an extraordinary variety of palms, giant ferns, wild bananas, rattans and a host of other striking plants. The Dipterocarp forest at the foot of the mountain is more open, being freer from undergrowth, and easier to get through; but as one ascends the mountain, the undergrowth is very dense, and one must exercise great care not to lose one's way in the thick jungle.

The wet banks along the trail are covered with beautiful ferns, liverworts and mosses, and although flowers are not very abundant or conspicuous, there were several worthy of notice. One of the prettiest was a Didymocarpus (Gesneraceae), with small foxglove shaped flowers, pale purple in color, borne on slender stalks rising from a rosette of dark green, almost black leaves, veined with snowy white. These dainty flowers grew abundantly on the mossy banks associated with delicate ferns, and made an exquisite picture. An occasional showy orchid, and some pretty Begonias were seen, and in one place, a number of plants of a pale yellow rhododendron (*R. salicifolium*). In the upper forest, a handsome Ixora, with scarlet flowers, somewhat like Bouvardia, was abundant.

Mt. Mattang has an especial interest to the botanist, as Professor Beccari, the great authority on palms, spent a long time here, and many of his species were first collected on this mountain.

The Dipterocarpaceae, so important as timber-trees throughout the Indo-Malayan region, are represented by many species in

Borneo, many of great size. There are also other large trees, especially Leguminosae. One of these, the "Tapang" (*Abauria excelsa*) is the tallest tree of the Bornean forest, a specimen 230 feet high having been measured.

Many species of Ficus are common, as well as species of Artocarpus, including the bread-fruits and Jack-fruit. Both the durian and mangosteen are represented by wild species. Rather unexpectedly there are several species of oaks, mostly in the mountains, but some at sea-level, as is also the case in the Malay States.

The coniferous trees of Borneo are few in number, and exclusively of southern types. The dammar-pines (Agathis), Podocarpus and Dacrydium are the only Bornean genera.

Borneo probably has more species of palms than any other area of equal extent; but many of them are small and relatively inconspicuous, or else they are climbing species of the rattan-type, which hardly suggest palms. There are, it is true, a considerable number of tall species, like the Sago-palm and Nibong; but as a rule, they do not dominate the vegetation to the same extent as in equatorial America. About 130 species have been described, mostly by Beccari, and all but 20 are peculiar to Borneo.

Many screw-pines occur in Borneo both as strand-plants, and in the forest up to 4,000–5,000 feet elevation.

The Araceae are also highly developed, and much resemble those of the Malay Peninsula.

One naturally expects to find many orchids, and, in fact, they are extremely numerous; but as every collector who has visited the tropics, knows, the showiest orchids are usually rare, and seldom abundant enough to make a striking display. Most species are insignificant, and would be overlooked by any but a botanist.

There are, of course, many very beautiful orchids in Borneo and other parts of the Malayan Archipelago, many of these being prized in cultivation. In the gardens of Singapore and Sarawak two handsome species are often seen, *Vanda teres* and *Arundina speciosa*. These are both ground orchids, and apparently easily grown. The genus Vanda includes many handsome species, some of which, like the Javanese *V. tricolor*, are often seen under glass in Europe and America. Perhaps the most striking of the Malayan orchids is the "tiger-orchid" (*Grammatophyllum speciosum*). This is a giant among orchids, and may be seen in great perfection in the famous botanical gardens at Buitenzorg in Java, where its pendent leafy shoots hang down from the trees to a length of ten feet or more. The numerous upright flower-stalks as tall as a man, bear many big brown and yellow striped blossoms. The genus Dendrobium is one of the largest in the eastern tropics, and many species are extremely beautiful and highly prized by collectors. A very interesting species is *D. crumenatum*, known in the British possessions as "pigeon orchid." It is very abundant and has the remarkable habit of flowering simultaneously over a large area, and only for a single day, when the long sprays of fragrant white flowers may be seen by thousands. The next day they are faded, and not a single fresh flower can be seen.

Among the noteworthy ferns of Mattang were species of Kaul- fussia, Angiopteris, and Schizaea, and some fine tree-ferns (*Al- sophila contaminans*). The handsome fern *Dipteris conjugata* was especially fine, the big fan-shaped leaves with stalks at least 8 feet high. Of the epiphytic ferns, the Hymenophyllaceae were not especially abundant, although represented by a number of species. Epiphytic species of Lycopodium included several conspicuous species like *L. Phlegmaria*, and an occasional speci- men of the curious *Psilotum flaccidum*, with leafless flattened, pendent shoots was seen.

At the summit of Mattang is a small area of comparatively open ground, with various sedges and grasses, but these are scarce in the heavy forest which covers most of the mountain.

Santubong, on the opposite side of the Sarawak delta, from Mattang, is much steeper, and the forest is more open and drier. At the summit, however, it is boggy, with abundant Sphagnum, like that of northern peat-bogs. The stunted trees are covered with a very heavy growth of epiphytes, among which were two very beautiful rhododendrons, and one of the finest pitcher- plants (*Nepenthes Veitchii*), which is prized in cultivation for its magnificent pitchers.

The beach skirting the foot of Santubong offers an excellent example of the Malayan strand-flora. Creeping over the sandy beach was the ubiquitous *Ipomoea pes-caprae*, found on pretty much every tropical beach the world over, and further back was a belt of trees and shrubs including many of the common Malayan strand species.

The largest trees were Casuarina, a genus especially developed in Australia, but extending as far as India. These peculiar trees have no leaves, but the slender green twigs look very much like pine-needles, and the tree suggests a long-leaved pine. Another characteristic tree is *Terminalia Catappa*, with branches arranged in regular tiers, and bearing very large glossy leaves. A rather

A   B

FIG. 62.—Strand vegetation at foot of Mt. Santubong, Sarawak, Borneo.
A. *Casuarina sp.*, *Terminalia Catappa*   B. *Pandanus sp.*

smaller and very beautiful tree, with leaves somewhat like those of Terminalia, is *Barringtonia speciosa*. The large four-angled fruits are conspicuous, and specially adapted for long journeys by sea, like the coconut, which explains the wide distribution of this tree throughout Malaysia. Another even more widely distributed species is the yellow tree-hibiscus (*H. tiliaceus*)—a denizen of most tropical beaches from the Malay Archipelago to Hawaii. The showy yellow flowered Wormia, already mentioned, is also very common, and a screw-pine with big red fruit-cones, looking like ripe pineapples, was very abundant. Associated with these trees were a number of leguminous shrubs with yellow or purple flowers, and climbing over trees and shrubs were various lianas, including several showy Ipomoeas, and a species of Gnetum, with salmon-pink berries. The latter represents a small family of gymnosperms, the Gnetaceae.

Forest Trees

As already indicated the most important trees are the Dipterocarps, but besides these is an extraordinary variety of other large trees. The most important families are the Rubiaceae, Leguminosae, Ebenaceae, Sapotaceae, Artocarpaceae, Tiliaceae, Bombacaceae, Dilleniaceae and Euphorbiaceae. The Rubiaceae take first place in the Bornean flora, the Orchidaceae second.

SUMATRA

Separated by the Straits of Malacca from the Malay Peninsula, is the great island of Sumatra, about 1,100 miles long, by 250 in breadth, and almost exactly bisected by the equator.

The topography of the island is comparatively simple. Parallel with the west coast, and descending to it abruptly, is a mountain range, in places exceeding 10,000 feet elevation. Between this range and the east coast is an extensive low alluvial plain.

The mountain ranges are composed largely of Palaeozoic rocks, granites, schists, quartzite, slate and limestone, but there are later deposits also, and some extensive volcanic formations including a number of active volcanoes, some of them approaching 10,000 feet altitude.

The climate is of the true equatorial type, with very little variation of temperature, and for the most part abundant rainfall. The west coast has a heavier rainfall than the east, approaching 200 inches annually at some points. The driest districts are in the northeast on the lee-side of the mountains.

While the vegetation has been pretty well investigated in some parts of Sumatra, much of the country is still very little known. The fertile eastern plains have been cleared of the heavy forest over considerable areas, and the usual tropical crops are grown. Of late years Sumatra has become a very important source of rubber, of which extensive plantations now exist. Tobacco culture is also a very important industry.

The cultivated districts are mostly in the fertile eastern plains, but extensive areas still await development. Although nearly four times the area of its neighbor Java, it has only about one sixth the population, and like Borneo, the development of its immense resources has only begun.

In the northern part the mountains approach the eastern coast so that the coastal plain is much narrower than further south, and in this region, the original forest has pretty well disappeared from the lowlands which are largely under cultivation. Tobacco is the chief crop, for which this Deli district is famous.

The most important town, Medan, is some distance inland, the immediate coast being occupied by extensive mangrove formations, composed of several species. There are also Nipa swamps, with the big fern, *Acrostichum aureum*, and back of this the graceful Oncosperma palms, as in Borneo.

Between the swamps of the coast and Medan, is a cultivated region, with the usual tropical growths, and in places, extensive teak forests.

This region is a rich alluvial plain presumably covered, originally, by heavy forest, now destroyed; but much of the land is covered with second growth jungle. Tobacco, which is most carefully handled and transplanted, is grown only for a short time on the same ground, which is then allowed to grow up to jungle for several years when it is again cleared for tobacco; so that only a fraction of the arable land is in use at one time.

The soil is very rich, and the jungle springs up quickly and comprises a great variety of trees and shrubs, as well as herbaceous flowering plants and ferns.

The writer had an opportunity of making a brief sojourn in the mountains west of Medan. Bandar Baroe, at an elevation of 866 metres has still some remains of the original forest, which has practically disappeared from the adjacent lowlands. At this elevation it is noticeably cooler than at Medan, and there is evidently a fairly heavy rainfall, although decidedly less than on the western side of the mountains; and the forest was much less luxuriant than at similar elevations in western Java, Borneo, and the Malay Peninsula. Some of the trees, however, were very large, especially some gigantic figs of the banyan type.

In general the vegetation of this part of Sumatra, is quite

similar to that of the Malay States across the Straits of Malacca, but less luxuriant. There is a considerable development of lianas, including species of Vitis, various climbing Araceae, e. g., Pothos, Scindapsus, and a good many small rattans.

Palms are not conspicuous, although there are a good many small species, and occasionally a sugar-palm (*Arenga sp.*) with enormous feathery leaves.

Fig. 63.—Rain-forest vegetation, Bandar Baroe, Sumatra. Wild banana (*Musa sp.*); wild ginger (*Eletteria sp.*).

In the rain-forest especially along the small streams is a rich vegetation of gingers, bananas, and other similar plants. A very common one is an Amomum, a ginger with leafy stems two or three yards high, the leafless flower stalks arising separately from the rhizomes. Others, e. g., Costus and Alpinia have showy flowers suggesting orchids. The latter are represented by many species, some of great beauty, e. g., Caelogyne, Spathoglottis, Arundina; and a small Nepenthes was also noted but the latter genus is much more abundant in some other parts of Sumatra.

Among the more abundant flowers, were numerous pretty balsams (*Impatiens spp.*), Melastoma, Clerodendron, Didymocarpus, and several Begonias and Solanums.

Screw-pines both Pandanus and the climbing Freycintia, were abundant. Tree-ferns were not uncommon, and the big Angiopteris was very abundant, and especially luxuriant, with huge fronds four or five yards long. Contrasted with these are

A   B
Fig. 64.—Rain-forest vegetation, Bandar Baroe.
A. At left, young palm (*Caryota sp.*).   B. The large fern is *Angiopteris sp.*

tiny epiphytic Hymenophyllaceae, only an inch or two high. Many other ferns, both epiphytic and terrestrial are common.

A number of interesting liverworts were collected at Bandar Baroe, which is richer in these plants than most parts of the Malay Peninsula, and approaches the extremely rich region of western Java where conditions are quite similar. Some of the rarest and most interesting species occur in these favored regions.

Above Bandar Baroe, at an elevation of about 1,200 metres,

is an extensive plateau, a sort of moorland covered with coarse "lalang" grass and bracken. Except in sheltered places, trees were absent, but where conditions permitted, tree-ferns, palms (Caryota, Arenga), and some other tropical types were noted; but with these were such characteristic northern plants as elder, raspberries, violets and several coarse Compositae. These grassy plateaus are said to be frequent in the mountain regions of northern Sumatra.

The western side of the main mountain range has a much heavier rainfall than occurs in eastern Sumatra and the vegetation is said to be extremely luxuriant. In the Padang Highlands, especially in the volcanic districts, the conditions are much like those in western Java, and the vegetation has much in common with that region.

The forests of the southwest are said to be characterized by unusually large trees, especially some of the Dipterocarps. Forbes[1] states that he measured trees whose trunks were 40–50 yards before they branched, and some of them ten to twelve feet in diameter. The species were not given. The principal products of this part of Sumatra are pepper and dammar-gum, the latter derived from several species of Dipterocarps, the most valuable being that obtained from *Hopea dryobalanoides*. These gums are highly prized for fine varnishes.

Even with its relatively scanty population, the destruction of the forests has been very great, owing to the very wasteful methods employed. Like all half-civilized peoples in a forest country the natives destroy the forest with no thought for the future. The ground is cleared, cultivated for a short time, and then allowed to revert to jungle, or as too frequently happens, to become invaded by the rank "lalang" grass (*Imperata arundinacea* and *Saccharum spontaneum*), which prevents the forest getting a foothold, and renders the land quite useless for cultivation.

The lowland forests have largely disappeared, and one must usually go to the mountains to see the primaeval forest. As in the Malay States, the great development of rubber plantations has been largely responsible for the destruction of the original forests.

Forbes [2] gives an interesting account of the flora of one of the

[1] Forbes, H. O., *A Naturalist's Wanderings in the Eastern Archipelago*, p. 221, 1885.

[2] *Loc. cit.*, p. 206.

higher volcanic peaks, Dempo, over 10,000 feet elevation. At an elevation of 3,500 feet there were extensive coffee plantations, above which, at about 4,000 feet, the virgin forest began, and for about 2,000 feet was extremely luxuriant, evidently much like the similar forests on the slopes of the great volcanic peaks of western Java.

Flowers were scarce, except for some epiphytes and climbers, but he discovered one remarkable new species, a strange parasite, *Brugmansia sp.*, related to the gigantic *Rafflesia Arnoldi*, also a native of Sumatra. The latter is an extreme parasite living within the tissues of a vine (*Vitis sp.*) very much like a parasitic fungus. The flower buds break through the tissues of the host-plant, and the huge flowers, sometimes nearly a yard across, look as if they belonged to the vine upon which they are parasitic. These giant flowers have a color and odor suggesting putrid flesh, and attract swarms of carrion-flies and other insects which doubtless serve as agents in pollination. Among the plants noted by Forbes in the lowland forest, was the gigantic arum, *Amorphophallus Titanum*, with leaves seventeen feet high!

The forest shows the usual profusion of gingers, bananas, tree-ferns, palms, aroids, etc. Forbes states that this region also, is remarkably rich in flowering trees, one of which, *Gordonia excelsa*, has two related species in the southern Atlantic states. Above 6,000 feet most of the palms, including the rattans, ceased, and the trees became smaller. These trees were mostly of the myrtle family, and their branches were heavily laden with epiphytes, especially ferns in great variety. Still higher up, long gray lichens became conspicuous, and Begonias, honeysuckles, and a very fine orchid (*Dendrobium secundum*) were abundant. The tall forest stopped at 8,600 feet, and changed to lower shrubby growths, largely Ericaceae. Of these, a species of Vaccinium (*V. Forbesii*), became a small tree. This was associated with scarlet rhododendrons, and many ferns. A few raspberries and a gentian were also noted, but the pitcher plants, so abundant on some of the mountains, were almost entirely absent.

While the trees of Sumatra are mainly Malayan types, they include a single pine (*Pinus Merkusii*), found in the north of the island, and several species of oaks. *Pinus Merkusii* probably marks the southermost extension of the true pines, but Sumatra shares with the rest of Malaya the Kauri-pines (Agathis) and Podocarpus.

JAVA

Probably no region in the world offers more to the botanical student than does Java, and because of the amazing wealth of the flora, and its accessibility, it has been visited by many botanists during the past century, and its flora is better known than that of any other part of the Malayan region.

Java is preëminently a volcanic country and contains many active volcanoes as well as numerous extinct ones. The volcanic soils are extremely rich, and together with the uniform high temperature and very heavy rainfall, induce a luxuriance of vegetation in many parts of Java, especially in the west, that can hardly be matched elsewhere.

Unlike Borneo and Sumatra, Java is very densely populated, and most of the available land is under cultivation. As elsewhere in Malaya, rice is the staple food, and is very carefully cultivated; but in addition to rice, practically all the tropical food-plants are grown, and the variety of fruits, especially, can hardly be equalled anywhere. In spite of the dense population, about 36,000,000 in an area less than 50,000 square miles, there is little evidence of this to the casual observer in western Java. The people live for the most part in small villages, "campongs," composed of bamboo houses so hidden by the groves of palms, bamboos, and fruit-trees, as to be quite invisible except at close range; and from an elevation the country appears to be covered by an unbroken forest, except for the larger towns and extensive rice fields.

Under the wise administration of the Netherlands government, Java is probably the most successful tropical colony in the world, and the output of all sorts of tropical products, rubber, coffee, sugar, tobacco, etc., is very great, and the country is extremely prosperous. Among the most important products of Java is quinine, which, introduced from South America, has been most successfully grown, and by careful selection trees have been developed which yield a much greater amount of quinine than any of the wild species of Cinchona.

Java is extremely mountainous, there being very little level country. Along much of the northern shores are mangrove and Nipa swamps, but the southern side of the island has a greater development of sandy beaches and dunes. The high mountains

PLATE XVIII.—Edge of jungle, Mt. Salak, Java.

are all volcanic, those in the west forming a more or less continuous
mass; at the east are several isolated peaks, including the loftiest
mountain, Merapi, about 12,000 feet high.

In general, the rainfall in Java is heavy, especially in the western
mountains, and in the southern part of the island. While in all
parts of Java, the period from November to March, the west
monsoon, shows the greatest precipitation, there is no pronounced
dry season, although in eastern Java the rainfall is scanty during
several months, and the vegetation is very different from that of
the wet western mountains.

The approach to Batavia, the old capital, is through a swampy
region in which the Nipa-palms are a conspicuous feature. The
residence district, outside the old town, is attractive, the gardens
full of fine foliage and flowers, but the surrounding country being
closely cultivated, offers little to the botanist who is likely to seek
the mountains as soon as possible.

The great centre of botanical activity is the famous botanical
garden at Buitenzorg, some forty miles from Batavia, at an elevation of about 1,000 feet. From Buitenzorg the richest botanical
regions are within easy reach, and together with the immense
collections in the garden, afford unequalled opportunities for the
study of equatorial vegetation.

In these gardens may be seen an unrivalled collection of tropical
plants, drawn from every quarter of the world. Java has been a
centre of botanical research for more than a century, and the collectors have brought to the gardens plants from all over the Archipelago, many new species having their types now growing in the
gardens. The conditions for tropical vegetation are ideal. The
average temperature hardly varies throughout the year, and is
about 78°F. A rainfall approaching 200 inches annually, an
absence of a marked dry season, and rich soil, give these gardens
a great advantage over any of the other important tropical
botanical gardens.

The country immediately about Buitenzorg is mostly under
cultivation, but nevertheless many interesting native plants may
be found growing outside the cultivated areas; and within a short
distance, on the lower slopes of the great volcano Salak, a magnificent forest of the most pronounced tropical type can be found.
Compared with the lowland forests of Sumatra and Borneo,

PLATE XIX.—Palm collection, Botanical Gardens, Buitenzorg, Java.

Dipterocarps are less in evidence. On the other hand the species of figs (Ficus) are developed to an extraordinary degree in Java, over a hundred species having been described, of which a majority are in western Java.

Belonging to the same family as the figs, is the famous Upas (*Antiaria toxicaria*), a very large tree, whose poisonous properties have been greatly exaggerated.

The myrtle family is also abundantly represented, especially the genus Eugenia, while other characteristic trees belong to the custard-apples (Anonaceae), and the Leguminosae have many representatives, e. g., Albizzia, Pterocarpus, Tamarindus, Cassia, etc. The canary-nut (*Canarium sp.*) belonging to the tropical family Burseraceae, is a large and characteristic tree. A magnificent avenue of these is one of the features of the Buitenzorg garden. The silk-cotton (Bombax), durian (*Durio spp.*) and several species of Artocarpus, are characteristic of the Javanese forest. In the lowland forest is a wealth of palms, including many species of rattans, as well as some fine tall species, e. g., Oncosperma, Areca, Caryota, etc.

Lianas and epiphytes are extremely abundant as elsewhere in the lowland Malayan jungles, and much like those in Sumatra and Borneo. Tall bamboos (Dendrocalamus, Gigantochloa), screw-pines, and fine tree-ferns, combine with the gingers, bananas, and giant arums, to make a magnificent undergrowth, wherever the shade is not too dense.

Western Java is one of the richest regions in the world for liver-worts and ferns. The banks and shady ravines are full of rare and beautiful species, in immense variety. Tree-ferns are especially abundant and beautiful, some specimens of a common species, *Alsophila glauca*, being said to reach a height of 20 metres. These are found at a lower elevation in western Java than is usual, but reach their maximum development at somewhat higher elevations in the cooler mountain rain-forest.

The lowland forest extends to about 2,000 feet elevation, above which up to about 4,500 feet, is a rain-forest, tropical in its main constituents, but with a considerable mixture of species allied to those of more temperate climates.

A forest of this character may be seen in great perfection on the great volcanic mass, the Gedeh, not far from Buitenzorg.

PLATE XX.—Banyan figs (*Ficus Benjamina*), Buitenzorg. The epiphytic ferns are the bird's-nest fern (*Asplenium Nidus*).

On this mountain, at about 4,000 feet elevation, is a botanical garden with accomodations for visiting botanists; and Tjibodas, the site of this garden, is familiar to many botanists who have explored the virgin forest which immediately adjoins the garden. From this point to the summit of Pangerango, 10,000 feet high, is an unbroken primaeval forest, in which one may study at his convenience the wonderfully rich vegetation of this great volcano.

The lower forest comprises over a hundred species of trees belonging to many genera. The figs and myrtles, so numerous in the lowland forest are much less abundant, while chestnuts, oaks, maples, Viburnum, and Vaccinium, recall the forests of the north temperate zone. The tallest tree of this region, the "Rasamala" (*Altingia excelsa*), is a near relative of the American Liquidambar. Magnificent specimens of this noble tree are growing close to the garden, and high up on the branches one catches glimpses of the bright orange flowers of an epiphytic rhododendron (*R. Javanicum*).

A number of trees belong to genera characteristic of the forests of Atlantic North America. Of these the beautiful *Gordonia excelsa* with its abundant big white flowers, is the most conspicuous. Others belong to the genera Nyssa, Celtis and Lindera. Other representative genera of this forest are Symplocos, Schima, Trema, Elaeocarpus, Flacourtia, Antidesma, Cedrela, Weinmannia, Myrsine, Pandanus, Vernonia, Michelia. The only gymnosperms are two species of Podocarpus.

Climbing plants are not so abundant as in the lowland forest, but there is an immense development of epiphytes, ferns, mosses, orchids, rhododendrons, and many others. Common and conspicuous are the species of Aeschynanthus with scarlet flowers.

Of the epiphytic ferns, the great bird's-nest fern (*Asplenium nidus*) is the most conspicuous. This fern sometimes has attached to its base another remarkable epiphytic species, *Ophioglossum pendulum*, and other epiphytic ferns are many Hymenophyllaceae, *Vittaria spp.*, *Polypodium spp.*, and others. There are several epiphytic species of Lycopodium, e. g., *L. Phlegmaria*, and also Selaginella.

Flowers are not very abundant, but sometimes a showy orchid is met with, and some extremely pretty balsams (*Impatiens spp.*) are very common.

Probably no tropical mountain has been more thoroughly explored than the Gedeh; and no mountain better illustrates the changing zones of vegetation as one ascends from the base to the summit, 10,000 feet above sea-level.

The forest, which at Tjibodas, about 4000 feet elevation, is predominantly a tropical rain-forest, two thousand feet higher shows a marked increase in such temperate types as the oaks and chestnuts. The foliage is less luxuriant, and the climbers and epiphytes (except mosses and ferns), become decidedly less developed. In the upper zone mosses become extraordinarily abundant, great cushions of moss covering the ground and fallen logs, and the trunks and branches being covered and festooned with mosses of many kinds. They seem to find an especially congenial habitat in these cool wet forests, and are much more important than the liverworts which are so abundant in the lower elevations, although there are some species confined to the higher altitudes.

At one point on the trail leading to the summit is an interesting illustration of the effect of increased temperature. This locality "Tjipanas," has a number of hot springs which issue from the mountain side and form a natural hot-house, where the vegetation has a genuine tropical luxuriance. Gorgeous orchids, pitcher plants, giant tree-ferns, and a dense drapery of ferns and mosses on the rocks, together presented a picture suggesting the hot zone 4,000 feet below.

At this time (April) the young foliage of the evergreen forest presented a great variety of beautiful tints, red, pink, yellow, adding much to the beauty of the scene.

Toward the top of the mountain, the forest trees are low and distorted, with scanty foliage, the branches covered with mosses and draped with long streamers of gray lichen.[1] The floor of this strange forest is covered with a carpet of dead leaves and twigs, among which a curious parasite with red and yellow flowers (*Balanophora elongata*), may sometimes be found, and with it a few ferns and a small terrestrial orchid are associated.

A very characteristic plant of this region is a tall yellow

[1] Schimper, *loc. cit.*, p. 723, gives the following as the most important trees, *Aralia sp.*, *Myrsine avenis*, *Vaccinium floribundum*.

primrose (*Primula imperialis*) not uncommon under the bushes, said to be confined to this mountain, and this is associated with a buttercup and raspberry, as well as several other common boreal genera. A very interesting plant is *Nertera depressa*, a little trailing plant growing at the base of the moss-covered trees. This same species is common in New Zealand and Australia and also occurs in temperate South America.

Somewhat lower down there was a rich growth of liverworts, mosses and lichens, as well as some remarkably fine tree-ferns, (*Cyathea sp.*) forty feet or more in height. Several species of Gleichenia, including a large climbing species (*G. arachnoides*) were noted by the writer, and species of Lycopodium, including the cosmopolitan *L. clavatum* and *L. complanatum*, as well as the large climbing *L. volubile* and others. Some fine orchids were seen, the most notable a crimson Dendrobium and a large orange-flowered terrestrial species (Phajus?).

The summit of Pangerango, the highest point of the Gedeh, is covered for the most part with scrub, but with open grassy patches between. The scrub is mostly a woody composite, *Anaphalis Javanica*, with whitish flowers, and associated with it are occasional low gnarled trees of *Leptospermum floribundum*. The latter belongs to the myrtle family, and the genus is especially abundant in Australia.

In general the summit vegetation of the Gedeh is distinctly boreal in type. Two fine rhododendrons, *R. retusum* and *R. Javanicum*, which at lower elevations are epiphytes, are here seen as terrestrial shrubs, and other members of the heath family, Vaccinium and Gaultheria, are abundant at the higher elevations. The latter is represented by two abundant species with white and black berries, having a strong wintergreen flavor, like their American relative, *G. procumbens*.

EAST JAVA [1]

Eastern Java on the whole, is decidedly drier than the west, and this is reflected in the forest growth which is intermediate in character between the very wet western rain-forest, and the monsoon forest with a preponderance of deciduous vegetation.

[1] Schimper, *loc. cit.*

There is greater variety in soil conditions than in west Java, and this results in a greater variety of forest trees.

In parts of east Java are extensive teak forests, almost pure stands of this important timber-tree. In the dry season the forest is quite leafless, and offers the strongest contrast to the exuberant luxuriance of the western rain-forest. There are some evergreen species associated with the teak, e. g., *Albizzia stipulata*, *Butea frondosa*, the latter, as in India, conspicuous for its showy red flowers. The deciduous forest is almost destitute of epiphytes, but some species of Ficus occur which begin life as epiphytes upon the teak and other deciduous trees.

A number of lianas, mostly Leguminosae, occur, and there is a rich growth of shrubs and small bushes, some with showy flowers like species of Cassia and Hibiscus. Palms and bamboos are comparatively scarce.

Where conditions permit an accumulation of humus, some of the rain-forest herbaceous plants, like the gingers (Curcuma, Amomum, etc.), and others with showy flowers, may be seen, and flowers in general are more noticeable than in the rain-forest, owing to the more abundant light. The display is greatest at the monsoon rains in November, before the new foliage appears on the deciduous trees.

KRAKATAU

A very instructive demonstration of the rapid development of vegetation under equatorial conditions is shown by the re-establishment of vegetation on the island of Krakatau which was blown up by the tremendous explosion of its volcanic crater in 1883. Life of all kinds was completely destroyed, and what was left of the island was buried deep in volcanic ashes. Krakatau lies in the Straits of Sunda, midway between Java and Sumatra.

The first visit made to Krakatau after the catastrophe, was by Professor M. Treub, director of the Buitenzorg garden. This was three years after the eruption, but by this time about a dozen species of ferns were well established, together with a considerable number of flowering plants.

The writer [1] had an opportunity of visiting the island twenty

[1] "The New Flora of Krakatau," *American Naturalist*, Vol. XLIII, August, 1909.

years later, in 1906, by which time the island was completely covered with dense vegetation in great variety.

In places there was a broad beach with the characteristic strand plants. The ubiquitous *Ipomoea pes-caprae*, the curious grass, Spinifex, and a yellow leguminous vine (*Vigna lutea*), as well as several others, occupied the beach, while back of this was a belt of trees. Floating fruits of the Nipa-palm were stranded on the beach, but no swamp formation had developed.

The most important tree of the belt above the beach was *Casuarina equisetifolia*, some at least 50 feet high, and a common member of the Malayan strand flora. Screw-pines and the handsome *Terminalia Catappa*, with its symmetrical whorls of branches and big, shining leaves, were common, and the fine *Barringtonia speciosa*, with its big white flowers and square fruits. In short, the predominant strand plants were the same as in Borneo. The commonest climber was a vine (*Vitis trifolia*). A grove of coconuts had become established, and in full bearing, and the cool liquid contents of the nuts were hugely appreciated after a walk through the stifling heat of the tall grass jungle which covered much of the interior of the island.

From Professor Treub's early study of the vegetation, it appeared that the first plants to establish themselves were certain very primitive blue-green algae, which prepared the way for ferns, which soon obtained a foothold, and were quickly followed by other plants, as soon as sufficient soil was developed. These first immigrants were presumably derived from both Java and Sumatra, which are about equidistant from Krakatau. Some, like the coconuts and Barringtonia, evidently travelled by water, while the spores of the ferns, the minute seeds of orchids, and the fruits of grasses and Compositae, were probably wind-borne. Birds undoubtedly have played an important rôle in the introduction of many species.

It is evident, both from the depth of the sea, and from the character of both plants and animals, that in recent geological time the great Sunda Islands were part of the Asiatic continent.

Extending eastward from Java is a chain of small islands, of which the last, and largest, is Timor. Between two of the islands nearest to Java, Bali and Lombok, is a narrow, but very deep strait, and Wallace [1] pointed out the fauna of the islands to the

[1] Wallace, A. R., *The Malay Archipelago.*

east of this line was predominantly Australian. A study of the vegetation shows plainly that the floras of these eastern islands also show a distinctly Australian influence, although much less marked than the animal life.

The subject has been investigated by later investigators, and a recent paper by Dr. E. D. Merrill [1] gives an admirable summary of the subject. Wallace's line is extended northward to the west of the Philippines, Palawan being the only large island lying to the west. This line is supposed to mark the edge of the Asiatic continental shelf. A second line, Weber's line, running close to New Guinea and Australia, marks the edge of a second continental shelf upon which are situated Australia and New Guinea. The two continental masses are separated by an archipelago, of which Celebes is the largest member.

There is a marked difference between the eastern and western Malaysian floras, although they have a very large number of forms in common. There are 356 Malaysian genera confined to western Malaysia, and 225 which do not occur west of Wallace's line.

It is assumed that the two continental regions have been relatively stable, but the region between shows evidences of frequent elevations and depressions, with probable temporary connections with one or the other of the continental areas, thus permitting an occasional interchange of plants. This accounts for the presence of such distinctly Australian types as Eucalyptus, Casuarina, and Melaleuca, in the western part of Malaysia.

The contrast between the floras of western and eastern Malaysia may be illustrated by the distribution of the essentially western Malaysian family, the Dipterocarpaceae. In the Sunda Islands, there are eleven genera and 144 species, while in the whole of the region east of Wallace's line, including the great islands of Celebes and New Guinea, there are but four genera and fourteen species, and possibly this number may be reduced as some of the recorded species are doubtful.

The Molucca or Spice Islands, lying between Celebes and New Guinea, were formerly of great importance commercially, as the main source for such spices as pepper, cloves, nutmegs. The

[1] "Distribution of the Dipterocarpaceae," *Philippine Journal of Science*, Vol. XXIII, No. 1., July, 1923.

cultivation of these spices in the islands has greatly decreased in late years, and the trade in these products is no longer of very great importance.

THE PHILIPPINES

Of special interest to Americans is the Philippine Archipelago, lying North of Borneo and Celebes, and extending nearly to latitude 20°.

The Philippines share many species with the Sunda Islands, and their flora is predominantly Malayan in character; but in the northern island, Luzon, especially in the mountains, is a pronounced infusion of temperate species, related to those of the Asiatic mainland, especially China.

The botany of the Philippines has been the subject of much investigation since the American occupation, so that our knowledge of the very extensive flora has been greatly increased. It must be said, however, that much important work was also done during the Spanish régime.

Like Java and western Sumatra, the Philippines are characterized by extensive volcanic formations, and the vegetation on the volcanic peaks has much in common with the similar mountain floras of the Sunda Islands.

The shore vegetation does not differ essentially from that already described for other Malayan coasts, and includes mangrove and Nipa swamps, and beaches with the same strand species. Near Manila a screw-pine (*Pandanus tectorius*) is abundant, and its leaves are used for many purposes by the natives. Calophyllum, with beautiful glossy leaves, Terminalia, Barringtonia and Casuarina, are the same as in Borneo, and elsewhere in Malaya, and the trailing morning glory (*Ipomoea pes-caprae*), grows everywhere along the beach. An interesting little water-fern (*Marsilea crenata*), was also noted by the writer, in low ground near the shore.

The writer had an opportunity of studying the vegetation on two of the volcanic mountains in the vicinity of Manila, Mt. Maquiling and Mt. Banajao.

The former is about 3,500 feet altitude and its vegetation has been very little interfered with. The forest at the lower elevations has several species of Dipterocarps, which, as elsewhere, are the most valuable of the timber-trees, as well as among the largest. Figs of several species are abundant, and of other common trees, the following may be mentioned: several oaks (*Quercus Luzonensis* and others), are common, especially at the higher elevations, and various species of Celtis, Trema, Artocarpus, Myristica (nutmeg), Cinnamomum, Pithecolobium, Pterocarpus, and many others.

At about 1,000 feet the vegetation is particularly luxuriant, and many ferns and palms are conspicuous. Among the latter are

Fig. 65.—Lowland rain-forest, Luzon, P. I.   *Photo., Dr. E. B. Copeland.*

numerous rattans, as well as some very beautiful species of Oncosperma and Areca, with slender trunks and graceful feathery foliage. The sugar-palm (*Arenga saccharifera*), with its immense leaves, also occurs in this forest. A fine fan-palm (*Livistona sp.*) is also common. The usual profusion of lianas and epiphytes, characteristic of the rain-forest, is present. Two especially showy lianas, both Leguminosae, were noted, species of Bauhinia and Strongylodon, the latter with flowers of a peculiar blue-green color.

Ferns are very abundant, and there are many liverworts and mosses on the trunks of the trees and on banks and fallen logs.

Of the herbaceous plants the most conspicuous was a huge

arum (*Alocasia sp.*) with immense leaves six or seven feet long. A single specimen of a curious parasite, *Rafflesia sp.*, was seen.

Some handsome orchids (*Phajus sp., Vanilla sp.*), bright scarlet Aeschynanthus, showy pink epiphytic Medinilla and Begonias, gave dashes of bright color to the prevailing green of the luxuriant foliage.

Near the summit of the mountain, some pitcher plants were seen, and also fine filmy ferns and tree-ferns.

FIG. 66.—Mountain forest, Luzon, P. I. *Photo., Dr. E. B. Copeland.*

Banajao is about twice the height of Maquiling, but the lower part has little forest remaining; and up to about 3,000 feet is to a great extent covered with the coarse "lalang" grass. The forest is less luxuriant than on Maquiling, with fewer palms, except rattans. At the higher elevation, up to the summit (7,500 ft.), the forest is predominantly coniferous, but the trees are all of the yew family, species of Dacrydium, Taxus, and Podocarpus. The liverwort flora is a very rich and interesting one, including a number of species collected by the writer in Java and Sumatra. A rather unexpected find was a peat-moss (Sphagnum), in fine fruit.

No showy orchids were seen on Banajao, but some other very beautiful epiphytes were common. Especially striking were some magnificent Begonias and Medinillas. The latter are very abundant in the Philippines, and the large drooping inflorescences, the flowers surrounded by big pink bracts, are extremely showy.

The northern part of Luzon is a rugged mass of mountains, with a rich and varied flora. At about 3,000 feet are encountered true pines (*Pinus insularis*), which at Baguio (5,000 ft.) form an extensive open forest, such as one is familiar with in the north tem-

A   B

FIG. 67.—A. Pines (*Pinus insularis*), Baguio, P. I.; B. Orchid (*Cypripedium Argus*), and fern (*Gleichenia sp.*); high mountains, Northern Luzon. *Photo., Dr. E. B. Copeland.*

perate regions, and not at all suggestive of the tropics. These pines are found up to nearly 8,000 feet in the drier soils, but for the most part the higher forest is a dense mossy jungle, composed of oaks, myrtles (*Eugenia spp.*), and Podocarpus. The trees are draped in a profusion of mosses, liverworts and lichens in great variety. Tree-ferns, and many others abound, and in general the vegetation is much like that of the higher mountains of western Java.

A few pitcher plants were noted, but the most striking feature of this high mountain region was the abundance of beautiful flowers, which at the time of the writer's visit, the end of May, were in their fullest bloom. Many remarkably handsome orchids were abundant, including several species of Dendrobium, Coelogyne, and Cypripedium. The beautiful Philippine lily (*Lilium Philippinense*), displayed its big white trumpets by hundreds, and great bushes of azalea and rhododendron were covered with white and red flowers, while thickets of pink Begonias as high as one's head, grew in profusion. Pink Medinillas hung from the branches of the trees, and on the ground were many familiar looking, but less showy things. Several species of raspberries, strawberry, violet, buttercups, a large white anemone, lobelia, and everlasting (Gnaphalium) recalled the summit of the Gedeh in Java, and one noted also the white-fruited wintergreen (Gaultheria), and species of Vaccinium, like those of the Gedeh. Other northern types were an elder, and a dwarf chestnut (Castanopsis), the latter having a representative in the Pacific forest of North America.

Peppers, myrtles (*Eugenia spp.*) and Begonias, as well as the orchids and pitcher plants are more reminiscent of the tropical forests of the lower elevations. A member of the Magnolia family, *Drimys piperita*, is interesting as the genus is also characteristic of New Zealand and temperate South America.

Club-mosses, species of Lycopodium, both terrestrial and epiphytic, are abundant, and the species are the same as on the Gedeh in Java, and include the wide-spread boreal species, *L. clavatum* and *L. complanatum*.

The Philippines, lying to the east of Wallace's line, combine in their flora elements derived on the one hand from the great Sunda Islands, and on the other from eastern Malaya and Australia.[1] Thus of the 356 genera peculiar to western Malaya, the Philippines possess 61%, while of the 225 genera of eastern Malaya, absent from the region west of Wallace's line, the Philippines show 25%. It is evident then, that the relationships are much more intimate between the flora of the Philippines, and that of the Sunda Islands, than with the more scattered islands to the south and east through which the eastern Malayan and Australian elements have presumably migrated into the Philippines.

[1] Merrill, *loc. cit.*

The occurence in northern Luzon of such boreal types as pines, oaks, buttercups, lilies, etc., indicates some former connection with the Asiatic mainland. It is unlikely that these entered Luzon *via* Formosa. The deep water separating the two islands implies a long period of separation, and this is clearly indicated by the very different floras, Formosa having a flora closely related to that of China.

AUSTRO-MALAYA

The great island of New Guinea or Papua, 1,500 miles long, and with an area of over 300,000 square miles, is the largest island in the Pacific, and with its adjacent small islands is the easternmost member of the Malay Archipelago. The flora is still very incompletely known, but it is evident that while it is predominantly Malayan in character, there is a large infusion of true Australian types.

The lofty mountain range forming the backbone of the island has the highest peaks of the whole Pacific area, except continental America, some of these being over 15,000 feet elevation. The great range of conditions, between the hot coastal plains and the highest summits where in places permanent snow is found, results in an extraordinarily extensive and varied flora. In most parts of Papua the rainfall is heavy, especially in the western part, but there are much drier sections in the south and east.

David [1] states that Papua is part of the great "Himalayan-Burman arc, prolonged through the Malay Peninsula, Sumatra, Java and Timor." This relation to the Indo-Malayan region is clearly indicated by the character of the vegetation which in its main features is essentially Malayan, with an intermixture in the cooler mountain districts of northern genera like the oaks and rhododendrons so characteristic of the Himalayan flora, as well as many northern herbaceous genera. While a majority of the genera, and a good many species are identical with those of the western Malayan region, there is a very large proportion of endemic genera and species, and the flora is a very distinct one. [2]

The greater part of Papua is heavily forested except where lalang grass has invaded cut-over or burned forest land. The forest

[1] David, T. W. E., *Federal Handbook for Australia*, p. 320, Melbourne, 1914.
[2] Maiden, J. H., *Federal Handbook for Australia*, p. 179.

PLATE XXI.—Tropical jungle, North Queensland, Australia. Center, tree-ferns (*Alsophila Australis* (?)); at right and in foreground, rattans (*Calamus sp.*).

trees are in general the same types as in western Malaya, but the Dipterocarps are very much less developed, while in the drier regions of the south coast, the vegetation is decidedly Australian. Here there are open savannas, with coarse grasses, e. g., *Imperata arundinacea*, Anthisteria, Andropogon, Pennisetum, etc., while the trees and shrubs are for the most part the same as those on the Australian mainland. Such distinctly Australian genera as Eucalyptus, Acacia, and various Proteaceae, comprise most of the trees and shrubs of this savanna flora.

This region is separated from the York Peninsula, the northernmost extension of Australia by less than 110 miles of water, and the very shallow sea which now separates Papua and Australia, as well as the great similarity in the animal life, indicates that the separation of the two regions is of comparatively recent date.

NORTH AUSTRALIA

Northern Australia lies well within the tropics and North Queensland has a genuine tropical flora, largely of Malayan origin. The northeast coast, which has a heavy rainfall, was visited by the writer in July, 1921.

The neighborhood of Cairns, the principal port, is flat and sandy, with a mixture of Australian and Malayan types, Eucalyptus trees being associated with species of Ficus, Pandanus, and other Malayan types. Where streams enter the sea, there is a mangrove formation of the same sort as that in the Malay Archipelago.

South of Cairns lies the Bellenden-Ker range, the highest mountains in Queensland, and in this neighborhood is the wettest district in Australia. From a few days sojourn at Babinda, which has an average yearly rainfall of 150 inches, the writer can vouch for the heavy precipitation of this region. The forest in the neighborhood of Babinda is a genuine rain-forest, much like the lowland forests of Java or Borneo in general appearance, except that the trees are not so large. This jungle is often quite impenetrable, the trees loaded down with lianas and epiphytes of various kinds, among them several species of rattans, which were only too much in evidence. Throughout the Malayan region, these are the greatest hindrance to travel in

the forest, their tough spiny stems, and leaves armed with recurved thorns, making absolutely impassable barriers, veritable
barbed-wire entanglements.   Climbing aroids, e. g., *Pothos
longipes*, *Rhapidophora Australasica*, are much in evidence,
as well as many other lianas, among which are several species
of Vitis, and a pepper (*Piper Mestoni*) the latter with very showy

Fig. 68.—Mangroves, Cairns, North Queensland, Australia.   At right, young
mangroves.

scarlet fruits.   The usual abundance of epiphytes, orchids, ferns,
Peperomia, etc., was noted.

Ferns, liverworts, mosses, were not remarkably abundant.
Of the ferns, the most striking were some gigantic specimens
of Angiopteris.

Palms are a conspicuous feature of the Queensland rain-forest.
The commonest and most beautiful are the species of Archontophoenix, whose straight slender stems, and crowns of graceful
feathery leaves, are among the most beautiful of the order.   *A.
Cunninghamiana* is often cultivated under the name *Seaforthia*

PLATE XXII.—Grove of *Archontophoenix Alexandrae*, North Queensland.

245

elegans. Two other palms were seen near Babinda, a curious fan-palm (*Licuala Muelleri*) and the pretty "walking-stick" palm, *Bacularia sp.*

Further north, in the York Peninsula, are several Indo-Malayan genera, Caryota, Borassus, Areca, and others, which were not seen in the Cairns district. Pitcher-plants of several species, have also been described from the York Peninsula.

A   B

FIG. 69.—Rain-forest, North Queensland, Australia.
A. Young palms (*Archontophoenix sp.*).
B. Edge of jungle, showing rattans and screw-pine.

Back of the coast, at an elevation of 2,000 to 4,000 ft. is a plateau which supports a fine forest, mostly of hard-woods, of great value as timber. These forests are rapidly disappearing before the inroads of the lumberman, but there are still accessible remnants of the forest which show their character. This forest is developed only on the rich basaltic and alluvial soils, the poorer sandy soils being occupied by open forests of gums, as elsewhere in Australia.

PLATE XXIII.—Hard-wood forest, table-land North Queensland. The tree in the center is a "cedar" (*Cedreal toona*).

The upland forest has fewer lianas and less dense undergrowth
than the coastal rain-forest, but the trees are much finer, being
very tall with straight clear trunks, sometimes of great size,
5 to 10 feet in diameter in the case of the Kauri (*Agathis Palmerstoni*) and the "red-cedar" (*Cedrela toona*). Trees known
locally as "beech," "maple," "hickory," etc., are not even
remotely related to their northern namesakes. They are mostly

A   B

Fig. 70.—A. Staghorn fern (*Platycerium grande*,) botanical garden, Brisbane.
B. Giant fig (*Ficus sp.*), North Queensland.

species of Flindersia, a genus usually placed in the mahogany
family (Meliaceae). Many of the large trees have extensive
buttresses at the base, a very common feature in the larger
trees of tropical forests.

In the Queensland "scrubs," the local name for the rain-forest, are a number of fine trees belonging to the peculiar family
Proteaceae, developed to an extraordinary degree throughout
Australia. One of these, *Grevillea robusta*, is not uncommon
in cultivation in California. Other genera are Embothrium
and Stenocarpus.

Other characteristic trees are species of Elaeocarpus (Tiliaceae), Sideroxylon (Sapotaceae), Eugenia and the wide-spread *Aleurites Moluccana*, the "Kukui" of Hawaii. Two species of Podocarpus also are found. The giants of this region are banyan figs which attain a prodigious size. Like so many species of Ficus, these giant Queensland figs begin life as epiphytes, and their huge trunks are formed by the coalescence of many aërial roots. The trunk of one of these, seen by the writer, was said to be 120 feet in circumference, and the spreading crown was in proportion.

A dreaded pest of these forests is the tree-nettle (*Laportea moroides*), a rank weed some ten or fifteen feet high, whose touch is agony. Another species, *L. gigas*, is a tree of large size.

Screw-pines abound in north Queensland, and there are several species of cycads. The genus Macrozamia is wide-spread in Australia, occurring in every state; but Cycas and Bowenia are confined to tropical Queensland, and the latter genus is exclusively Australian. Bowenia differs much in appearance from the other cycads, having a bipinnate leaf which in form suggests a fern.

POLYNESIA

Occupying the whole central area of the Pacific, from Fiji, Samoa, and Tahiti on the south, to Hawaii on the north, are the innumerable islands of Polynesia, all lying within the tropics and enjoying a tropical climate modified by the cooling trade winds of the great ocean.

Except for Hawaii, the flora of the Polynesian regions is still quite imperfectly known; but in spite of the small size of the islands, and the great isolation of many of them, the floras have much in common, and on the whole may be considered as predominantly Malayan in type. There is also a strong infusion of Australasian elements.

Many of the Polynesian islands are low coral formations rising only a few feet above sea-level, but others like Tahiti, the Samoan Islands and the Hawaiian Archipelago, are volcanic masses, forming rugged mountains, which in Hawaii reach an altitude of over 13,000 feet. These highest mountains are recent volcanic cones, and in Samoa and Hawaii there are still active craters.

Fig. 71.—Forest interior, Samoa. *Photo., Mrs. D. S. Jordan.*

The low coral islands are evidently recent formations, and incapable of supporting any but a scanty flora which has presumably reached them from outside in recent times.

PLATE XXIV.—Lake Lanuto, Upolu, Samoa. *Photo., courtesy of Dr. D. S. Jordan.*

251

Fig. 72.—Hawaiian rain-forest. At back, "ohia" (*Metrosideros polymorpha*);
in center, lobelia (*Cyanea coriacea*). *Photo., Dr. J. F. Rock.*

The case of the large volcanic islands is very different, as the
recent volcanic deposits are probably superimposed upon more

ancient sedimentary rocks, the remains of some much larger sub-merged land-masses. Indeed there is much reason to suppose that all of Polynesia represents the remnants of extensive con-tinental, or sub-continental masses once connected with the Ma-layan region.

The flora of the southern larger islands has much in common with that of the Malay Archipelago and there are many identical species, as well as endemic species belonging to wide-spread Malayan genera. There is also a marked Australasian element in the floras of Polynesia.

Of course one must distinguish between the plants which man has carried with him all over the tropics, and those which are truly indigenous. The coconut, bread-fruit, bananas, sugar cane, etc., are universal in tropical countries. But leaving these aside, there is no question of the close relationships existing be-tween the southern islands of Polynesia and those of the Malay Archipelago.

The traveller between San Francisco and Australia or New Zealand, can get a glimpse of the Polynesian vegetation, as the ship stops in Hawaii, Samoa, Fiji, or Tahiti. A short sojourn in any of these islands will suffice to give one an idea of the general character of the vegetation, which has much in common through-out Polynesia.

Along the shore in Tahiti one sees the yellow Hibiscus, the "Hau" of the Hawaiians, screw-pines, and the handsome Bar-ringtonia, so characteristic of the Malayan strand vegetation, while the forest trees, as well as the rich undergrowth of herba-ceous plants, recall the rain-forests of the Malayan regions. This is especially true of the very abundant ferns, club-mosses and liverworts, many of which are wide-spread Malayan species. Among the ferns, giant specimens of Angiopteris are especially conspicuous, and there are a good many orchids, also belonging to Malayan genera. In Tahiti, the only orchid cultivated for commercial purposes, Vanilla, is a crop of considerable impor-tance. Climbing plants are much less developed in the Polynesian forests than is usual in the Malayan rain-forest.

PLATE XXV.—Forest interior, Samoa. *Photo., courtesy of Dr. D. S. Jordan.*

Hawaii

At the extreme northern limit of Polynesia lie the remote Hawaiian Islands, separated from the nearest land of any extent, by over 2,000 miles. In spite of their great distance from the islands to the south, the general character of the flora is much the same, and Malayan types are dominant as they are throughout Polynesia. Nevertheless it is evident that the islands have been isolated for a very long time, and in consequence the great majority of the species, and a good many genera, are restricted to the Hawaiian Archipelago. Hardly any part of the world has so large a proportion of.endemic species, upwards of 75% of the ferns and flowering plants being unknown outside these islands.

North America is the nearest continental land to Hawaii, being a little more than 2,000 miles distant; but the floras of the two have very little in common, in spite of the fact that the usually accepted agents in distribution, viz., ocean currents, winds and migratory birds, are all active between western America and Hawaii.

That the Hawaiian islands have been isolated for a very long period is amply proven by the peculiarities of both the animal and plant inhabitants whose nearest relatives, however, are for the most part found in the Malaysian and Australasian regions, and not in America.[1]

The Hawaiian Archipelago consists of several large islands, with a total area of nearly 6,500 square miles, lying between 18° 22′ and 21° 15′ north latitude. From the main group a long series of reefs and small islets extends for about eighteen degrees to the northwest.

There is ample evidence that the large islands were formerly united into a single land-mass which through gradual subsidence has become separated into the islands as they now exist. The northernmost island, Kauai, was the first to be cut off, as is indicated by the broad and deep channel between it and its neighbor to the south, Oahu. The long period of isolation of Kauai is also indicated by the greater degree of endemism in the flora.

The topography of the islands, especially the older ones, is excessively rugged. The prevailing northeast trades bring torren-

[1] Campbell, D. H., *The Derivation of the Flora of Hawaii*, Leland Stanford Junior Publications, 1919.

PLATE XXVI.—Lower forest, Hawaii. The light patches are "Kukui" (*Aleurites Moluccana*).

tial rains to the windward side of the islands, while the lee sides may be very dry. Where the mountains are low, as in Oahu, the rain may pass over the crest and fall at the head of the valleys on the lee side. An annual rainfall of 500 inches has been recorded from a station in Kauai.

The lowlands are closely cultivated, sugar and pineapples being grown on a very large scale, as well as the usual tropical fruits; and in some localities rice is grown.

Most of the vegetation seen about Honolulu and the other towns is exotic, and a great variety of beautiful flowering trees and shrubs is cultivated. The two commonest trees, the "algaroba" (*Prosopis sp.*) and "iron-wood (*Casuarina equisetifolia*), are both introduced, but have become completely naturalized.

The strand-vegetation includes such wide-spread types as *Hibiscus tiliaceus, Ipomoea pes-caprae,* Scaevola, Pandanus, Calophyllum—all familiar strand-plants of the eastern tropics; but the strand-flora as a whole is not an extensive one.

The commonest trees of the lowland forest, where it has survived, are two—the "Kukui" or "candle-nut" (*Aleurites Moluccana*), and the "mountain-apple" (*Eugenia Malaccensis*). As both of these are wide-spread in Malaysia and are of considerable economic value, it is thought that they may have been introduced by the early immigrants from the South Seas.

The upper forest zone, on the windward side of the islands, is a pronounced rain-forest with dense growth and many epiphytes; but lianas are not abundant, the most important being a climbing screw-pine, *Freycinetia Arnotti.* The most abundant tree of the upland forest is *Metrosideros polymorpha,* a near relative of the New Zealand rata. The showy red flowers are a great attraction to the honey-sucking birds of the peculiar Hawaiian family Drepaninidae. Another important tree is the "Koa" (*Acacia Koa*), much resembling some of the Australian species.

The trees and shrubs of the lower forest zone are largely genera common to the eastern tropics and Australia, but absent from America. Among these may be mentioned Pittosporum, Gardenia, Coprosma, Metrosideros, Santalum, Dracaena. The ferns and liverworts show a remarkable number of species identical or closely related to those of the Malayan-Australasian area.

There are a good many endemic Hawaiian genera, e. g., Platydesma (Rutaceae), Gouldia (Rubiaceae), Raillardia (Compositae), Cyanea (Lobeliaceae). The latter family is especially interesting from the standpoint of evolution. It is developed to a remarkable degree in the Archipelago, the greatest number of species, as well as the most specialized ones, occurring in Kauai, the oldest island—the number of species being much less in the more recently isolated islands, Maui and Hawaii, although these islands are very much larger than Kauai.

Fig. 73.—*Gunnera petaloidea*, characteristic of the wet mountain forests of Hawaii. Note the man at right of center. *Photo., Dr. J. F. Rock.*

There is but a single native genus of palms, Pritchardia, while there are no gymnosperms; and some wide-spread tropical genera, especially Ficus, are also entirely absent. The cosmopolitan family Araceae has no certainly indigenous representatives, although the staple food-plant of the natives, the "taro" (*Colocasia antiquorum*), is an aroid. Orchids, so abundant in most tropical countries, have only three species. One of the most conspicuous denizens of the upper wettest rain-forest is *Gunnera petaloidea*, with great rhubarb-like leaves four to five feet across. This much resembles the species from Chile.

PLATE XXVII.—Tree-fern swamp, Kohala Mountains, Hawaii, elevation 4,000 feet. *Photo., Dr. H. L. Lyon.*

As in all volcanic islands, ferns play an important rôle in the vegetation of the mountain forests, and this is notably the case in Hawaii. As has already been mentioned in regard to the restoration of the vegetation of Krakatau, after the great eruption, so in Hawaii, ferns are among the pioneers on the new lava discharged from the active craters.

Doubtless one of the important factors determining the peculiarities of these volcanic island floras, is the preponderance of volcanic soils which are not always suited to plants from outside. Thus in Hawaii it has been observed that only the strictly indigenous species seem able to get a foot-hold on the new lava.

FIG. 74.—Tree-lobelia (*Delissea longifolia*).
Photo., Dr. J. F. Rock.

It has been very commonly held that these isolated volcanic islands have always been completely separated from any larger body of land, and that the vegetation has been introduced from outside since the first appearance of the islands. There are very serious objections to this view, the greatest being the overwhelming preponderance of plants of Malayan and Australasian affinities, although very many of these are quite unfitted for natural transportation from these remote regions by any agency that is comprehensible. On the other hand, the number of strictly American types is very small, and can mostly be explained as introduced into the islands by currents, wind, or by birds, of which there are many regularly migrating between the American mainland and the islands.

The palms, screw-pines, acacias, and most of the indigenous

trees and shrubs, are unmistakably of South Pacific origin, and the same is true of many delicate plants of the wet mountain-forests, whose seeds could hardly survive an ocean voyage of several thousand miles, and then find their way to the cool mountain forests where alone they can grow.

CHAPTER VIII

THE NEOTROPICAL REGIONS

The distribution of the tropical vegetation of the new world is very different from that in the eastern hemisphere. The whole tropical region from northern Mexico to Argentina and Chile is continuous, and traversed by the great western mountain range of the Cordillera; and there is nothing comparable to the great expanses of desert separating the African wet tropics from the Indo-Malayan regions. This condition results in a much more homogeneous vegetation than is found in the Palaeotropics, although there is an exceedingly rich and varied flora.

The great Cordillera traversing western America from Alaska to Patagonia is a factor of the first importance in the distribution of plants in western America, both within and outside the tropics. This great mountain system has served as a highway for the migration of many plants, both north and south, and the influence of this great mountain barrier on both rainfall and temperature is very great, and is a controlling factor in the character of the vegetation within its influence.

The area of land within the equatorial belt is very much greater in America than in either Asia or Africa. While in the old world the northern tropics are largely deserts, like the Sahara, Arabia and northwest India, in corresponding latitudes in America the land areas are of relatively limited extent, and where deserts exist, they are insignificant compared with the great deserts of tropical Asia and Africa.

The equator crosses the broadest part of South America, through the immense Amazon valley, with its net-work of great rivers; and this whole region is occupied by the greatest continuous extent of tropical forest in the world. This immense region, extending from the Atlantic to the Andes is quite unequalled for the extent of its equatorial forests, which for variety and luxuriance can only be matched by the much less extensive forests of the equatorial forest belt in West Africa and the Malayan regions.

The American tropics, except for the West Indies and Galapagos Islands, constitute a single continental area.

MEXICO

The northern part of Mexico, both geographically and biologically, is part of the region which includes much of the states of Texas, New Mexico, Arizona and California.

The southern plateau region of the United States is continued southward into Mexico, where it becomes much higher, reaching

FIG. 75.—Sub-tropical vegetation, Mexico. Branches covered with epiphytes, largely Bromeliads. *Photo., Mr. G. N. Collins.*

7,000 feet in the vicinity of Mexico City. The greater part of Mexico is occupied by this central plateau, to the west of which the mountains form a continuation of the California Sierra. Part of this system forms the central range of the long peninsula of Lower California. The plateau of the Mexican mainland is separated from the Gulf of California by a high mountain range, which extends southward along the whole coastal region which forms a narrow strip between the mountains and the sea. Eastward the plateau descends more gradually to the Gulf of Mexico.

Much of Mexico is volcanic, and the great volcanic cones, one of which, Orizaba, over 18,000 feet elevation, is the highest peak in North America south of Alaska, are important factors in plant distribution.

With such great range in elevation, and also great differences of rainfall, it is not remarkable that the Mexican flora is a very extensive one.

Northern Mexico, in common with the southern plateau region of the United States, has a scanty rainfall, and a vegetation de-

Fig. 76.—Mountain forest, southern Mexico. Pines predominate. San Cristobal, State of Chiapas. *Photo., Mr. G. N. Collins.*

cidedly xerophytic in character, in which Cacti form a conspicuous feature. In northwest Mexico and Lower California true desert conditions prevail over much of the country, but southward there is an increase in precipitation, and below the Tropic of Cancer fairly abundant summer rains occur over most of the country, and vegetation is much more luxuriant than further north.

However, owing to the elevation of the plateau, the climate of Mexico City, although it lies well within the tropics, is temperate rather than tropical.

Travelling southward over the Mexican table land, one is at once impressed by the great number and variety of the Cacti, which here attain their maximum development, some of them being candelabra-like trees 40–50 feet high. With these are associated various other xerophytes, notably the century plants (*Agave spp.*), Yuccas and other characteristic American desert types.

With the diminishing breadth of Mexico toward the south, the plateau becomes restricted, and is broken by numerous hills, and in places by swampy areas and lakes, as in the vicinity of Mexico City, so that the flora is much more diversified than in the northern plateau. The climate of this region is mild, with a dry winter and rainy summer, much like that of parts of South Africa.

The Valley of Mexico for centuries has been the seat of a large population, and is to a great extent under cultivation, or supports herds of cattle. Remains of extensive irrigation and drainage works show that formerly an even greater area was under cultivation than at present.

While much of the drier parts of the plateau are covered with Cacti, Agaves, mesquit, and other xerophytes, there are moist canyons and open valleys where vegetation is more luxuriant, and the remains of forest at Amecameca, and some other hills, indicate that much of the open country was once covered with forest.

About Mexico City are extensive fields and gardens where corn, wheat, and the usual vegetables, fruits and flowers of the region are grown. In the summer, the markets show quantities of oranges, mangoes, avocadoes, strawberries and the fruits of certain Cacti. Some of these, like the mangoes, probably are brought from the lower country "Tierra caliente."

The great plantations of century plants, "maguey" in the vernacular, are a feature of the environs of Mexico City. The national drink, "pulque," is the fermented sap obtained by cutting out the great flower-stalk, just before it begins to elongate. The sap collects in the cavity left, and is gathered from day to day as long as it continues to flow. Enormous quantities of pulque are shipped to the capital daily. From other species of Agave a potent liquor "mescal" is distilled, and several species yield fibres of great strength. Sisal hemp is the product of *A. rigida* var. *Sisilana*.

The forests of this region are made up mostly of trees of boreal genera. Oaks in great variety, both evergreen and deciduous, are especially abundant in these mountain forests, and several species of pines and firs, a juniper and elder, are reminiscent of the forests of Arizona and California. A species of Arbutus, much like the Californian madroño is also found in the Mexican highlands.

With the evergreen oaks, pines, and firs, there are deciduous trees closely related to those of the temperate United States, such

Fig. 77.—Xerophytic vegetation, South Mexico, State of Michoacan. Cacti, Euphorbia (*E. fulva*). *Photo., Mr. G. N. Collins.*

as walnuts, sycamores, ashes and poplars, much like species found in California and Arizona.

Above the forest zone, on the higher mountains, the shrubs and herbaceous plants are almost exclusively of northern types, grasses and sedges, a great development of Compositae (Baccharis, Eupatorium, etc.), Ericaceae, Rosaceae, Umbelliferae and Cruciferae.

The railway to the coast from Mexico to Vera Cruz passes through the sub-tropical zone, "Tierra templada," into the tropical zone, "Tierra caliente" reaching some 3,000 feet above the coast.

As one descends, the oaks, pines, and other boreal genera become mingled with trees of more tropical aspect, such as members of the myrtle and custard-apple families, laurels, and especially

PLATE XXVIII.—Sonoran desert vegetation, Punto Kino, Western Mexico. At left, *Idria columnaris. Photo., Dr. W. S. Cooper.*

267

the distinctly American family Malpighiaceae. Bamboos, small palms, tree-ferns, lianas and epiphytes become more and more abundant as the tropical zone is approached. Among the epiphytes are some true parasites of the mistletoe family, (Loranthus, Phoradendron), and the exclusively American family Bromeliaceae is represented by a great number of species. This family is represented in our Gulf States by the "Spanish moss," and others,

FIG. 78.—Coastal desert. Shore of Gulf of California at Libertad, Sonora; *Frankenia Palmeri*, dominant. *Photo., Dr. W. S. Cooper.*

especially in Florida. Orchids are also extremely abundant in this region, and include some very beautiful species.

The region between 1,000 and 2,000 metres [1] has a heavy rainfall pretty evenly distributed. It is a region of evergreen oaks, and tree-ferns, and has many epiphytic orchids, and some small palms, (*Chamaedoria spp.*). This region has more species than the tropical belt below it.

The immediate coastal area is not so luxuriant in its vegetation as the region above 500 feet, as parts of it are quite barren, and only in the low ground and along the streams, is a true forest

[1] Drude, *loc. cit.*, p. 507.

developed. In the zone between 500–1,000 metres, a true tropical rain-forest is found. This zone is rich in palms (Acrocomia, Sabal,

Fig. 79.—Tree cactus (*Pachycereus Pringlei*), near Libertad, Mexico. *Photo., Dr. W. S. Cooper.*

Oreodoxa, etc.), and among the characteristic forest trees are giant silk-cottons (Bombax), laurels, Terebinthaceae, Combretaceae, and others. In some places fertile savannas occur.

The great volcano Orizaba offers a fine example of the zoning of vegetation from the rank tropical jungle at its base, to the regions of perpetual snow. The first pines appear at 2,200 metres, and the oaks reach to about 3,400 m., above which for another 1,000 metres a number of conifers extend. Above this forest, is an alpine region where the vegetation is composed of coarse grasses, and a variety of shrubby and half shrubby plants, especially Compositae, Labiatae, Rosaceae, etc., as well as some herbaceous species, grasses, sedges, Compositae, and others, all decidedly boreal types.

In the upper forest, the epiphytic orchids and Tillandsias of the lower elevations, give place to mosses and lichens.

The western coast of Mexico is much drier, and the tropical forest less developed. Pines and other northern forms grow at lower elevations than in the eastern part of the country.

Central America,[1] Nicaragua, Honduras, Guatemala and Costa Rica in the character of their vegetation are intermediate between Mexico and equatorial South America. There is a gradual disappearance of the oaks, pines, and other northern genera characteristic of the Mexican highlands, and an increasing number of palms, and other tropical types. As might be expected, the boreal genera ascend to higher elevations as the latitude diminishes, and finally disappear completely in the equatorial forests of Panama and South America.

As in Mexico, the Pacific slope of Central America is much drier than the Atlantic coast, but nevertheless supports a forest, mostly of tropical species, up to an elevation of about 3,000 feet. Above this tropical forest belt are open savannas, and still higher, forests of pines.

The eastern slope is covered with a heavy rain-forest, in which palms form a very conspicuous feature, these belonging to such tropical South American genera as Bactris, Geonoma, Iriartia. The central plateau in the more southern part, at an elevation of about 5,000 feet, supports a forest in which many trees like the silk-cotton and Spanish cedar are leafless during the dry season.

The forests of Costa Rica are notable for the great profusion of ferns and orchids, this being one of the richest regions for these plants known to the botanist. Palms, tree-ferns, Scitamineae (Canna, gingers, etc.), are very abundant as they are everywhere in the tropical American rain-forests.

[1] Drude, loc. cit., p. 509.

SOUTH AMERICA

Tropical vegetation in America reaches its greatest development in the enormous area drained by the Amazon and its tributaries. This immense expanse of rich alluvial country lying immediately under the equator, and for the most part having an extremely heavy rainfall, supports the largest area of tropical rain-forest in existence.

The eastern slopes of the Andes, at the headwaters of the Amazon, receive an enormous rainfall, and this region, and the portions of the Amazon Valley immediately east of the mountains, are covered with a forest growth of unrivalled luxuriance.[1] Further down the river are regions of much lighter precipitation where open savannas occur, while in northeastern Brazil to the south of the mountains of Guiana and Venezuela, the country is said to be very arid due to the interception of the moisture-laden winds from the Caribbean by the intervening mountains.

The coastal region, however, from the Amazon delta to and including the coast of the Guianas, is one of heavy rainfall, and with very dense forests. This northeast corner of Brazil and coastal Guiana constitute a very natural botanical province.

The forests of the Amazon region are of three kinds.[2] First are the great forests of the immense regions of the flat valley, which are regularly inundated by the flood-waters, and remain covered with many feet of water for a long period. All trees and shrubs of this flood-forest ("Igapó," "gapó") must be able to survive this long submergence.

Above the gapó is the great virgin forest occupying land above the flood-mark, and this is the most extensive and luxuriant forest, and contains the greatest number of species.

Finally, in drier regions are extensive much more open forests of relatively low trees, known by the Brazilians as "Caatinga."

About the middle of the last century the English botanist Spruce, spent about fifteen years in the Amazonian country, and has given an excellent account of the most important features of this vast region.

[1] Bates, H. W., *The Naturalist on the River Amazon*, Reprint in EVERYMAN'S LIBRARY.

[2] Spruce, R., *Notes of a Botanist on the Amazon and Andes*, edited by Alfred Russel Wallace, London, 1908.

PLATE XXIX.—Brazilian tropical forest. *Photo., Dr. Bailey Willis.*

272

While there is an immense number of species there are certain general resemblances throughout the great Amazonian forest area. Thus while the species of the different types of forest, riparian, upland and dry, are mostly different, the genera are largely the same, and some of the most important species occur over a very large extent of country.

The riparian forests, or gapó, are flooded for long periods, and the members of this association must necessarily be such species as can endure this unusual condition. The trees of the gapó are rarely as tall as those of the virgin forest which lies above the high-water mark, but the two formations merge into each other at the upper limit of the gapó whose outer margin is composed of low shrubs and bushes, and many aquatics, like arums, rushes, sedges, etc.

The gapó is notable for the great variety and abundance of palms, many of which overtop the other forest trees, and sometimes occur in groves forming long avenues of columnar trunks along the shore.

When the water recedes, the gapó develops a dense undergrowth of herbaceous plants, and every tree and shrub is draped with a curtain of herbaceous creepers, passion-flowers, morning glories, and others, often having flowers of great beauty.

The virgin forest is distinguished by the very tall and closely set trees, whose lofty trunks, often with great buttresses at the base, support a thick canopy of foliage which shuts out most of the light, so that there is relatively little undergrowth, except young trees of the predominant species, and slender palms which carry their crown of leaves toward the light. Stout lianas, like cables looped from tree to tree, belong to many species, but their foliage and flowers, borne high up in the tops of the trees, are rarely recognizable from the floor of the forest. This virgin forest covers an enormous area in the Amazon valley, the gapó, of course being confined to the lowland area subject to the annual inundation.

The "caatinga" open or white forest, occupies areas of poor soil in the drier districts, and is composed of low trees and shrubs, with few lianas and palms, the latter when present being peculiar forms, quite distinct from those of the wet forest.

To these might be added the second growth forests, where a tangle of trees and shrubs fight with each other for the possession of the soil.

The "campos" or savannas, open grassy or scrubby districts, occupy but a small part in the valley proper, but north and south merge into the great llanos or prairies of Venezuela and Argentina.

Comparing the different types of the Brazilian forest Spruce makes the following statement: [1] "And yet when the constituent plants of the different classes of forest come to be compared together, they are found to correspond to a degree quite unexpected; for although the species are almost entirely diverse, the differences are rarely more than specific. It is only in the caatingas that a few genera, each including several species, seem to have taken up their exclusive abode; such are Commianthus among Rubiaceae, Bugamea among Loganiaceae . . . and there are a few other peculiar genera, chiefly monotypic. But of the riparial plants nearly every species has its congenor on terra firma to which it stands so near that, although the two must of right bear different names, the differences of structure are practically such as might have been brought about by long exposure even to the existing state of things without supposing them to date from widely different conditions in the remote past; this is especially true of such genera as Inga, Pithecolobium, Lecythis, and of many Myrtles, Melastomes and Sapotads, etc."

Some characteristic species are very wide-spread. Thus Spruce mentions the Brazil nut (*Bertholletia excelsa*), perhaps the finest and most characteristic tree of the virgin forest. It grows almost throughout the Amazon valley where the soil is suitable, from Pará to a point more than 1,200 miles west on the Amazon proper, and for many hundred miles up its principal affluents and the regions of the upper Orinoco. One of the finest palms, *Maximiliana regia*, with huge leaves 30–40 feet long, is even more widespread.

As a rule, however, the most wide-spread species do not belong to the heavy forest, but to the open savanna.

Very often a species restricted to a somewhat limited area, is replaced elsewhere, under similar conditions by a similar, but distinct species.

Two types of rivers are found in the Amazon system, clear or "black" rivers of which the Rio Negro is the type, and the "white," or turbid rivers like the Amazon itself. The riparian vegetation

[1] *Loc. cit.*

along these two sorts of streams, is very different, but is very similar throughout along streams of the same type. Many identical species occur in the riparian forest of the Amazon from its mouth to the base of the Andes. As a typical example, Spruce mentions the "Mulatto" tree (*Eukylista sp.*) found everywhere along the shores of the Amazon, and prized for fuel.

Like all tidal rivers in the tropics the great delta of the Amazon has very extensive mangrove formations, in which the most important species, *Rhizophora mangle*, is the same as in the mangrove swamps of West Africa, on the opposite side of the Atlantic.

Ascending the streams, the mangroves gradually disappear, with the decreasing salinity of the water, and are replaced by the riparial forest or gapó.[1] The trees of the gapó include many Leguminosae, e. g., Inga, Pithecolobium; Brazil nuts, myrtles, custard-apples (Sapotaceae), and especially a great profusion of palms.

Trees and shrubs are almost hidden by a dense tangle of creepers. These climbing plants include many species with showy flowers,— passion-flowers, Bignonias, morning glories, and the less familiar Malpighiaceae, very abundant in the American tropics, and with showy yellow or pink flowers. Another very striking creeper is *Cacoucia coccinea* (Combretaceae), with brilliant scarlet flowers.

Just above the inundated area, in the drier waste places, there is a dense growth of shrubs and coarse herbaceous plants. Solanum, Cassia and various other showy Leguminosae, and peppers, some being large shrubs, and many climbing plants like those of the gapó.

The primaeval forest near Pará is very vividly pictured by Spruce.[2]

"There were enormous trees crowned with magnificent foliage, decked with fantastic parasites, hung all over with lianas which varied in thickness from slender threads to huge python-like masses, were now round, now flattened, now knotted and now twisted with the regularity of a cable. Intermixed with these trees, and often equal to them in altitude, grew noble palms; while other and far lovelier species of the same family, their ringed stems sometimes scarce exceeding a finger's thickness, but bearing plume-like fronds and pendulous bunches of black or red berries, quite like those of their loftier allies, formed along with shrubs

[1] Spruce, *loc, cit.*, Vol. 1, p. 4. [2] *Loc. cit.*, p. 17.

and arbuscles of many types, a bush undergrowth not usually very dense or difficult to penetrate. The herbaceous vegetation was almost limited to a few ferns, Selaginellas, Sedges, here and there a broad-leaved Scitaminea, and (but very rarely) a pretty grass (Pariana). . . . In some places one might walk for a considerable distance without seeing a single herb or even rarely a fallen leaf on the bare black ground. It is worthy to be noted that the loftiest forest is the easiest to traverse; the lianas and parasites (which may be compared to the rigging and shrouds of a ship, whereof the masts and yards are represented by the trunks and branches of trees) being in great part hung too high to be much in the way; whereas in the low gapó that sometimes skirts the rivers, they have not yet got hoisted high enough to allow one to pass beneath, but bar the way with an awful array of entangled, looped, and knotted ropes, which even the sword itself can sometimes with difficulty unloose."

The Brazil nut and the related monkey nuts (*Lecythis spp.*) are among the commonest and largest trees of the high forest. Spruce measured a specimen whose nearly cylindrical trunk was 42 feet in circumference, and about 100 feet to the first branch. This he states was the largest tree he found. The Brazil nut and species of silk-cotton (*Bombax spp.*) are the tallest trees of the Brazilian forest, but they probably never exceed 200 feet in height.

Many of the trees of the virgin forest show an extraordinary development of buttresses at the base, which may reach a great size. These are especially marked in the silk-cotton trees, but Spruce notes that among the laurels, some of the finest trees of the Amazonian forest, buttresses were quite wanting. These trees have deep roots, and where they predominate is a certain indication of deep soil.

The lianas belong to many families and show much variety in the shape of their stems; while the stem of the free swinging forms is usually cylindrical, they are sometimes curiously twisted or flattened. Spruce[1] cites the case of a leguminous species (*Schellia splendens*), whose flattened wavy stem is sometimes a foot broad, and climbs over the trees for 200–300 feet. The trumpet creepers (*Bignoniaceae*) often have strongly angled stems.[2]

While most of these giant lianas are twiners, others climb by

[1] Spruce, *loc. cit.*, p. 28.   Ibid., p. 28.

means of stout hooked thorns, which earn for them such popular names as "devil's fish-hook," "cat's claws," etc. The rattans of the eastern tropics are replaced by a genus, Desmoncus, which like its eastern relatives, is dreaded by the explorer in the forest, where its barbed-wire entanglements are a formidable obstacle. Like the eastern rattans, the prolonged leaf-axis is armed with recurved claw-like spines.

Epiphytes of many kinds abound in the equatorial forest. Among the most notable are many aroids, and species of Cyclanthaceae, the latter looking like small palms, and confined to the American tropics. These, as well as some of the Araceae, develop thick, pendent aërial roots, which hang down like plumb-lines, and may sometimes reach the ground. Aërial roots are also common in epiphytic orchids, but as a rule are too small to attract attention. Many aroids climb up the trunks of the trees by means of the aërial roots, and the leaves of some of them are of gigantic size.

While epiphytes are developed to a remarkable degree in the high forest, they are often quite invisible from below, as they grow far aloft in the crowns of the trees.

The Cyclanthaceae, referred to above, have terrestrial species as well, among them the species of Carludovica from whose leaves are manufactured the Panama hats.

Another peculiarly American family, the Bromeliaceae, also largely epiphytes, includes the pineapples, and the "Spanish moss" of our Gulf States. The family is very abundantly represented throughout tropical America, most of them resembling the pineapple in habit. Some have showy flowers, or the inflorescence is surrounded by brightly colored leaves.

Epiphytic orchids are common, but are less conspicuous than in the mountain forest or the lower and more open forest of the caatinga. Small epiphytic peppers (*Peperomia spp.*) are also abundant, and the scarlet Aeschynanthus of the Malayan regions is replaced by related, but different genera of Gesneraceae.

Strangling figs, like those of the eastern tropics, occur in the Amazonian forest, but are less common than in the Andean region, and some other parts of tropical America.

In the dark virgin forest the herbaceous undergrowth is scanty; but in the lower wet forest there is a rank growth of ferns, Araceae, Scitamineae (bananas, gingers, arrow-root, etc.). These are mostly different genera from those of the old world, but there are some genera in common: e. g., Costus, Thalia; and Cannas of several species are frequent, their showy red or yellow flowers lighting up the open places at the edge of the forest and spreading as a weed into waste ground. The Canna family is peculiarly American, although some have become naturalized as weeds in the old world. The banana family (Musaceae), gingers (Zingiberaceae), and arrow-roots (Marantaceae), are also represented in the old world, but mostly by different genera.

There are no true bananas native to America, but the family is abundantly represented by several species of Heliconia, handsome plants with banana-like foliage, and brilliant red and yellow floral bracts. Another interesting member of this family is *Ravenala Guianensis*, closely related to the famous "traveller's tree" of Madagascar.

The gingers of the genus Costus have handsome orchid-like flowers, and the Marantaceae have leaves often of velvety texture and beautifully variegated. These are sometimes seen in cultivation.

Among the many conspicuous Araceae growing in low wet ground is *Montrichardia arborescens* which forms dense thickets along the river banks, the tall, bare, palisade-like stems bearing a tuft of big arrow-shaped leaves. These aquatic aroids and the many other aquatics associated with them, sedges, grasses, pickerel-weeds (Pontederiaceae), etc., form the outer fringe of the gapó, and inland are replaced by the shrubs and trees which occupy the land exposed by the subsiding water.

Another common and conspicuous genus of terrestrial Araceae is Caladium, whose arrow-shaped leaves are beautifully marked with white and crimson, which in cultivation have produced many extremely beautiful varieties. The large genus Anthurium is also prized in cultivation, both for the handsome foliage of some species, and the showy white or red Calla-like inflorescences of others.

Of the climbing Araceae, Philodendron and Monstera are perhaps the most conspicuous. Their gigantic leaves are often fantastically cut and perforated, and at once attract attention. *M. deliciosa* is often seen in conservatories where its big perforated leaves and thick spikes of edible fruit at once attract notice.

The equatorial forests of South America have little in common with those of temperate North America or Eurasia. The coniferous trees are absent, and deciduous trees are almost entirely wanting. The characteristic deciduous trees of the boreal forests, oaks, beeches, chestnuts, walnuts, poplars, birches, maples, etc., are entirely unrepresented. A single willow (*Salix Humboldtii*), which is common in the Amazon district, is about the only representative of the catkin-bearing trees. It is true that in the warmer parts of the United States, especially in southern Florida, which almost touches the tropics, there are a good many trees and shrubs which are evidently outposts of the tropical vegetation which culminates in the great Amazonian forest.

Our locusts and mesquit represent the great family of Leguminosae, which probably has the greatest number of species in the equatorial forest, and the sassafras and in the south Persea, a tropical genus which includes the "avocado," represent the laurels which have many tropical genera and species. Other cases might be cited, but they are relatively unimportant.

Rivalling the Leguminosae in number are the species of the madder family (Rubiaceae). The most important of these, Andean, however, rather than Amazonian, is the genus Cinchona, the source of quinine. The Rubiaceae of temperate climates are mostly insignificant herbs, like the bedstraws (Galium) and the little bluets (Houstonia) of the Atlantic States. Both in the Palaeotropics and Neotropics, a very large number of trees belong to this family.

The Leguminosae comprise an enormous assemblage of trees, shrubs, and lianas, many of which have extremely abundant and showy flowers at certain seasons. The sub-family Mimoseae often have delicately cut graceful foliage, and flowers with clusters of slender stamens, e. g., Inga, Pithecolobium; or like Cassia and Bauhinia of the sub-family Caesalpineae, the flowers are open, often suggesting an orchid. The pea-flowered type (Papilionaceae), is less common, but still abundantly represented.

The fig-family (Moraceae) includes a large number of species other than Ficus. Among these are bread-fruits (*Artocarpus spp.*), and other genera, one of the most notable being Cecropia, a genus of trees, usually of comparatively small size, growing in the riparian forest. They have hollow branches in which colonies of ants are said to have their abode, and the long-stalked palmate leaves, usually woolly beneath, are suggestive of the castor-bean. The Cecropias are everywhere abundant and conspicuous in the wet American tropics.

The myrtle family is an important one in tropical South America, and comprises many species of Eugenia, Myrcia, Psidium, and others. Several species of the latter genus, yield the well-known guavas, now extensively cultivated in most tropical and some subtropical countries.

Among the giants of the Amazonian forest are the silk-cottons (Bombax, Ceiba) whose huge trunks are supported by enormous buttress-roots. The silky down attached to the seeds of some species furnishes the silk-cotton or "Kapok" used for stuffing mattresses and similar purposes.

Of the many trees yielding useful commercial products, the Pará rubber (*Hevea Braziliensis*) takes first place, and until quite recently was the most important export from Brazil. It belongs to the Euphorbia family, and is a tree of moderate size with trifoliate leaves, something like a Laburnum. It grows in the low forest over much of the Amazon valley, and now is cultivated on a great scale in many tropical countries, but with especial success in various parts of the Malayan regions, where the plantations furnish most of the rubber requirements of this age of automobiles. Another large and common tree of the same family, the "sand-box" (*Hura crepitans*) is abundant in the virgin forest.

The custard-apples (Anonaceae), and the sapodillas (Sapotaceae), include many important fruits of the Amazonian region, some of the latter also furnishing that remarkable substance "chicle," the basis of one of America's noblest products, chewing gum.

The Brazil nut represents the purely tropical family Lecythidaceae, especially developed in northern Brazil, while the "Spanish cedar" (*Cedrela spp.*), and species of nutmeg (*Myristica spp.*), are also characteristic of the old world tropics.

These are but a few samples of the thousands of species of trees that make up the great equatorial American forest.

Palms are much more conspicuous than in most parts of the eastern tropics. Whether the number of species is greater might be questioned; but as regards conspicuous arborescent species, there is no question that the American tropics surpass any part of the old world. Leaving out the coco-palm which has been distributed over the tropics of the whole world, the American palms, with two significant exceptions, belong to genera quite unrepresented in the eastern hemisphere.

The fan-palms of the genus Mauritia are very abundant, but the pinnate-leaved genera are much more numerous. Some like the wide-spread *Maximiliana regia* have immense leaves 30–40 feet long, and recall the sugar-palms of the East Indies. A particularly abundant and beautiful species is *Euterpe oleracea*, with slender stems, and graceful feathery leaves. This occurs in great numbers along the banks of the northern South American rivers. The genus Bactris, mostly small palms, often with clusters of showy black or red berries, is very common in the undergrowth of the forests, and other small palms (*Geonoma spp.*) with almost entire leaves are also abundant. The only climbing species belong to Desmoncus, which in habit is much like the rattans of the eastern tropics, but is really not closely related to them.

Many palms are very important economically, the fruits furnishing food, while the stems and leaves yield fibres, and building material for the primitive dwellings of the natives, the leaves being the usual thatch for the roofs. The "peach-palm" (*Gulielma speciosa*) is extensively cultivated for its fruit, but according to Bates [1] is unknown in a wild state. It bears immense clusters of fruits of the size of a peach, which they resemble in color. They are very nutritious, and an important article of diet among the natives.

In the virgin forest the trees are so tall that even when they bear showy flowers, they are scarcely perceptible from below, and the general effect is that of luxuriant foliage with flowers rare, or inconspicuous. Indeed a large proportion of both trees and shrubs have inconspicuous flowers, although there are numerous exceptions. In the more open forest, and along the banks of streams, there is sometimes a very magnificent display of flowers, and there are some lofty trees, which in their flowering season are covered with masses of brilliant bloom.

Spruce [2] states that near Pará the Leguminosae and Bignoniaceae furnished the greatest number of showy trees and lianas. Among the former are species of Cassia, Sclerolobium and Bauhinia. The

[1] *Loc cit.*, p. 290. [2] *Loc. cit.*, p. 41.

Bignoniaceae include many extremely showy creepers and trees, the latter being mostly species of Tecoma, allied to the common trumpet creeper. Other trees with showy flowers belong to the Myrtaceae, Rubiaceae, Lecythidaceae and Bombacaceae.

Mention has already been made of the showy-flowered lianas,— passion-flowers, Bignonias, Malpighiaceae, etc., and the showy herbaceous plants: Heliconia, Caladium, Canna, etc. of the wet gapó.

The Amazonian forest reaches its maximum development in the portion of the river above its junction with the Rio Negro. Between this and the foot of the Andes there is an excessively heavy rainfall, and the whole country is covered with unbroken forest which ascends to 3,000–4,000 feet on the eastern side of the mountains.

A tropical rain-forest much like that of the Amazon valley in its composition is found along the eastern coast of Brazil from Pernambuco southward to a point beyond the Tropic of Capricorn. This includes Rio Janeiro, and the adjacent country.

The interior plateau rises to the east and near the coast forms an escarpment which is cut by many abrupt gorges, and the edge of the plateau forms two broken ranges of mountains parallel with the coast. The seaward slopes of these ranges, and the coastal plain, when present, receive a copious rainfall, which together with uniformly high temperatures, develops a luxuriant rain-forest which extends far south of the Tropic of Capricorn, but finally loses its tropical character and merges with the temperate vegetation of the coast of Argentina.

Forming the eastern boundary of the great Amazon basin are the extensive continental highlands of Brazil, whose eastern edge consists of the coastal mountain ranges already mentioned. Inside this coastal mountain rim, the plateau slopes westward to the Amazon valley, but is much broken up by mountain masses of greater or less extent. From the mouth of the Amazon to Uruguay, this great table land is drained by many rivers belonging to the Amazon system.

The rainfall is fairly heavy over much of the plateau, but a good deal of the country is semi-arid, and the vegetation more or less decidedly xerophytic. Extensive savannas suited for grazing, and open forest cover large areas.

The dry open forest "caatinga" is a feature of much of the

plateau. The trees are low, and often thorny, and are associated with shrubs of many kinds. Many of both trees and shrubs cast their leaves in the dry season. In the caatinga are found many Cacti, Bromeliads, and other succulents, and there is a marked development of bulbous plants, which are only evident in the rainy season, when the trees renew their foliage, and many are adorned with showy flowers.

Southern Brazil has a remarkably large number of extremely showy trees, shrubs and climbers, many of which adorn the gardens of the warm temperate zone, like the Riviera, California and Australia. The well known Bougainvilleas, Bignonias, and passion-flowers, mostly come from this region, and the Jacaranda with its delicate foliage and masses of beautiful blue flowers.

The caatinga of Brazil may be compared to the bush-veldt of the south African plateau.

In the region of the Orinoco, according to Spruce, the caatinga formation is mainly due to poor soils, and the trees are evergreen with the profusion of epiphytic growths associated with a humid atmosphere.

The coastal mountains of Venezuela and the adjacent region of Colombia show a large percentage of deciduous trees. As one sails in sight of these coasts in the summer, the mountain slopes present a very dreary picture due to the large number of bare deciduous trees. This is a striking contrast to the rich evergreen vegetation of the Guiana lowlands and Trinidad, and more resembles the caatinga of the eastern Brazilian highlands.

The tropical Amazonian forest ascends the eastern slopes of the Andes to a height of 3,000–4,000 feet, above which there is a gradual increase of temperate types and a corresponding disappearance of the lowland species.

The eastern slopes of the Andes, at the headwaters of the Amazon have an extremely heavy precipitation, and the difficulties of exploring these dense forests have been graphically described by Spruce who spent several years in this region. Owing to their inaccessibility, as well as the fevers and other drawbacks to exploration, these forests are still very imperfectly known.

Except where the forests have been cleared there is little open country at the lower elevations, although there are a few spots, which owing to their topography, are relatively dry, and free from heavy forest. Ferns, mosses and liverworts become much more abundant in the Andean mountain forests, and become extraordinarily developed, a phenomenon to be noted everywhere in the tropics.

Spruce found the development of mosses and liverworts especially great in the region known as the "montaña of Canelos," in the neighborhood of the great volcanoes of Cotopaxi and Tunguragua. This forest which extends from 1,000–5,000 ft. elevation is very wet, and Spruce says the growth of these plants is the most luxuriant he had ever seen. "Even the topmost twigs and the very leaves were shaggy with mosses and from the branches overhanging the river depended festoons of several feet in length composed chiefly of Bryopterides . . . in beautiful fruit."

So great is the load of mosses, that when soaked with water they often broke off the branches to which they were attached.

A very interesting plant of this forest was a giant horse-tail (*Equisetum sp.*), twenty feet high and with a stem almost as thick as one's wrist.

Palms are common in these mountain forests, but less varied than in the lowlands. The commonest species is *Iriartea ventricosa*, which forms extensive groves. Species of Wettinia and Euterpe are also characteristic of the Canelos forests, and also the vegetable-ivory palm (*Phytelephas sp.*).

The most important trees of the Andean forest are several species of Cinchona yielding quinine. Spruce's long sojourn in this region was mainly for the purpose of securing young plants and seeds of the most valuable species, the "Red-bark" (*C. succirubra*). Different species are found at elevations from 2500 to 10,000 feet, *C. succirubra* growing from 2,500 to 5,000 ft. The plants and seeds sent by Spruce to England marked the beginning of the cultivation of Cinchona in the tropical British colonies, which, however, have never met with the success of the plantations in the Dutch East Indies, especially Java, which now furnishes a large part of the world's supply of the drug. There are now, also, plantations of Cinchona in Colombia and other parts of the Andean region. The family Rubiaceae, to which Cinchona belongs, has furnished another plant of great importance, viz., coffee, now grown in immense quantities in southern Brazil, which furnishes the greater part of the commercial product.

PLATE XXX.—Riparian forest, Para River, Surinam. *Euterpe oleracea, Heliconia sp.*

285

The Cinchona region has a flora of the same general type as that of the Amazonian forest, and a good many of the same species. Bamboos and other giant grasses are a feature of this region, among them the giant arrow-grass (*Gynerium saccharoides*), related to the familiar "pampas-grass" of the gardens, but sometimes 30–40 feet high.

There are many orchids, but mostly inconspicuous species. The richest collecting grounds for showy orchids are further north in the mountains of Colombia, and Central America, from which come many of the choicest ornaments of our conservatories. The many species of Cattleya, Odontoglossum and Oncidium, and other extensively cultivated orchids, come from these countries.

Except in the higher altitudes, the trees and shrubs of the mountain forest belong to the same families as those dominating the forest lower down, e. g., Rubiaceae, Leguminosae, Myrtaceae, Malpighiaceae, etc. At higher elevations, however, temperate genera occur, and at the highest altitudes there is a distinct alpine flora. In the cool highlands we may find such familiar northern plants as brambles, mallows, chick-weed, huckleberries, pig-weed (Chenopodium), Geranium, catch-fly and a good many others; but there are also certain distinctly Andean genera, like Fuchsia, and Calceolaria, while the sub-alpine flowers including gentians, valerian, paint-brush (Castilleia) and lupins, remind one of the sub-alpine flora of the Californian mountains.

The western slopes of the Andes are much dryer, and as Spruce says "The Amazon side of the Andes is incomparably richer than the Pacific side." The former has a continuous rainy season with little variation in temperature, while the Pacific slope has a long dry season, and much of the coastal part of Peru, Ecuador and northern Chile is an absolute desert where rain is almost unknown, and except along the streams descending from the mountains, vegetation is often completely absent.

The writer's first-hand impressions of the equatorial South American vegetation are derived from brief visits to Panama, Guiana, and Trinidad, where, however, the vegetation is very much the same as that of the Pará district of the Amazon.

The coast of the Guianas is mostly low and swampy, and the tide extends for a long way up the rivers, whose lower reaches

PLATE XXXI.—Riparian forest, Para River, Surinam. *Cecropia palmata* (?) in background.

are bordered by impenetrable mangrove swamps composed almost exclusively of *Rhizophora mangle,* the common American species.

As one ascends the stream, the Rhizophora gives way to the "white mangrove," (*Avicennia nitida*) which sometimes becomes a large tree with very long aërial roots pendent from the upper branches. Back of the mangrove belt are slightly elevated ridges upon which grow large trees of various kinds.

Still higher up the rivers, the mangroves disappear completely, and the banks are overgrown with a dense jungle of trees and shrubs corresponding to the gapó of the Amazon. Leguminosae of many species are especially abundant, particularly species of Inga; and the big arum, *Montrichardia arborescens,* already referred to, forms a close palisade at the outer margin of the jungle.

Continuing above the tide limit palms become a conspicuous element in the forest, and along the banks, and in the typical riparial forest occur in large numbers and variety, and add a great charm to the river shore. First in abundance and beauty is *Euterpe oleracea,* whose tall slender stems and feathery crowns occur in thousands. Other characteristic palms are species of Maximiliana and Attalea, with gigantic pinnate leaves, and less striking species of Astrocaryum and Manicaria. Of the smaller palms occurring as undergrowths in the forest, the commonest are many species of Bactris, with slender stems, sometimes hardly an inch thick, and with clusters of showy red or black berries. The climbing species of Desmoncus, already referred to, are very common. Their flexible spiny stems, and graceful feathery leaves, armed with savage hooked spines, are festooned from tree to tree, and remind one of the East Indian rattans. The clusters of scarlet fruits are very conspicuous, and attract attention, as the boat skirts the dense jungle along the shore.

Next to the palms, perhaps the most striking trees of the riparial forest are the numerous Cecropias, with their big palmate leaves and jointed stems, which occur everywhere along the rivers.

A bewildering tangle of climbing plants forms a heavy drapery over trees and shrubs, sometimes quite concealing them. These lianas belong to very diverse families, and include morning glories, passion-flowers, trumpet creepers, as well as less familiar genera of Apocynaceae, Melastomaceae, Malpighiaceae and others.

PLATE XXXII.—Lowland forest interior, Surinam.

Many of these have flowers of great beauty which are admirably set off by the background of luxuriant jungle foliage.

The primaeval forest in the vicinity of Paramaribo in Surinam (Dutch Guiana) is largely a swampy one, but with elevations of drier sandy soil where the tallest trees grow. The largest trees of this forest are the silk-cotton (*Ceiba pentandra*) and the sand-box (*Hura crepitans*) which reach gigantic size.

The trunks and branches of these great trees are covered with numerous epiphytes, among which the Bromeliads take first place. Several species of Tillandsia, including the "Spanish moss" of the southern United States, were the most abundant of these. Clinging to the trunks of the trees, or festooned from tree to tree, were many lianas, some of great size. These included morning glories of several kinds, Bignonias, and especially the great climbing aroids:—Monstera, Philodendron, Syngonium, and others, which were conspicuous in the tangle of creepers.

A luxuriant undergrowth of dwarf palms, Cannas, Heliconias and showy arums, gave the finishing touch to a truly tropical picture.

Ferns, mosses and liverworts are not abundant in this forest, and this seems to be true of much of the Amazonian forest region, to judge from Spruce's notes. A few epiphytic ferns, species of Vittaria and Polypodium were noted at Paramaribo, but they were not specially abundant.

A very different type of vegetation is found in the savannas which are sometimes met with in the coastal regions of Guiana. One of these visited by the writer was an expanse of coarse gritty soil covered with a sparse growth of coarse grasses and sedges, with scattered clumps of low shrubs. A number of terrestrial orchids were seen, but only one of these, a Catasetum, was in flower. The flowers of this curious species are quite large, greenish in color.

Here and there were shallow pools in which grew tiny bladder-weeds (Utricularia) with yellow flowers, and minute rush-like plants belonging to the families Eriocaulaceae and Xyridaceae. Small patches of Sphagnum grew under the bushes, and in these were little sundews (*Drosera sp.*) reminding one of the northern peat-bogs. A beautiful blue gentian (*Chilonanthus sp.*) was common, and a few ferns, including the common bracken, were noted.

PLATE XXXIII.—Jungle interior, Surinam; at left, *Ravenala Guianensis.*

The shrubs for the most part belonged to the mainly tropical families Malpighiaceae, Melastomaceae and Rubiaceae. To the latter belonged an undetermined shrub with a profusion of large rose-colored flowers. A butterfly-pea (*Clitoria sp.*) with large purple flowers, was also common.

The outstanding feature of this savanna was a noble fan-palm (*Mauritia flexuosa*) which formed groves of considerable extent.

Surrounding the savanna was a forest occupying rather dry soil, and traversed by clear streams, but with areas of boggy soil. Palms were abundant as an undergrowth, and a very interesting plant was a sort of wild banana (*Ravenala Guianensis*) much resembling its congener the traveller's tree of Madagascar. Ferns were more abundant than in the forest about Paramaribo, but still played a very subordinate rôle in the vegetation.

One of the common trees of this forest is the "Balata" (*Mimusops sp.*) belonging to the Sapotaceae. This yields a rubber of fair quality, but much inferior to the Pará rubber.

The writer was struck with the abundance of showy flowers in the neighborhood of Paramaribo, a rather unusual condition in the wet tropics. The showy climbers have already been noted, and were especially abundant. A rose-red passion-flower, and the big golden bells of an Allamanda (Apocynaceae), were truly magnificent, and many of the shrubs, Leguminosae, Rubiaceae, Melastomaceae, Malphighiaceae, bore very abundant and showy flowers.

Of the herbaceous plants perhaps the most notable were the very common Heliconias, looking somewhat like Cannas, or the larger species like bananas. The brilliant scarlet and yellow bracts of the flower clusters are extremely showy. Red and yellow Cannas were also very abundant, and wild ginger (*Costus sp.*) and arrowroot (*Maranta spp.*) were common and handsome forms, and with these were growing Caladiums with gayly painted arrow-shaped leaves.

This brilliant floral display was seen at the edge of the forest, and in open places, such as railway embankments, which were veritable flower gardens. Red and yellow milkweed, weedy Compositae and Verbenaceae were everywhere common.

PLATE XXXIV.—Savanna vegetation, Surinam. *Mauritia flexuosa.*

TRINIDAD

The island of Trinidad while separated from the mainland of South America, nevertheless has a vegetation closely resembling that of the adjacent coast. The wetter lowland forest abounds in palms, aroids, Scitamineae, etc., identical with, or closely related to those of the coastal belt of the Guianas.

A　　　　　　　　　　　　　　　B
FIG. 80.—A. Tree with epiphytic ferns, Port of Spain, Trinidad.
B. Palm (*Attalea sp.*), Para River, Surinam.

The drier hillsides, however, show a quite different vegetation, such as a very common palm (*Acrocomia sclerocarpa*), common in Jamaica and other islands of the Antilles. Ferns are decidedly more abundant than in Guiana, although not especially conspicuous in the lower forest. Two particularly interesting species were noted near Port of Spain, viz: A climbing fern (*Lygodium sp.*) and *Anemia phyllitidis*. In the lowland wet forest ferns were more abundant, but much less so than at higher elevations.

Port of Spain, with its fine botanical garden and attractive parks, offers much of interest to the botanist. There are many species of palms, native and exotic, and splendid specimens of other native trees. Of the commonly planted palms, the finest is *Oreodoxa oleracea*, the "Palmiste" of the French, "cabbage-palm" of the English, a much handsomer species than the royal palm (*O. regia*) with which it is sometimes confused. *O. oleracea*, with its perfectly cylindrical trunk, sometimes more than 100 feet high and its magnificent crown of rich plumes, is perhaps the finest of all palms.

Fig. 81.—Lowland vegetation, Trinidad. At left, "groo-groo" palm (*Acrocomia sclerocarpa*).

Silk-cotton trees, sand-box, Spanish cedar (*Cedrela odorata*), and mahogany, are commonly planted, and enormous specimens of the wide-spreading "monkey-pod" (*Pithecolobium saman*) adorn some of the parks. The curious cannon-ball tree (*Couropita Guianensis*), related to the Brazil nut, is sometimes seen, the large red flowers, borne upon short branches growing directly from the main trunk, and followed by big globular fruits to which it owes its popular name.

In the low wet forest near Port of Spain, there was a luxuriant growth much like that in Guiana. A fine arum (*Spathiphyllum cannaefolium*) was very abundant along the streams, the large white spathe recalling the common calla, while other handsome members of the same family, e. g., Montrichardia, Philodendron, Anthurium, were abundant. Epiphytic orchids were frequent, but mostly out of flower at this season (June), but several very handsome flowers were noted, especially Bromeliads with brilliant red bracts, and the wild "Poinsettia" (*Warczewiczia coccinea*), in which one of the calyx-lobes is greatly enlarged and bright scarlet in color. Big clumps of *Heliconia bihai* gay with the bright red and yellow flower-spikes, made fine masses of color amid the rich foliage, and presented a magnificent picture of tropical vegetation in its fullest development.

Savannas, like those in Surinam, also are found in Trinidad. One of these visited by the writer, the Aripa savanna, was much like the one already described, but the vegetation was more luxuriant. The fan-palm of Guiana was represented by an even finer species, *Mauritia setigera*, forming groves of considerable size. Ground orchids, sundews, and bladder-weeds were abundant, but like the palms, different species from those of Surinam. An interesting fern, *Schizaea pennula*, and two club-mosses, *Lycopodium cernuum* and *L. Carolinianum*, were noted among other plants.

A fine forest adjoined this savanna, with many beautiful palms: Euterpe, Bactris, Attalea and Maximiliana, and there was an abundant growth of epiphytes, including some small filmy-ferns.

Among the trees in this forest, were numerous species of Clusia, a peculiarly American genus, some of which begin life as epiphytes, sending down aërial roots which finally strangle the host tree. These parasitic Clusias, with their glossy magnolia-like leaves, are very handsome, and resemble some of the strangling figs of the eastern tropics.

The highest mountain of Trinidad, Tucuchi, has an interesting flora. The lower part of the mountain is largely occupied by plantations of cacao (*Theobroma cacao*), but the upper part is covered with heavy primaeval forest. At about 1,500 feet one enters a splendid forest of lofty trees, with a heavy undergrowth of ferns, palms, Heliconias, and various aroids, with shrubs and lianas in great variety, altogether a fine example of a tropical rain-forest.

At the top, some 3,000 feet elevation, the trees are smaller, but dwarf palms were still abundant, and ferns were numerous and beautiful. Several fine tree-ferns were common, and among others, the most interesting were several species of Danaea, a member of the ancient order Marattiales. The prothallia of these ferns were abundant, and so large that they may be easily taken for

PLATE XXXV.—Jungle near Port of Spain, Trinidad.

liverworts. Of the latter there were many interesting species, with club-mosses and lichens in profusion.

One of the most interesting of the epiphytes, is a species of bladder-weed (*Utricularia montana*), whose drooping racemes of large white flowers might well be mistaken for an orchid.

To the botanist who visits equatorial America for the first time, the abundance and variety of palms will probably first attract atten-

A   B

FIG. 82.—A. Cannon-ball tree (*Couropita Guianensis*), Port of Spain, Trinidad.
B. Cabbage-palms (*Oreodoxa oleracea*), Port of Spain.

tion. There are many exceptionally beautiful species, and as they often are gregarious, they give a characteristic stamp to the forest vegetation. They are a much more conspicuous feature than in any part of the eastern tropics with which the writer is acquainted.

The Araceae, too, are more numerous and varied than in the tropics of the old world, and none of the old world species can rival the giant climbing species like Anthurium, Philodendron, and Monstera, so characteristic of the American tropics.

PLATE XXXVI.—Silk-cotton tree (*Ceiba pentandra*), Port of Spain, Trinidad.

THE GALAPAGOS ISLANDS

The Galapagos Islands, 580 miles west of Ecuador and lying directly on the equator, are of great interest both to the zoölogist and the botanist. The islands are entirely volcanic in formation and attain a height of 2,000 to 2,500 feet. Both animals and plants give evidence of a very long period of isolation.

The most comprehensive account of the vegetation is given by Professor B. L. Robinson with the co-operation of several other specialists.[1]

The climate is very hot and dry, and at the lower elevations the vegetation is decidedly xerophytic, made up of scattered small-leaved shrubs, wiry grasses and undershrubs, and a few tree Cacti.

Inland are saline lakes, and about these and in brackish swamps, as well as along the coast, are a good many saline plants or "halophytes." First in importance are the mangroves (*Rhizophora mangle, Avicennia officinalis*), while other characteristic forms are species of morning glories (Ipomoea, Calystegia), Verbena, Heliotropium, Atriplex, and several others.

Epiphytes are infrequent, but there is a Bromeliad (Tillandsia) and an orchid (Epidendrum) and several species of Peperomia. Showy flowers are scarce.

As to the origin of the Galapagos flora, Robinson says: "While it is clear that the Galapageian flora is only an outlying portion of the American flora . . . it is impossible to trace its relationship closely to any one section of the Pacific American vegetation."[2]

Omitting the algae, fungi and bryophytes, which have a few peculiar species, there are 499 species of vascular plants recorded. Of these 52 are ferns and 445 spermatophytes (flowering plants). Only three ferns are endemic, while 202 species, 15 varieties, and 19 forms constituting 44.4 per cent of the whole spermatophyte flora are peculiar to the islands.

---

[1] "Flora of the Galapagos Islands" (Papers from the Hopkins-Stanford Expedition to the Galapagos Islands), *Proceedings of the American Academy of Arts and Sciences*, Vol. XXXVIII, No. 4, October, 1902.

[2] *Loc. cit.*, p. 239.

The Antilles

Aside from Trinidad, which is essentially South American in its flora, the archipelago of the Antilles or West Indies, in the Carribbean Sea, has a sufficiently individual flora to warrant separating the West Indies from continental America, as a distinct botanical province. Each of the larger islands has many peculiar species, but there are many common to other islands, and to the Mexican and central American mainland. The southern end of Florida, with the "keys," is essentially West Indian in its flora, and has many species in common with the islands. Examples of these West Indian species are *Pinus Cubensis*, the royal palm (*Oreodoxa regia*), mahogany, and species of figs, orchids and many ferns.

The larger islands are all very mountainous, the mountains in Haiti exceeding 10,000 feet in height, while in Jamaica, the Blue Mountains are over 7,000, and in Cuba the highest summits exceed 8,000. The trend of the ranges is mostly east and west, and this, together with their elevation, exercises a marked influence on the climate. The northeast trade-winds precipitate their moisture mostly on the northern slopes of the mountains, the lee side being much drier. This is well shown in Jamaica in making the journey from Port Antonio on the north coast, to Kingston on the south side of the island, about 40 miles away, the two places separated by the high and steep range of the Blue Mountains. At Port Antonio the annual rainfall is nearly 200 inches, while at Kingston it is less than 40. The whole northern coast was originally clothed with dense jungle, a typical rain-forest of great luxuriance.

About twenty-five years ago, when the writer first visited Jamaica, the newly constructed railway between Port Antonio and Kingston traversed a region of luxuriant forests, which have since disappeared, and been replaced by extensive plantations of bananas, which are grown on an immense scale for the American market. Of late years this trade in bananas and other tropical fruits has assumed vast proportions, and has been extended to Mexico and Central America, as well as to the other West Indian islands.

The mountains intercept a large part of the moisture of the trade winds, and when one approaches Kingston, instead of the rain-

PLATE XXXVII.—Mountain forest seen from above, Blue Mountains, Jamaica. *Photo., Dr. Forrest Shreve.*

302

forest one sees an open semi-arid plain or savanna with Cacti, mesquit, and Agaves, suggesting the semi-deserts of Mexico and Arizona. As in those countries there is a dry winter, most of the rain falling in the summer months.

In the Blue Mountains, the lower rain-forest extends to about 2,000 feet elevation and in general is quite like the South American equatorial forest, but is much poorer in palms. Araceae and the showy Heliconias are conspicuous, and ferns are much more abundant than in the lowland forest of South America.

Above this forest is a rain-forest of somewhat mixed character; mingled with laurels and other tropical types are genera common to the forests of temperate America, like walnuts, and Clethra, the latter belonging to the Ericaceae. The yew family is represented by species of Podocarpus, already referred to in connection with the floras of the East Indies and Australasia.

In the drier hot lowlands are found trees which shed their leaves at certain seasons. Among these are the giant silk-cottons (Ceiba, Bombax), mahogany (*Swietenia*), and Spanish cedar (Cedrela). An important tree of the hot lowlands is log-wood (Haematoxylon), an extremely valuable dye-wood belonging to the Leguminosae, a family with many representatives in the West Indies, as in other tropical countries.

The Antilles are less rich in palms than the equatorial forests of the Amazon region, but nevertheless they play an important rôle in the flora of the larger islands, and include some of the handsomest members of the order, such as the royal palm (*Oreodoxa regia*) and the still finer *O. oleracea*, the "cabbage-palm" of Jamaica. The beautiful *Euterpe oleracea*, so abundant in Guiana, occurs also in Jamaica but is much less common, and the same is true of the genus Bactris. Palmettoes and the spiny-stemmed "groo-groo" (Acrocomia), and fan-palms of the genus Thrinax, are characteristic genera, absent from the Amazonian forests.

The upper rain-forest is characterized by an extraordinary development of ferns, and allied forms, Jamaica probably excelling in this particular any other known region of like extent. While the island has an area of only about 4,000 square miles, the great variety of soil, elevation and rainfall induces an unparalleled development of these plants, the total number of species being nearly or quite 500.

PLATE XXXVIII.—Interior of mountain forest, showing profusion of ferns, Blue Mountains, Jamaica.
Photo., Dr. Forrest Shreve.

In the Blue Mountains at elevations of 3,000–5,000 feet this fern-flora reaches its culmination, and ferns form the most conspicuous features of the vegetation, ranging from stately tree-ferns, 40–50 feet high, to tiny filmy-ferns looking more like delicate mosses than like ferns. Nowhere in the world can the student of these beautiful plants find a richer harvest.

In addition to the true ferns, there are many lycopods or club-mosses, and occasionally one encounters in the stream-beds, groves of giant horse-tails (*Equisetum giganteum*), suggesting a forest of the coal period.

The summits of the highest mountains have a sub-alpine flora, composed in part of the usual boreal genera.

CHAPTER IX

THE SOUTH TEMPERATE ZONE

SOUTH AFRICA

As the whole of Africa lies north of 35° south latitude, the Cape and the adjacent regions of South Africa all are within the warm temperate zone; and on account of the elevation of the central plateau, temperate conditions prevail over much of the area lying close to the Tropic of Capricorn, and even extending beyond it.

As a whole, South Africa is a region of moderate or scanty rainfall. The best watered regions are near the south and eastern coasts, while the west coast, except for a small part of the extreme southwest, including the Cape, is very arid and is continuous with the great desert regions of the Karroo and Kalahari, north of the Cape district.

The southwest coast of the Cape has a rainfall of 60–70 cm. of which the greater part falls in the winter months: May–September. The summer is nearly or quite rainless as in the Mediterranean region, California and southern Australia, and there is a marked superficial similarity in the vegetation, although it is composed for the most part of very different species.

To the east of the Cape is a small strip (Knysna forest) where the mountains approach the coast, and this is the rainiest portion of the south coast. The mountains in places support a fairly heavy evergreen forest, but elsewhere in the Cape region the forests have been almost entirely destroyed, and they have been replaced by a dense growth of evergreen shrubs resembling the "macchie" of the Mediterranean countries, or the Californian "chaparral."

Following the coast eastward the rainfall becomes more evenly distributed through the year, and grasslands or savannas take the place of the evergreen forests and chaparral on the hills to the west. Further north, the summer rainfall exceeds that of the winter, and in the interior nearly all the rain falls in the summer months. This is much less favorable for vegetation, owing to the great loss of moisture due to evaporation. Because of the light rainfall, most of South Africa, except near the coast, is destitute of proper forests, and is either grass-land and savannas, where there is sufficient rainfall, or a more or less complete desert, as in most of the great Kalahari and the Karroo.

The Cape is famous for the beauty and variety of its flowers, many of which are familiar denizens of our gardens and conservatories. Such are the common calla lily, Pelargoniums, Gladioli, many species of Oxalis, Mesembryanthemum, Lobelia, and many others. The profusion of showy flowers adorning the sandy flats

FIG. 83.—Karroo vegetation near Beaufort West, Cape Colony. *Carissa ferox* (?), *Euphorbia Mauretanica*, *Grewia cana*, *Lycium sp.*, *Mesembryanthemum sp.* Photo., Dr. W. A. Cannon.

near Cape Town in September and October, is equalled only by the display in Western Australia under very similar conditions.

In the chaparral on the mountain sides, are heaths of many kinds, and along the railways are millions of brilliant flowers of every shade of vivid color. Among these are many of the Iris family, especially species of Babiana, with blue, purple or lavender flowers. Others of the same family are species of Moraea, looking much like a true Iris, and with flowers of purple, yellow or bright orange; Pelargoniums of many species, callas, gorgeous Gazanias (Compositae), and giant sundews (Drosera), orchids, Proteas (Proteaceae), and endless other brilliant flowers.

A feature of the Cape flora is the abundance of bulbous and tuberous plants of the Iris family, which has a very large number of species.   In addition to numerous species of Gladiolus, there are the less familiar Watsonias, with pink and scarlet flowers, white, red and yellow Ixia and Sparaxis, blue and purple Babianas, yellow, pink and white Romuleas.   There are no proper species of Iris, but Moraea, which closely resembles it has many attractive species.   Many of these beautiful Cape bulbs find a congenial

FIG. 84.—*Aloe Schlechteri*, north slope of kopje near Beaufort West. *Photo.,*
Dr. W. A. Cannon.

home in California and Australia and are common ornaments of the gardens.

The lily family and the Amaryllis family are abundantly represented, and some are familiar in cultivation.   The blue Agapanthus and pink *Amaryllis bella-donna*, which in late summer sends up its leafless stalks crowned with rosy flowers, are the best known of these.   Less commonly seen in cultivation are species of Nerine and Brunsvigia.

There are many beautiful ground orchids at the Cape, which in this respect, also, recalls West Australia.   Among the characteristic genera are Satyrium, Disperis, Disa, Eulophia, and others.

One is immediately struck by the abundance and beauty of the species of Oxalis, white, yellow, pink and crimson, which occur in great profusion. One of these, the yellow *O. cernua*, is a rampant grower which has become a troublesome weed in parts of the Mediterranean and Australia, where it was introduced as an ornamental plant.

Very abundant and conspicuous are the many species of Mesembryanthemum ("ice-plant," etc.) which are so extensively planted in California and other warm temperate countries.

Giant sundews with pink flowers the size of a half dollar, are

Fig. 85.—Vegetation of very dry central Karoo. *Mesembryanthemum calamiforme, Cotyledon hemisphaerica* (?). *Photo., Dr. W. A. Cannon.*

common, and again remind one of West Australia, where this genus is also extraordinarily developed.

The Compositae, as in most other countries, are much in evidence, and include very showy species many of which have been introduced into cultivation. Especially showy are the many species of Gazania, with white, yellow or orange flowers. Much like these are Dimorphotheca and Arctotis, also sometimes seen in cultivation.

Leguminosae are common, and include some showy species, e. g., *Sutherlandia frutescens*, but they are much less abundant than in Australia.

Grasses and sedges are not specially abundant in the open places where so many showy flowers are found, but nevertheless there are numerous species. Much resembling sedges are the Restionaceae, a family especially characteristic of the Cape region, but also found in Australia. Elsewhere the family is almost unknown.

The thickets covering the hillsides are composed of a great variety of shrubs and small trees. Some of these belong to familiar genera, like the evergreen sumacs (Rhus); but the greater number belong to genera quite unknown in the northern hemisphere. Among the most abundant of these chaparral shrubs are many species of Protea, Leucadendron, and other members of the family Proteaceae, whose headquarters are South Africa and Australia.

Some species of Protea are very showy, the big heads of flowers being enclosed in broad scales, pink or purple in color, the whole inflorescence reminding one of an artichoke; indeed one of the finest species, *P. cynaroides* emphasizes this fact. The species of Leucadendron may become small trees, and while the flowers are less conspicuous than those of Protea, the broad silvery leaves of the best known species, *L. argenteum*, the "silver-tree" of Table Mountain, make it very ornamental, and it is not infrequently seen in cultivation in California and elsewhere.

A curious leafless twiner, *Cassytha sp.* is often seen climbing over the shrubs. While this reminds one of the common dodder, it is quite unrelated to the latter, but belongs to the laurel family. The genus is wide-spread through the warmer parts of the world.

Among the most attractive of the Cape flowers, are the many true heaths (Erica), developed in South Africa to an extraordinary degree, the Cape flora alone having no less than 350 species. They are most abundant on its hills and in mountainous districts, and in the spring one may see great bunches of these beautiful flowers offered for sale in the streets of Cape Town, indeed one fears that some of the rarer species are threatened with extinction.

The writer, unfortunately, was unable to make the ascent of Table Mountain, which is famous for its beautiful and interesting vegetation.

The distinguished German botanist, Professor Engler,[1] has given an interesting sketch of a trip made at the time of the writer's visit to South Africa. Engler's account, however, is confined to

[1] Engler, A., *Die Pflanzenwelt Africas*, p. 494, DIE VEGETATION DER ERDE, IX, 1910.

the region below 2,000 feet. He notes a fine grove of silver-trees, and compares the thick growth of evergreen shrubs to the "macchie of Corsica and Algiers," but notes that this formation at the Cape is much richer in species than the corresponding formation in the Mediterranean regions, and that there were more species with showy flowers. Especially conspicuous were species of Podalyria (Leguminosae) Polygala (milk-wort), sumacs, and many others.

White, pink and scarlet heaths were abundant and among the rocks were stone-crops (Crassula, Cotyledon, Rochea) with fleshy leaves and showy pink or scarlet flowers.

The blue African lily (Agapanthus) is also a common plant of this region, as well as many of the showy Iridaceae already mentioned.

The fine *Protea cynaroides* belongs to Table Mountain also, and one of the handsomest orchids, *Disa grandiflora*, with large scarlet flowers.

Among the common Compositae are species of Helichrysum, a genus also abundant in Australia, and furnishing some of the showiest of the garden "everlastings." Engler calls special attention to two of the chaparral shrubs: viz., *Cunonia Capensis* and *Grubbia rosmarinifolia*. The former is a monotypic species, belonging to the essentially southern family Cunnoniaceae. Grubbia represents a family, Grubbiaceae, confined to the Cape region.

The Cape is not rich in ferns, as the long dry summer is not favorable to most of them. Nevertheless there are some interesting species in the sheltered gullies, or rock crevices. One of the most notable is *Todea barbara*, a very handsome fern which also occurs in Australasia. In some of the gulches of Table Mountain, a small tree-fern, *Hemitelia Capensis*, occurs, and a single small filmy-fern (Hymenophyllum) was noted by Engler. At Muizenberg, near Cape Town, the writer collected specimens of the interesting *Gleichenia polypodioides* belonging to a family having no representatives in Europe or the United States, but common in the warm temperate regions of the southern hemisphere.

Just as many plants native to the Cape have been introduced into other countries, so one may see in Cape Town a great many trees, shrubs, and herbaceous plants brought from abroad. One

PLATE XXXIX.—Hillside vegetation near Durban, Natal. Arborescent Euphorbias are conspicuous.

312

is at once struck by the magnificent European oaks and the stately stone pines from the Mediterranean which are perfectly at home and completely naturalized. Two Californian conifers are extensively planted, the Monterey pine (*Pinus radiata*) and the Monterey cypress (*Cupressus macrocarpa*). These two trees are very restricted in their natural range on the coast of central California, but are easily grown and are now extensively planted in many warm temperate countries.

Australian gums, wattles (Acacia), and Casuarinas are also frequently planted, the Acacias being grown extensively for their bark, which is of great value for tanning. *Hakea suaveolens*, one of the Australian Proteaceae, has escaped from cultivation in some places and become quite naturalized.

All the fruits of the warm temperate zone flourish at the Cape. Peaches, apricots, figs, oranges and grapes, are extensively grown, the latter yielding wine of great excellence.

It is supposed that much of the Cape region was originally forested, but at present almost no forest is left, and only in a few mountainous districts can one see the remnants of the original forest. The most important trees are species of Podocarpus; *P. latifolia*, and *P. elongata* are said to reach a gigantic size. Two species of Callitris, small trees resembling junipers or cypresses are the only representatives of the true conifers.

In the low wet ground the common calla-lily is very abundant, and on the ponds are white and blue water-lilies, and various other aquatics, some of the common pond-weed types, rushes, and sedges, but others peculiar to the region, like the curious *Aponogeton distachya*, whose forked clusters of white flowers at once attract attention.

NATAL

On the east coast of Africa, the transition from the strictly tropical to the temperate regions is a very gradual one. Durban, the port of Natal, in lat. 30°, has a sub-tropical climate suited to the growth of many tropical products: sugar, bananas, pineapples, etc., and in the attractive botanical gardens of the town, one may see coco-palms, royal palms, bamboos, and many gorgeous tropical trees and shrubs growing luxuriantly.

Fronting the Indian Ocean, the climate is warm and humid,

with a pretty heavy rainfall, so that the coastal vegetation is luxuriant, and made up to a great extent of species related to those of the tropical regions to the north. Such are the wild date-palms (*Phoenix reclinata*) and another palm, *Hyphaene crinita*, several species of Ficus, the banana-like Strelitzias and many others.

In the valleys between the coastal hills is a forest formation of moderate sized trees, mostly of tropical affinities like the species of Ficus, the "water-boom" (*Syzygium cordata*), of the Myrtaceae; Albizzia, Mimusops, Strychnos, Combretum, etc.

Along the coast, in places, are mangrove swamps, in which the principal species is the white mangrove (*Avicennia officinalis*). Back of the mangroves, the wide-spread yellow tree-Hibiscus (*H. tiliaceus*) and a species of Barringtonia, a handsome genus of trees characteristic of the strand-floras of the eastern tropics.

Many handsome evergreen shrubs form the undergrowth of the forest; among them the writer noted the brilliant scarlet flowers of a trumpet creeper (*Tecoma Capensis*), the fragrant white flowers of the "Natal plum" (*Carissa sp.*), and several species of Gardenia.

Adding much to the tropical aspect of the jungle were great masses of the stately *Strelitzia Augusta*, much resembling the traveller's tree (Ravenala) of Madagascar. Lianas are conspicuous, among them an evergreen grapevine (*Vitis Capensis*), growing to the tops of the trees, and many less rampant vines—cucurbits, morning glories, and some curious asclepiads scrambled over the shrubs and smaller trees.

A very splendid sight was the "Kaffir-boom," *Erythrina Caffra*, the leafless branches bearing clusters of vermilion flowers.

Engler [1] reports two epiphytic orchids, *Angraecum sp.* and *Polystachya sp.* as common in this region, but these were not seen by the writer.

In the sheltered valleys two tree-ferns, *Cyathea Dregii* and *Hemitelia Capensis*, occur, and also *Todea barbara*.

The floral display in Natal is less remarkable than in the Cape region, but there are nevertheless many very beautiful species. Near Durban are "flats" like those around Cape Town, and in these are many showy flowers, especially Compositae, e. g., Gazania, Senecio, Gerbera, everlastings; Lobelia, sundews, and many

---

[1] *Loc cit.*, p. 411.

PLATE XL.—Vegetation near Ladysmith, Natal. To the right, *Aloe sp.*

others. The Liliaceae and Iridaceae, are perhaps not so numerous as at the Cape, but they include some very showy species of Kniphofia, Anemotheca, Tritonia and others.

While most of the trees belong to tropical genera, there are a few related to northern ones, such as species of sumac (Rhus), Celtis, and Vernonia, a shrubby composite of the same genus as the ironweed of the eastern United States.

On the drier hills are xerophytic forms, related to those of the arid parts of Africa. Especially conspicuous are the great candelabra Euphorbias (*E. grandidens*), recalling the giant Cacti of Arizona and Mexico. Aloes, some of them almost trees, much resemble in appearance the century-plants of the American southwest. The flowers of some of the Aloes are extremely showy, great spikes of flaming scarlet or orange bloom. Another showy flower of this region is Haemanthus, which sends up from a bulb a short stalk crowned by a dense head of scarlet flowers, with a fringe of long stamens. Of the Liliaceae with less showy flowers, are many species of Asparagus, one of which, *A. plumosus*, is common in cultivation under the name "Asparagus fern."

Among the most interesting botanical features of Natal are the cycads. Two genera are found, Encephalartos, with several species, and *Stangeria paradoxa*, the most fern-like of all the cycads, and when first discovered, mistaken for a genuine fern.

The sub-tropical type of vegetation in Natal reaches from the coast to about 1,500 feet elevation, above which, is a temperate belt extending to the foot of the Drakensberg, the mountains separating Natal from the Orange State and Transvaal.

The railway from the coast ascends through a fertile and picturesque country, which in places is broken by bold ravines or "kloofs," in which there is a fine growth of timber. Plantations of Eucalyptus and Acacia are frequent, these Australian immigrants appearing to be as much at home in Natal as they are in California. Peach trees apparently have become naturalized in many places in the higher parts of Natal, and in the spring (October) were in full flower, presenting a beautiful sight. A stop at Ladysmith, gave opportunity to examine the very typical formation of this region, flat-topped "Kopjes" rising from the plateau. The slopes of these rugged hills were clothed with a variety of more or less xerophytic plants, among which the Aloes were conspicuous, being in full-bloom, the great candelabra flower spikes a blaze of orange and scarlet, a truly splendid sight.

The Drakensberg has peaks 10,000–11,000 feet high, the loftiest mountains in Africa south of Kilimanjaro, and in winter, snow clad. The valleys of the streams flowing to the sea are often deep and abrupt, and are clothed with heavy forest, but the open country is mostly grass-land or savannas.

Among the most valuable timber-trees are Podocarpus and mountain cypress (*Callitris cupressoides*).

Fig. 86.—High Veldt, Transvaal.

Passing the barrier of the Drakensberg, one enters the extensive table land of the Orange State and Transvaal, the "High Veldt" of the Boers, a plateau with an average elevation of 4,000–5,000 feet. The mountains intercept much of the moisture from the Indian Ocean and the climate is a relatively dry one, with an annual precipitation of 20–25 inches (53–64 cm.). As the rain falls mostly in the hot weather, and often in violent thunder storms, much moisture is lost by evaporation, and the country for the most part, is treeless, except in sheltered places or along the streams.

The high veldt reminds one of our own western plains, but the climate is much milder in winter. About Johannesburg one may see orchards of oranges and other vegetation which show that the cold is never severe, a great contrast to the arctic winters of Wyoming and Montana.

The writer's acquaintance with this region is confined to a brief visit in the early spring (September) before the summer rains had started the dormant vegetation, and the monotonous veldt was an almost unbroken expanse of dead grass, with only here and there an occasional low bush or stunted tree.

In summer there is a vigorous growth of tall grasses which furnished feed for the hosts of antelopes and other big game that once roamed these great natural pastures, much like the buffalo and antelopes of our western plains.

According to Engler [1] the predominant grass is *Antistheria imberbis* associated with species of Andropogon, Panicum and several others. The bulbous plants, so abundant in the Cape region and Natal, are much less common, but on the slopes of the hills and in the moist depressions, are showy species of Crinum, Gladiolus, Ornithogalum and others. Dicotyledonous herbs are abundant and include representatives of many families.[2] While many of these belong to wide-spread genera, like Lepidium, Cassia, Indigofera, Polygala, Heliotropium, Lobelia, etc., a large number represent genera unknown in the northern hemisphere.

On the rocky slopes of the kopjes, one may see such conspicuous plants as the fleshy-leaved Aloes and Euphorbias, stone-crops, and the showy Mesembryanthemums.

The most abundant trees of the veldt are the thorny Acacias, especially the "Kameel-dorn" (*Acacia giraffae*) which grows mainly along the stream-banks together with several other species of small trees, among which is an olive (*Olea chrysophylla*), sumacs, a willow (*Salix Capensis*) and several others.

While the high veldt is mostly a pastoral region, one may also see orchards of oranges and peaches, the latter in full bloom in September and presenting a beautiful sight, especially when, as was often the case, they were associated with weeping willows just bursting into leaf, a tree which is very often seen about the farms in the neighborhood of Johannesburg and Pretoria.

[1] *Loc. cit.*, p. 458.   [2] Engler, *loc. cit.*

Successful experiments have been carried out on field and orchard crops in this region where climatic conditions are comparable to those of California, and the orchards are cultivated in much the same way. Maize is a staple crop in South Africa, and in places alfalfa is also proving profitable.

North of Johannesburg is Pretoria, and not far away from the latter is a range of low mountains, the Magalisberg, a region with a flora quite different from that of the open high veldt. This marks the beginning of the "bush-veldt," a savanna region with an open growth of trees, sometimes becoming a continuous thin dry forest.

The trees of the bush-veldt are mostly deciduous, and in September looked much like the leafless winter forests of the north. There is, however, a considerable number of evergreen species, notably the figs, which remind one how near this region is to the tropics.

Near Pretoria a small stream breaks through the range of hills, and along its banks is a thin growth of small trees and shrubs. Among these were noted two sumacs, a hackberry (Celtis) just unfolding its leaves, and several unfamiliar species. Close to the water was a willow, and tall reeds (*Phragmites communis*) and sedges grew in the moist sand.

In the clefts of the rocks were various succulents, Aloes and stone-crops; and a club-moss (*Selaginella Dregei*) not unlike the American *S. rupestris*, was quite common. Two xerophytic ferns, *Notochlaena lanuginosa* and *Pellaea calomelanos*, were also noted. Another interesting fern was *Mohria Caffrorum*, of the family Schizaeaceae.

Of the various shrubs growing on the rocky banks, one in particular attracted attention by its profusion of pretty white flowers. This shrub, *Dombeya Natalensis*, is occasionally grown in California.

To the northwest of the Magalisburg, the bush-veldt is continued and the trees sometimes reach quite respectable size, indeed one of these, a banyan fig, may become quite an imposing tree. A specially fine example of this species (*Ficus cordata*) known locally as the "wonder-boom," is one of the sights of this region. The great dome of foliage was said to be 160 feet in diameter. Other trees and shrubs of this neighborhood noted were species of Acacia, the scarlet-flowered *Erythrina Caffra*, *Strychnos pungens*, *Burkea*

Africana, and a poisonous plant, *Dichapetalum toxicarium* belonging to the predominantly African family Dichapetalaceae.

West of Transvaal and Rhodesia the precipitation falls off, and along the Atlantic coast true desert conditions prevail. The bush-veldt gives place to open formations with a fairly extensive vegetation in the less arid portions, but over much of the region the vegetation is extremely scanty. This great arid region is the Kalahari Desert, and occupies most of the table land west of the Transvaal and Rhodesia. The whole region has a scanty rainfall, in some places an annual precipitation of only about four inches.

At the extreme north there are a good many species of tropical origin, but on the whole the species are the same as those of the adjacent regions, and there are few peculiar to the Kalahari. The grasses are thin and scattered, and there are scrubby bushes and stunted trees in many places, the commonest being the widespread *Acacia giraffae*.

Among the herbaceous plants of the Kalahari are several of the melon family, including, according to Engler, true water melons (*Citrullus vulgaris*), which are highly prized by man and beast.

Travelling southward from the Orange State one descends from the high table land toward the lower arid region of the Karroo. This has a very dry climate, sometimes almost rainless for periods of a year or more. When, however, the rains come, there is a surprising amount of vegetation developed, many species having underground tubers or bulbs which may remain dormant indefinitely, only waiting for sufficient moisture to put forth leaves and flowers. Shrubs and trees quickly unfold fresh green leaves which are destined soon to wither away.

Trees are scarce, but there are many low shrubs scattered over the landscape, which is not unlike that of parts of Nevada or Arizona. As in the southern American deserts, there is a marked development of succulents, but the place of the American Cacti and Agaves is taken by cactus-like Euphorbias and Aloes. In some places, however, true Cacti (*Opuntia spp.*) may be seen, but these prickly-pears, although completely naturalized, are escapes from cultivation.

As in the Cape region, there are many showy species of Mesembryanthemum, and the curious Stapelias, members of the milkweed family are characteristic of the Karroo. The latter have fleshy leaves and dull purplish flowers, with a most evil scent of carrion, which attract flies and other insects that doubtless play their part in pollination of the flowers.

The writer travelled through this region in September, 1905, a season of unusually abundant rains, so that the Karroo was seen in its most attractive aspect. While the low bushes, looking like sage-brush were perhaps the most obvious feature of the landscape, there were also many bright flowers, the most conspicuous a pink Mesembryanthemum which occurred in large masses, and in the distance reminded one of the heather on Scottish moorlands.[1]

The railway through the Karroo ascends to a height of about 3,500 feet (1,150 m.) and then descends through picturesque scenery to the beautiful valley of the Hexe River, one of the most attractive regions in South Africa. The vegetation of the Hexe valley is a combination of that of the Karoo and the true Cape flora. In September, the height of the spring season, the wonderful Cape flora was in its glory, and is unsurpassed by anything the writer has seen unless, perhaps, the somewhat similar floral display in West Australia.

On the rocky hillsides were masses of beautiful heaths and other showy shrubs, and along the railway were millions of exquisite flowers of every shade and color: white, yellow, pink, vivid orange, scarlet, blue and purple. Particularly abundant were the Babianas, beautiful plants of the Iris family, sometimes seen in Calfornian gardens. These have all shades of blue, purple and crimson, and in mass are extraordinarily effective. This region is also the home of many species of Freesia, Ixia, Sparaxis and Gladiolus, all garden favorites.

AUSTRALASIA

Australia and New Zealand, isolated as they are, show a very high degree of endemism both among plants and animals. The outlying islands share in this, and the great island of Papua, or New Guinea, and the adjacent islands to the west, are to a certain extent Australian in their vegetation, and connect the Australasian floras with the more strictly Malayan vegetation of the large western islands of the Archipelago.

[1] For details of the flora of the Karroo, see Engler, *loc. cit.*, pp. 468–477. Also Cannon, W. A., Carnegie Institution of Washington, Publication 354; 1924.

PLATE XLI.—Bunya pine (*Araucaria Bidwillii*), Queensland Australia.

Australia

Australia comprises much the greater part of Australasia, equalling in area the whole United States exclusive of Alaska. The northern portion lies within the tropics, while its southernmost part corresponds in latitude to New York City. The climate, therefore, ranges from a true tropical one at the north, to a warm temperate one in the south, comparable to that of the Mediterranean, or southern California.

Australia is lacking in high mountains and there is a dearth of large rivers and lakes, and much of the country is occupied by monotonous plains of great extent, and largely arid. The highest elevations are near the eastern coast, where a succession of highlands and mountain ranges extends from the York Peninsula to Victoria and Tasmania. Along the coast of North Queensland are some definite mountain ranges, but for the most part the highland is a plateau sloping westward to the interior with more or less definite escarpments near the coast. These escarpments are sometimes deeply indented by abrupt gorges, such as may be seen in the Blue Mountains west of Sydney. The highest point in Australia, Mt. Kosciusco (7,300 ft.) is in New South Wales near the Victoria border. The eastern highlands and the coastal strip, have, as a rule, a good rainfall, but there are no large rivers. The heaviest rainfall in Australia is in the coastal region of North Queensland, at the foot of the Bellenden-Ker range. At one station, Babinda, visited by the writer, the annual precipitation sometimes exceeds 200 inches.

Inland, however, the rainfall diminishes rapidly, and a third of the continent, some 1,000,000 square miles, is said to receive less than ten inches annually, while another third has less than twenty. This means that a large part of Australia must be considered as too arid for most agricultural purposes except under irrigation. Vast areas, however, are adapted to grazing, and sheep raising is at present the most important industry of the commonwealth.

There is a more or less pronounced wet and dry season in most parts of Australia. In the south, the rains come mostly in the winter months—May–September,—while at the north, summer is the rainiest period.

The rain-forests of North Queensland contain many wide-

PLATE XLII.—Eucalyptus forest, Victoria, Australia.

spread Malayan types, like the figs, screw-pines, palms, arums, and many epiphytic ferns and orchids. The Malayan character of the flora is especially marked in the northernmost region, the York Peninsula, which has many genera absent from the rest of Australia, like the pitcher plants (Nepenthes), and palms of the genera Caryota, Borassus and Areca.

As one travels southward, beyond the tropics, one still meets a considerable number of the Malayan rain-forest species where the conditions of soil and moisture are favorable, but these gradually disappear, and are replaced by more strictly Australian types.

Among the most notable of Australian trees are the conifers of the genus Araucaria. The finest is *A. Bidwillii*, the "Bunya-pine," of southeastern Queensland, where in one district it forms forests of considerable extent. A more wide-spread species is *A. Cunninghamii*, which is very abundant along parts of the Queensland coast, forming pure stands, like some of the pines and spruces of the Pacific coast of North America.

Other species occur in some of the adjacent islands, New Caledonia and Norfolk Island. The Norfolk Island pine (*A. excelsa*) is the most familiar. Two South American species are the only others known to science.

The coastal region of New South Wales shows much the same type of vegetation as southern Queensland; but the tropical types become less abundant and there is an increasing number of such true Australian genera as Acacia and Eucalyptus. The rain-forest, however, still has a decidedly tropical aspect, with tall palms, tree-ferns, and lianas.

Away from the coast, and wherever the soil is poor, the dense rain-forest is replaced by open Eucalpytus-forest with an undergrowth composed of a great variety of smaller trees and shrubs, all more or less decidedly xerophytic in character. Herbaceous plants are not very abundant, but there are a good many grasses and sedges, and numerous bulbous and tuberous species including many showy orchids and Liliaceae, which with the profusion of showy flowered shrubs, make a magnificent show in the spring. Many species of Eucalyptus, Leptospermum, Melaleuca, Callistemon, often seen in cultivation, as well as others less familiar, represent the myrtle family; while the Leguminosae are even more abundant, and comprise a host of showy species. Of these

PLATE XLIII.—Giant Eucalyptus (*E. regnans*), Victoria, Australia.

Acacia leads in number of species, but the pea-family is also extremely abundant. About Sydney several species of Boronia and Eriostemon (Rutaceae), are common and beautiful shrubs, and many other unfamiliar flowers abound.

As elsewhere in Australia, New South Wales has many Proteaceae, a family which reaches its maximum development in Australia. The commonest genera are Grevillea, Banksia and Hakea. To this family belongs also the "Waratah" (*Telopea speciosissima*) one of the most gorgeous of Australian flowers, whose magnificent clusters of scarlet are the pride of New South

Fig. 87.—Desert vegetation, Transcontinental Railway, Australia.

Wales. Another very splendid plant, common near Sydney is the giant torch-lily (*Doryanthes excelsa*) which bears aloft on a stout stem, 10–15 feet high, a huge cluster of immense scarlet lilies.

The southeastern part of Australia is occupied by Victoria, the smallest state in the commonwealth, being about the size of Kansas. Much of Victoria has a temperate climate, adapted to the staple crops of the temperate zones, and better suited to European settlers than the hotter parts of Australia.

Its smaller size and more uniform climate result in a lesser variety of vegetation than in the larger states; but in the well watered mountains of the east are found magnificent forests of giant gums (*Eucalyptus regnans*), close rivals in height of the

Californian redwoods. The forests of giant gums, with their undergrowth of tree-ferns and other luxuriant vegetation, are among the finest in the world.

Travelling overland from Victoria to the west coast of Australia, one traverses, for the most part a region of deserts, or dry steppes comparable to those of Arizona or southern California. Extensive tracts show only a sparse growth of salt-bush (Atriplex, Kochia, etc.) reminding one of the sage-brush desert of Nevada and Utah; but for the most part there is a growth of stunted trees and shrubs,

Fig. 88.—Sandy desert near Oodnadatta, South Australia. *Eucalyptus sp. Photo., Dr. W. A. Cannon.*

with scattered bunch-grasses, and sometimes a few showy herbaceous plants.

The commonest trees are gums of several species, the shrubby ones known locally as "Mallee." Other common trees noted were species of Casuarina, whose thin leafless twigs simulate pine-needles, and the tree suggests a scrubby straggling pine. Casuarina is essentially an Australian genus, although a few species, especially as strand-forms, reach the western Malayan region.

Of the shrubs, several species of Acacia and a sandal-wood (Santalum), may be mentioned. In October, the golden flowers of the wattles relieved the monotony of the prevailing dull green of the foliage of most of the desert shrubs. Showy flowers were not abundant, but here and there masses of pink and white everlastings were seen, and the splendid scarlet flowered "Sturt-pea," (*Clianthus Dampieri*), is abundant in some localities.

As the west coast is approached the country becomes less arid, and presently the increasing moisture is evident in the more luxuriant vegetation and the profusion of showy flowers which in the spring adorn the country. The train passes through a veritable garden of brilliant bloom. The variety and beauty of this floral

Fig. 89.—Coastal vegetation, Perth, West Australia. Red gum (*Eucalyptus calophylla*), *Banksia grandis*.

show must be seen to be appreciated. While some of the flowers, especially the many Papilionaceae and lilies, seem more or less familiar, most of them are quite strange to the northern botanist, many belonging to families entirely wanting in the northern hemisphere. The family Goodeniaceae includes many species of yellow Goodenia, and blue Dampiera and Leschenaultia, one of the latter, *L. formosa* of a blue so magnificent, that once seen, can never be forgotten.

Ground orchids are remarkably abundant in West Australia, mostly characteristic Australian genera, e. g., Caladenia, Diuris, Thelymitra, and others quite strange to the European or American botanist. Many of these are very beautiful. Another striking feature of this region are the many species of sundews which abound in the sandy moorlands, some of them slender, half-climbing plants four or five feet high, with pink flowers like small single roses, while others are tiny rosettes of leaves lying close to the ground.   Yellow Hibbertias (Dilleniaceae), several pretty Liliaceae (e. g., Thysonotus, Burchardia), and species of Pattersonia, of the Iris family; Boronias and many species of the curious "trig-

A   B

Fig. 90.—A. Wild flowers, Perth.   At extreme left, "Kangaroo paws" (*Anigozan-thus Manglesii*); B. *Banksia grandis.*

ger-flowers," Candollea, are common and characteristic.   Among the many strange and showy flowers peculiar to West Australia none are more remarkable than the "Kangaroo-paws" of the genus Anigozanthus (Amaryllidaceae).   These flowers show the most bizarre coloring—green and scarlet, yellow and black, red and yellow, or pure green.

Besides the many species of Eucalyptus, Acacia and Casuarina, the smaller trees and shrubs include many Proteaceae, of which Grevillea, Banksia and Hakea are the most abundant; Myrtaceae, with numerous species of Leptospermum, Melaleuca and Callistemon, and many others less common.

The only gymnosperm seen by the writer in Western Australia was a cycad, *Macrozamia Fraseri*, which was very common and a serious pest, as animals are often poisoned by eating the young foliage in times of drought.

Especially abundant in West Australia, but found also in the

Fig. 91.—Cycad (*Macrozamia Fraseri*), West Australia. *Photo., courtesy of Mr. C. E. Lane-Poole.*

other states, are the "grass-trees" (Xanthorrhoea), striking if not beautiful features of the vegetation. The larger species have a stout trunk and recall in habit the tree-Yuccas of Southern California and Mexico; but the numerous drooping leaves are much more slender and the innumerable flowers, borne on a tall club-like spike, are insignificant and quite lacking in the beauty of the Yucca.

Throughout the less arid parts of West Australia, the spring display of flowers from August to November, is quite unrivalled elsewhere, and perhaps culminates in the Albany district, to which are confined many species, among them the curious pitcher plant,

(Cephalotus). In variety and beauty, the flowers of the Albany district surpass anything the writer has ever seen.

The visitor to Australia is at once impressed by the dominance of the gum forests. Although the prevailing dry open forest is very monotonous, one must remember that some of the species of Eucalyptus are among the stateliest and most striking of trees. The Karri (*E. diversicolor*) of West Australia, and the giant gums of Victoria, as well as other species of the moister regions of New South Wales and Queensland, are among the finest of all trees. Many species show beautiful golden or ruddy tints in the young leaves, contrasting beautifully with the gray-green of the adult foliage, and the flowers are often very showy, especially in some of the species of West Australia. The best known of these is the scarlet flowered *E. ficifolia*, which is often cultivated.

The Myrtaceae, which include Eucalyptus, number about 800 Australian species, among which are other fine trees, related to Eucalyptus. Among these are Tristanea, Angophora and Syncarpia. In the moister and warmer regions, are also found species of Myrtus and Eugenia, both wide-spread genera.

Even more numerous than the Myrtaceae are the Leguminosae, with over 1,000 species. First in importance is Acacia, with over 400 species, everywhere abundant, and ranging from tiny shrubs, a few inches high, to trees of large size. They are generally known as "wattle," and the masses of golden flowers of many species are a feature of the spring landscape all over Australia. Many of them are favorites in the gardens of California and the Riviera, where they often go by the name of "mimosa."

The pea family, or Papilionaceae, contributes a host of showy flowers to the spring show. Their colors are extremely brilliant— pink, scarlet, orange, yellow, blue and purple, and the flowers are borne in great profusion. Many of the genera, e. g., Chorizema, Gastrolobium, Jacksonia, etc., are strictly Australian, but only a few of them are in cultivation.

The Proteaceae, which have no representatives in the United States, and are almost entirely wanting north of the equator, are third in number in the Australian flora. They are mostly shrubs, but some are trees of considerable size, the latter most abundant in the rain-forests of Queensland and New South Wales. Of these, the silk-oak (*Grevillea robusta*) is often

PLATE XLIV.—Grass-trees (*Xanthorrhoea Preissii*), West Australia. *Photo.,
courtesy of Mr. C. E. Lane-Poole.*

333

cultivated, and less frequently others are seen, e. g., Stenocarpus, Macadamia.

Few Australian trees are more characteristic than some species of Banksia, whose stiff serrate leaves, and big oblong heads of flowers are very striking. Except for a few trees of the northern rain-forests, most of the Proteaceae are xerophytic in habit.

Other characteristic Australian families with few or no representatives elsewhere are the Tremandraceae, Goodeniaceae, Candolleaceae and Casuarinaceae.

The gymnosperms of Australia, apart from the cycads, Kauri, and Araucarias, are mostly of the yew family, the most important being species of Podocarpus. Most nearly related to the northern conifers are several species of Callitris, much resembling cypresses.

Tasmania has a number of peculiar Taxaceae, absent from the mainland, but also found in New Zealand. The most important of these are Dacrydium and Phyllocladus.

Ferns and their relatives are scarce, or wanting in much of Australia, owing to the prevalence of arid or semi-arid conditions. Where there is sufficient moisture, however, as in the mountain forests of Victoria, New South Wales and Tasmania, they are abundant and luxuriant, and form an important element of the vegetation.

Tree-ferns are abundant in these regions, especially species of Alsophila and Dicksonia, and in the wetter districts, filmy-ferns, and other epiphytic species abound. Among these the extraordinary stag-horn ferns (Platycerium), are common and conspicuous.

Club-mosses (Lycopodineae) and the curious Psilotum and Tmesipteris, are sometimes seen, and many interesting liverworts and mosses may be found by the student of these plants.

Tasmania, unlike most of the Australian mainland, is extremely mountainous, and in the west especially, has a heavy rainfall. Both in topography and climate it has much in common with New Zealand, and like the latter there is an important element in the flora closely related to that of Patagonia and the Chilean Andes. Some of these "Fuegian" plants occur also in southern Victoria and the higher mountains of New South Wales and Queensland. The most important of the Fuegian types are the antarctic beeches (Nothofagus), the sole representatives of the oak family in Australia.

PLATE XLV.—Interior of Kauri forest, North Island, New Zealand.

New Zealand

New Zealand, lying over 1000 miles from Australia, and like it, completely isolated, consists of two main islands of about equal size, and a number of small outlying ones. The two principal islands lie between 34° and 47° S. lat., and the total area is a little more than 100,000 square miles.

New Zealand presents a strong contrast to Australia, both in topography and climate. Its relatively small area results in a decidedly insular climate with very much less range of precipitation and temperature than is found in continental Australia. Owing to the higher latitude, the climate as a whole is rather cool, but severe frost is rare in the lowlands, and the effect of the surrounding ocean is seen in the relatively small range of temperature due to latitude. Thus between Auckland in the North Island, and Invercargill, ten degrees further south, there is less than 10°F. difference in the mean annual temperatures.

For the most part, rain is abundant and well distributed, and originally extensive forests covered much of the country. Most of the forest has disappeared, especially in the North Island. There are, however, in the South Island, areas of light rainfall, which are natural grass-lands, and may be compared to the American prairies. The most important of these is the Canterbury Plain.

New Zealand is very mountainous, and there are extensive volcanic formations especially in the North Island. The Rotorua district, familiar to tourists, recalls the Yellowstone Park, with its geysers and thermal springs.

The lofty snow-clad Southern Alps parallelling the west coast of the South Island, culminate in Mt. Cook, over 12,000 feet high, from which extensive glaciers descend, almost to its base. These mountains greatly influence the climate of the South Island, intercepting a large part of the moisture from the ocean, so that in the narrow strip of territory, Westland, between the mountains and the coast, there are stations with as much as 200 inches of annual rainfall; while Christchurch, on the east coast has only about 25 inches, and some eastern stations even less.

This eastern dry region is mostly treeless, the ground covered with coarse tussock-grasses, especially *Festuca Novae-Zeylandeae,*

PLATE XLVI.—Giant Kauri (*Agathis Australis*), New Zealand.

and *Poa caespitosa*. The contrast between this region and the dense evergreen rain-forest of Westland, is very marked.

The most important tree of the great forest which once covered most of the North Island, is the Kauri (*Agathis Australis*). Very little remains of this primitive forest, and the Kauri is almost extinct except in a few reservations. This magnificent tree is very different in appearance from any northern conifer. While the young tree has the same symmetrical pyramidal form, this is

Fig. 92.—Cabbage-trees (*Cordyline Australis*) and native flax (*Phormium tenax*), North Island, New Zealand. *Photo., Mr. W. D. Reid.*

later lost, and the mature tree has an almost perfectly cylindrical bole, 60–80 ft. high, sometimes 8–10 feet in diameter, or even more, which divides abruptly into several widely divergent branches, supporting an immense spreading crown, which over-tops all the other trees.

The interior of the Kauri forest with its huge smooth gray pillars is most impressive. Associated with the Kauri are other characteristic trees. Among these are several members of the yew family, e. g., "Totara" (*Podocarpus Totara*); "Rimu" (*Dacrydium cupressinum*), both valuable timber-trees, and the curious *Phyl-locladus trichomanoides* whose flattened leaf-like shoots, or "clado-des" look like fern leaves. Other common trees are *Weinmannia sylvicola* (Saxifragaceae), and *Beilschmiedia taraire*, of the laurel family. Weinmannia is said to be the commonest tree of New Zealand.

Many very ornamental evergreen shrubs are common, e. g., Coprosma, Pittosporum, Nothopanax, and as everywhere in

FIG. 93.—*Todea (Leptopteris) superba.* Tree-ferns in background.

New Zealand, ferns are much in evidence. The tree-ferns of New Zealand are especially beautiful and abundant. *Cyathea medul-laris*, sometimes upwards of 50 feet high, is probably unsurpassed in beauty by any tree-fern.

In the wet forests lianas and epiphytes are abundant, the latter including many bryophytes and ferns, as well as a good many flowering plants, among which several orchids may be noted; but these are much inferior in beauty to those of northern Australia. A very common epiphyte, belonging to the lily family is *Astelia Solanderi* whose great bunches of sword-shaped leaves

PLATE XLVII.—Tree-ferns (*Cyathea medullaris*), North Island, New Zealand.

cling to the trunks and branches of the trees. It is often found attached to the slender trunk of the "Nikau" (*Rhopalostylis sapida*), very common in the North Island, and the only palm native to New Zealand.

Where the cleared land has been abandoned, it is often invaded by the ubiquitous bracken (*Pteridium aquilinum*), and another plant which quickly takes possession is the "Manuka" (*Leptospermum scoparium*), a shrub closely resembling some of the Australian species. When in bloom, the profusion of pretty white flowers is quite ornamental.

In open moist places, all over New Zealand, two characteristic plants at once attract attention. The native flax (*Phormium tenax*) and the "cabbage-tree" (*Cordyline Australis*), both handsome plants, are often seen in cultivation. The latter, sometimes in California known as "Yucca-palm," is not very distantly related to our native Yuccas. The flax yields an abundant strong fibre which is manufactured on a large scale and is one of the most important products of the country. In November, when these two plants are in bloom, they present a fine picture. The flax sends up from its great tufts of broad leaves, four or five feet high, flower stalks of twice that height, bearing racemes of dark red flowers, which are frequented by the honey-sucking birds. The stately cabbage-trees have big clusters of small white, very fragrant flowers.

Among the common trees of New Zealand are several species of Metrosideros (Myrtaceae), a genus distributed over Polynesia and Australasia. *M. robusta*, the "Rata," is a handsome tree with glossy foliage, and a profusion of bright red flowers, the stamens, as in many other Myrtaceae, being the showy part of the flower. *M. tomentosa* is very common about Auckland, and *M. lucida* in the South Island. Some of the species are climbers, and *M. robusta* begins life as an epiphyte behaving like many of the tropical banyan figs.

Further south the forest is of much the same type, but the Kauri is entirely absent, and finally the Nikau-palm disappears. In the extreme southern part of the North Island, near Wellington, one first encounters the evergreen beeches, which are very characteristic of many districts in the South Island.

The predominant forest near Wellington is a mixed one. Fine

PLATE XLVIII.—Nikau-palm (*Rhopalostylis sapida*), North Island, New Zealand.

specimens of *Knightia excelsa*, one of the two species of Proteaceae found in New Zealand, were seen about Wellington. This is a handsome tree somewhat resembling the Australian Banksias. Another interesting small tree, is a species of Fuchsia (*F. excorticata*). New Zealand has three species of this otherwise American genus.

The beech forest near Wellington is composed exclusively of two species, *Nothofagus fusca* and *N. Menziesii*. The forest is more open than the mixed, forests of the North Island. Except for their very small leaves, they are not unlike the beeches of the northern forests, and also remind one of the alders of the northern Pacific coast.

Cook's Strait separating the North and South Islands seems to afford no appreciable barrier to plant migration, there being little difference in the vegetation on the two sides of the strait, indicating that the separation of the islands is too recent for any marked changes in the vegetation.

The eastern part of the South Island is largely occupied by open grass-land, the Canterbury Plain, in which is situated the important city of Christchurch, being the most extensive. This is a rich agricultural and pastoral region. Where it has not been cultivated it is covered by coarse tussock-grasses, and this is also true of the eastern foot-hills of the mountains. In a few localities, where the ground is low and moist, and in some sheltered ravines in the coastal hills, there are patches of forest.

Crossing the South Island from Christchurch to the west coast, one traverses a great variety of country, with a correspondingly varied vegetation.

The tussock grass-land of the Centerbury Plain extends over the lower slopes of the mountains but gives place, very abruptly, to dense woods of the mountain beech (*Nothofagus Cliffortioides*), marking the beginning of the western rainy district.

At Arthur's Pass, about 3,000 feet elevation, the increasing moisture is still more evident. The country is an open rocky moorland, with a great variety of herbaceous plants and low shrubs. Preëminent among the flowers is the superb giant buttercup (*Ranunculus Lyallii*), with great clusters of big snow-white blossoms, and immense almost circular entire leaves. Another common and beautiful flower is *Ourisia macrocarpa*, somewhat like a white Mimulus.

Fig. 94.—Beech forest (*Nothofagus fusca*), South Island, New Zealand. The fern is *Polystichum vestitum*. Photo., Mr. W. D. Reid.

There is a very characteristic sub-alpine scrub, including several species of Veronica, a genus remarkably developed in New Zea-

land, as well as many others. Among the latter are various woody
Compositae (Olearia, Celmisia, Senecio); a leafless leguminous
shrub (Carmichaelia); Gaultheria, Pseudopanax, and most striking of all the conspicuous Dracaena-like *Dracophyllum Traversii*, a
low tree with bunches of long reddish leaves at the tips of the
straggling branches. In spite of the Yucca-like aspect, it is a
heath, of the family Epacridaceae, especially developed in Aus-

Fig. 95.—Tussock grass-land (*Poa caespitosa*), South Island, New Zealand. *Photo.*,
Mr. W. D. Reid.

tralia. A second species of flax (*Phormium Colensoi*) is common
in this district.

The descent toward the west coast through the magnificent
Otira Gorge, is one of the finest pieces of scenery in New Zealand.
Luxuriant forest completely covers the precipitous walls of the
canyon, and testifies to the heavy rainfall of the western slopes of
the mountains.

The beech forest of the higher elevations gradually gives way
to the typical Westland rain-forest, and there is an increasing

luxuriance in the roadside vegetation, where there is a profusion
of moisture-loving plants like liverworts and ferns, and such herbaceous flowers as violets and the interesting genus Gunnera,
which is especially developed in New Zealand. Tree-ferns become
more and more abundant as one descends, and in the typical
Westland forest are developed in magnificent profusion.

The Westland rain-forest is one of extraordinary luxuriance.
The very heavy precipitation and mild temperature result in a rich
vegetation that recalls the Malayan jungle. Composed entirely
of evergreen trees and shrubs, draped with giant creepers and
epiphytes, and with groves of tall tree-ferns, it is hard to realize
that this forest, in S. lat. 43°, corresponds in latitude to Buffalo
or Milwaukee.

This forest is dominated by two trees of the yew family, *Podocarpus dacrydioides* and *Dacrydium cupressinum*, and has been
called a "Taxad" forest for this reason. However, other trees
are also common, especially Weinmannia, already referred to in
connection with the forest of the North Island. Related to this
is another abundant species, *Quinquinia acutifolia*. A very common shrub is *Aristotelia racemosa*, with rather pretty pinkish
flowers; other abundant shrubs and small trees are species of
Coprosma, Metrosideros and Pseudopanax.

Ferns, mosses and liverworts luxuriate in these wet forests, and
club-mosses are abundant, both terrestrial and epiphytic species.
The interesting Tmesipteris, formerly associated with the lycopods, but now assigned to a class of its own (Psilotineae) is
common as an epiphyte in many places.

Of the tree-ferns the commonest is *Dicksonia squarrosa*, sometimes 20–30 feet high. Less abundant is *Hemitelia Smithii*. Of
the epiphytic ferns, the beautiful filmy-ferns are especially abundant and luxuriant. Of these the very characteristic kidney-fern
(*Trichomanes reniforme*), with vivid green, rather leathery leaves
is peculiar to New Zealand, as are several other species of Hymenophyllum and Trichomanes. Another abundant and beautiful fern, confined to New Zealand is *Todea* (*Leptopteris*) *superba*,
belonging to the same family, Osmundaceae, as the royal fern and
cinnamon fern of the United States.

As might be expected, these saturated forests are a veritable
garden of mosses and liverworts which drape the trunks and

branches of the trees, and form thick carpets on the forest floor, and great cushions over every stump and fallen log. Big tussocks of Sphagnum grow in the forest pools, and here and there are colonies of the giant *Dawsonia superba*, the last word in moss-evolution.

The abundance and luxuriance of the liverworts is astounding; it is doubtful if anywhere else in the world is a richer growth of

Fig. 96.—Giant moss (*Dawsonia superba*), Kauri forest, North Island, New Zealand. *Photo., Dr. L. Cockayne.*

these interesting forms. They include some of the giants of the class, one in particular, *Monoclea Forsteri*, being the largest liverwort that the writer has ever seen.

The New Zealand rain-forests are rich in climbing plants and epiphytes. Of the latter some are permanent epiphytes, others begin life as epiphytes but later send roots downward and assume a terrestrial habit. The permanent epiphytes include many mosses, liverworts, lycopods and ferns, as well as a good many flowering plants like orchids, Peperomia, Astelia and others. Several New Zealand trees begin life as epiphytes. The seeds germinate on

the branches of trees, and presently the young plant sends down
roots which descend along the trunk of the host until they reach

Fig. 97.—Sub-alpine scrub, Arthur's Pass, South Island, New Zealand. *Dracophyllum Traversii;* in front, *Suttonia divaricata. Photo., Dr. L. Cockayne.*

the ground. Sometimes these roots coalesce into a more or less
solid trunk, and the host may be completely strangled. The
"rata" is the most conspicuous of these temporary epiphytes.
Other species are *Dracophyllum arboreum* and *Griselinea littoralis.*

Compared with Australia, New Zealand has few showy flowers, a remarkable number of the plants having white or greenish flowers. There is, however, a considerable number of marked exceptions to this, like the scarlet flowers of the rata and native flax; the bright yellow of *Sophora tetraptera*, and the showy blue or purple of many species of Veronica and various Compositae, like Celmisia.

When the floras of New Zealand and Australia are compared, there are fewer correspondences than might be anticipated, and these are largely of northern genera which are also common to the Malayan flora. The Malayan element, however, is relatively of much greater importance in New Zealand, where in spite of the much cooler climate, a large proportion of the trees and shrubs are more or less evidently related to Malayan types. There is very strong evidence of former land extensions to the north of New Zealand, and it is quite likely that the Malayan genera which New Zealand shares with Australia, have reached the former country quite independently.

The distinctly Australian genera are relatively few in New Zealand, some of the most important like Eucalyptus, Acacia and Grevillea, being totally absent. The myrtle family, with over 800 species in Australia has a scant 20 in New Zealand, and the Proteaceae, with approximately 650 in Australia, have but two species in New Zealand. The characteristic Australian family Epacridaceae is well represented in New Zealand, as well as several Australian genera of Orchidaceae, Leguminosae and Compositae; but it has been suggested that some of these may have originated in New Zealand, and later migrated to Australia.

The Sub-antarctic Flora

Reference has already been made to the presence in southeast Australia and Tasmania of certain plants which are evidently related to species found in sub-antarctic South America. This "Fuegian" flora is much more evident in New Zealand, and has been the subject of many careful investigations. In one of the more recent of these publications [1] it is stated that 47 families

[1] Scottsburg, K., "Notes on the Relation between the Floras of Sub-antarctic South America and New Zealand," *Plant World*, May, 1915.
Cockayne, L., *New Zealand Plants and Their Story*, Wellington, 1919.

and 68 genera are common to the two regions, and there are even several identical species. The southern beeches (Nothofagus) have already been mentioned, but there are other more or less familiar genera, like Fuchsia, Geranium, Myosotis, Veronica, Ranunculus, etc., as well as others, e. g., Ourisia, Drimys, Pernettya, Libertia, Laurelia, Astelia, Mühlenbeckia, etc.

So difficult is it to explain the transport of so many forms across the immense stretch of ocean between New Zealand and South

FIG. 98.—Westland rain-forest, South Island, New Zealand. *Photo.,*
Dr. L. Cockayne

America, that one is compelled to assume some former land connections, probably *via* some northern extension of the present antarctic regions. Such fossil evidence as is available shows that some of these common types formerly existed in the Antarctic.

Further investigation may show that there was a northward extension of the antarctic regions, with climatic conditions suitable for vegetation. If further discoveries of fossils should indicate, as in the northern hemisphere, that a uniform vegetation existed in Tertiary time throughout what is now the antarctic regions, it would explain much of the present plant distribution in the southern hemisphere. Migrants from such a common temperate flora, shut off in the at present widely sundered regions, would in course of time show greater or less divergence, depending upon the difference in environment. The cool humid climates of Fuegia, Tasmania and southern New Zealand would be more likely to preserve these ancient forms with little change, than the hot arid-climate of most of Australia and South Africa.

There is sufficient similarity in the floras of South Africa and Australia to warrant the assumption of some former land connections; but such, if they did exist, were severed at a very remote period. The high degree of endemism in the two regions, points to a long period of isolation; and while, for example, such a peculiarly southern family as the Proteaceae, is abundantly represented in both regions, there is not a single genus common to the two.

The rain-forests of Queensland and New South Wales are probably the remnants of a once much more extensive flora of Malayan type. It is certain that at no very remote period, geologically speaking, northeastern Australia and Papua were united, and this is amply shown by both the floras and faunas of the two regions.

Western Australia, however, is supposed to be part of a very ancient continent which was at one time completely separated from what is now eastern Australia. In this ancient western continent it has been thought that most of the peculiar autochthonous Australian types originated. The typical Australian flora shows a very high degree of endemism, this reaching its maximum in Western Australia. The proportion of both endemic genera and species is very high, but the number of families represented is relatively small. The large number of species in certain genera is notable. Thus the genus Eucalyptus has over 200 species, and of the Leguminosae, the largest family in the Australian flora, over 400 species, or approximately one third of the total number, belong to the single genus Acacia. The Myrtaceae, the second largest Australian family, has over 800 species and the Proteaceae more than 650.[1] Several families, e. g., Candolleaceae, Goodeniaceae, are almost exclusively Australian, and especially developed in West Australia.

The typical Australian types are largely adapted to dry conditions, and after the union of eastern and western Australia, it may

[1] Maiden, *loc. cit.*, p. 166.

FIG. 99.—Vegetation of coastal cliff, southern part of South Island, New Zealand. At center, *Celmisia Lindsayi;* foreground, *Poa Astoni.* Photo., Dr. *L. Cockayne.*

be assumed that the extreme aridity and poor soils of the central part of the continent would be much better adapted to the xerophytes from the west than to the Malayan rain-forest types, which seem to have been to a great extent evicted by the drought-resistant western immigrants, and are now restricted to comparatively limited areas of good soil and adequate moisture.

Fig. 100.—Alpine grass-land, elevation 4,500 feet. *Gentiana corymbifera* in flower. South Island, New Zealand. *Photo., Mr. W. D. Reid.*

The autochthonous types have for the most part remained in Australia. Eucalyptus, Acacia, and a few Proteaceae, and a few others are found in the savannas of southern Papua, and some even reach the drier parts of the Philippines, and range through Polynesia; but the great majority of the true Australian types are unknown beyond the Australian continent.

Agriculture and Horticulture in Australasia

The cooler parts of Australia and all of New Zealand are adapted to the usual crops of the temperate zones. In Australia wheat is grown on a large scale and is much the most important agricultural product. Corn, oats, and barley are grown in considerable quantities, and alfalfa is an important forage crop in many places. Fruits and vegetables of many kinds thrive, and some fruit is exported, especially apples from Tasmania. Grapes, figs, passionfruit and oranges thrive in southern Australia, and wine of excellent quality is an important product, especially in South Australia. Dried fruits are made under much the same conditions as in California, but as yet the industry is still on a relatively small scale.

In Queensland sugar is grown in considerable quantities, and tropical fruits, pineapples, bananas and papayas, are produced on a commercial scale.

The climate of New Zealand is too cool for tropical fruits, and the cultivated fruits and vegetables are all the familiar ones of the temperate zone.

Weeds

As in all other lands settled by Europeans, there have also come many plant immigrants, not always welcome. These weeds hail from many countries. In the hotter and dryer parts of Australia, many of the weeds have come from India, Brazil or Africa, while in the temperate parts of Australia and New Zealand, they are the familiar European and American weeds, like sorrel, dock, thistles, plantain, etc.

Parts of Australia, especially Queensland, have been invaded by the American prickly-pears (*Opuntia spp.*) which have proved a very serious pest. It is said that in Queensland, 30,000,000 acres have been overrun by one species, causing immense damage. America has also contributed the cockle-bur (Xanthium), Stramonium and some other troublesome weeds. In the cooler and moister parts of Australia and New Zealand, European blackberries, sweet-brier, gorse and broom, have escaped from cultivation and become very difficult to eradicate.

South Africa, whose climate is so like that of Australia, has contributed a number of plants which have become more or less completely naturalized. The common calla lily may often be seen growing in ditches in southern Australia, and several handsome South African Iridaceae, Ixia, Sparaxis, Watsonia and

Homeria, are sometimes seen growing along the railway embankments and elsewhere. Homeria is said to be poisonous, and may be ranked as a weed. A showy yellow Oxalis (*O. cernua*) has also run wild, and the "Cape-weed" (*Cryptostemma calendulacea*) covers acres with its light yellow daisy flowers.[1]

TEMPERATE SOUTH AMERICA

The transition from the tropical regions of Brazil to temperate Argentina and Uruguay is very gradual. Southern Brazil extends beyond the Tropic of Capricorn, and the highlands have a climate not unlike that of parts of South Africa. Like the South African plateau, the rain, which is much heavier than in central Africa, falls mostly in summer, and very hot summers contrast with relatively cold winters.

Much of the country is open grass-land, but the valleys show a luxuriant sub-tropical vegetation, and there are many beautiful flowering trees, shrubs and creepers, some of which are not rare in cultivation. Among these may be mentioned, the beautiful Jacaranda, with its masses of blue flowers, and graceful foliage; the gorgeous orange *Bignonia venusta*, and the purple Bougainvillea.

Southern Brazil is also the home of an Araucaria (*A. Braziliana*), a very peculiar genus of conifers, confined to South America and the Australian region. This tree forms pure stands, like the northern pines, and associated with it is an undergrowth of "maté" (*Ilex Paraguayensis*), a shrub of the holly family, whose leaves yield the maté tea, extensively used by the natives, and now beginning to be an article of export.

Among the sub-tropical types of southern Brazil and northern Argentina, are various palms, some of which are in cultivation, like *Cocos plumosa* and *C. datil*, often seen in southern California.

Paraguay, like southern Brazil, has a sub-tropical climate with abundant precipitation especially in the eastern portion, so that there are luxuriant forests mainly of evergreen trees, but with predominantly deciduous species on the drier soils. Westward the forest becomes more restricted in its range and is interspersed with open prairies, with some palms and scattered thickets.[2] The

[1] For a fuller account of the Australasian vegetation, see the writer's papers in the *American Journal of Botany*, Vol. X, January, April, December, 1923.

[2] Hardy, M. E., *Geography of Plants*, Oxford, 1920, p. 158.

Plate XLIX.—Argentine pampa. *Photo., Dr. Bailey Willis.*

Paraguay tea, or maté, is abundant in this region and collected in great quantities.

The Paraguay river is subject to great floods, and the low country is then inundated so that the land adjacent to the river becomes an immense swamp.

South of Brazil and Paraguay, and east of the Andes lies the great plain of Argentina, the pampas, covering thousands of miles with a sea of grass, like the North American prairies. As in North America, the western portions of these plains are arid and broken, and sparsely covered with bunch-grasses, interspersed with tufts of dry thorny shrubs and Cacti, much like the deserts of Arizona and southern California. Salt pans, where the barren ground is covered with a film of white alkali are also reminiscent of our own southwest.

The pampa proper extends from Uruguay to the Rio Colorado near the northern boundary of Patagonia. The general aspect of the pampas must be much like the plains of the central United States. The grasses are mostly bunch-grasses belonging to several genera—Stipa, Aristida, Andropogon, Paspalum, Panicum and others, and these completely dominate the landscape. Where water settles in the hollows of the rolling prairie, there may be a continuous turf of finer grasses, and flowering herbs. Originally great numbers of ostriches, guanacos, and many small rodents inhabited these grass-lands; but with the coming of the white man, these have become greatly reduced in numbers, and now the pampas furnish pasturage for vast herds of cattle and horses. With the rapid settlement of the Argentine, vast areas have gone under the plow, and the Argentine wheat and corn compete in world markets with the grain of North America, Australia, India and Russia.

As in all newly settled countries, plant immigrants have come, and European weeds have invaded the cultivated areas. Especially notable is the cardoon-thistle (*Cynara Cardunculus*) which is said to cover extensive tracts of country almost to the exclusion of other vegetation.

South America narrows rapidly southward and nowhere is the climate of the pronounced continental type found in most parts of the northern hemisphere in corresponding latitudes, although there is a marked difference between winter and summer.

Buenos Aires, in about the same latitude as Los Angeles, has much the same range of temperature, viz., 104°–32°F., but the rainfall is twice as great. The southern extremity of Patagonia, has a harsh, but not extreme climate, comparable with that of the extreme north of the British Islands.

The greater part of Patagonia is a most forbidding semi-desert, a sandy or stony broken plain, with scanty vegetation comprising only the hardiest of plants. The scrubby bushes have small leathery leaves, and are often hairy or sticky. Showy flowers are almost wanting, weedy Compositae, plantain and verbenas being among the characteristic plants.[1]

The southernmost part of Patagonia has much more rain, and the climate is a moist, cloudy and windy one, with much less range of temperature than the drier region to the northeast. The stormy climate is not conducive to tree growth, but conditions favor the development of a moorland vegetation. Tussock-grasses (*Poa flabellata*) form huge tufts over the dreary moorland, and prostrate evergreen shrubs cover the ground in places.[2]

The flora of the Falkland Islands whose climate is even less genial than that of the mainland, has been somewhat carefully studied.[3] 130 species of flowering plants have been described, of which 26 are endemic. The ferns and mosses number 75, and the algae and fungi, 173. The most conspicuous plants are the tussock-grasses, and of the prostrate shrubs, two are notable, a peculiar umbellifer (*Azorella glebaria*) and a myrtle (*Myrtus nummularia*).

Fuegia

The great Andean chain gradually diminishes in height as it approaches the extreme southern part of the continent. The lower slopes, and the adjacent coast receive much more rain than the east coast of Patagonia, and the climate is much milder, so that conditions are favorable for a relatively rich vegetation. The same conditions prevail in Tierra del Fuego, across the Straits of Magellan, and the Fuegian region develops a low scrub forest composed mainly of the southern beeches (*Nothofagus antarctica* and *N. betuloides*), with a dense undergrowth of shrubs and herbaceous flowering plants, and a rich growth of ferns, mosses and lichens. The Fuegian flora has a considerable number of species either

---

[1] Drude, *loc. cit.*, 535.   [2] Hardy, *loc. cit.*, 162.   [3] Drude, *loc. cit.*, 540.

identical with or related to forms found in New Zealand, Tasmania and parts of Australia. Among these are the species of Gunnera, Astelia, Nertera, and Nothofagus. A single conifer, *Libocedrus tetragona*, is found in the Fuegian region. Other species occur further north in the Chilean Andes, and another is *L. decurrens*, the incense cedar of California.

Hardy compares the climate and vegetation of Fuegia with that of the north of Great Britain.

Chile

Chile occupies the Pacific coastal strip of South America, between latitude 18° and 55°, corresponding in North America to the coast from Central Mexico to southern Alaska, and there is a striking similarity in the climates of the two regions in corresponding latitudes, due to similar conditions. As in North America, the narrow coastal belt is bounded on the east by the great Cordillera, and the climate is a pronounced maritime one being dominated by the winds from the Pacific.

Of course, as Chile lies in the southern hemisphere, the seasons are reversed when compared with North America, and the northern regions are the hot ones. Like the west coast of the United States, winter is the rainy season, and is associated with northerly winds corresponding to the rain-bringing south winds in California; while the summer fair-weather southwest winds correspond to the prevailing northwest summer winds along the Californian coast.

All of northern Chile is extremely dry—practically rainless, in fact, and almost destitute of vegetation. This is the region of the famous nitrate deposits, the source of great wealth to the country. This long stretch of arid country extending into the tropics, forms an effectual barrier to the southward migration of tropical plants, which are almost entirely wanting in the temperate parts of Chile.

The scanty rainfall of all of northern and much of the coastal region of central Chile prevents the growth of any plants except those adapted to long periods of drought. It is not remarkable, therefore, that as in corresponding regions of North America, Cacti play a very important rôle in the flora. Other dry region plants like species of Euphorbia, Croton, Cassia, Ephedra, as well

PLATE L.—Coniferous forest, Chile; Libocedrus, Fitzroya. *Photo., Dr. Bailey Willis.*

360

as a good many bulbous plants and short-lived annuals, are also characteristic of the region.

The country about Valparaiso, which in latitude and climate may be compared to southern California, has a flora which is decidedly reminiscent of the latter region.[1]

There are many genera familiar to the Californian botanist, e. g., Calandrinia, Baccharis, Gilia, Lupinus, Sisyrinchium, etc., but there are also many which are exclusively South American. Some of these are very showy, and are cultivated in our gardens and greenhouses. Calceolaria, Schizanthus, nasturtiums and Petunias, are familiar instances of these herbaceous plants, while in the moister localities like ravines and the higher mountains, are many trees and shrubs which are highly prized in cultivation.

Some of the common weeds have come from the Mediterranean regions, and are also common in California. Among the earliest plants to respond to the first autumn rains are two common weeds, the bur-clover (*Medicago denticulata*) and the "Alfilaria" (*Erodium cicutarium*) both very common in California, where the seeds sprout within two or three days after the first good rain and soon cover the bare ground with a film of fresh green.

Among the characteristic species of Valparaiso, a few may be mentioned.[2]   Near the shore on granite banks are species of Bahia, Eupatorium, Leuceria, Senecio, Eryngium, Puja (Bromeliaceae), Lobelia. Of the herbaceous plants Calceolaria, various Cruciferae, Sisyrinchium, Cerastium, and various grasses.

On the mountain slopes and on the plateau back of Valparaiso Reiche mentions, among others, the following as characteristic. Low bushes and scrub included species of Baccharis, Mühlenbeckia, Azara, Flourensia, Haplopappus, and several others; associated with these were many showy herbaceous plants, e. g., Sisyrinchium, Scilla, Stenandrium, Thecophilaea, while occasionally a Puja or Cereus was seen. A few climbing plants were also noted, especially a yam (Dioscorea), and *Aristolochia Chilensis*.

Near Valparaiso are numerous mountain gorges in which there is a dense growth of tall shrubs, including some showy forms like Fuchsia, Eupatorium and Lobelia, as well as others less familiar. Among the interesting herbaceous plants is a wild potato, *Solanum*

[1] Reiche, K., *Pflanzenverbreitung in Chile*, DIE VEGETATION DER ERDE, VIII, 196.
[2] Reiche, *loc. cit.*

PLATE LI.—Beech forest (*Nothofagus sp.*), Chile. *Photo., Dr. Bailey Willis.*

Maglia. In this region also, is a fine palm (*Jubaea spectabilis*). One of the largest groves of this palm occurs at Cocolan, in lat. 34° 10′. In California, in almost the same latitude north, is the only native palm, *Washingtonia filifera.*

South of 35° the rainfall increases and in favorable localities, true forests begin, increasing southward in extent and luxuriance with the rapidly augmented precipitation.

Along the coast, opening to the sea, are protected valleys, re-calling the redwood canyons of central California, and harboring a fairly heavy forest in which the beeches, some evergreen, others deciduous, are the most important trees. These beeches are as has been pointed out, a prominent feature of the sub-antarctic forests of Fuegia, New Zealand, Tasmania, and associated with them are also other tree genera common to the southernmost parts of South America and Australasia, e. g., Weinmannia, Podocarpus, Drimys, as well as a good many shrubs and herbaceous species. One in particular, *Nertera depressa,* a pretty little evergreen trail-ing plant, has an extraordinary range, being common in New Zealand and Tasmania, and also known from some of the moun-tains of western Malaya.

Southward from Valparaiso there is a rapid increase in the rain-fall, and ferns, mosses and other moisture-loving plants become more and more abundant, and coniferous trees play a much more important rôle in the forest. The myrtle family is represented by species of Myrtus and Eugenia, both genera also abundantly represented in the Australasian and Malayan rain-forests. The myrtle family is largely developed in the tropical forests of South America, as it is in Australia, and another characteristic Australian family, the Proteaceae, has also a number of genera, two of which, Embothrium and Lomatia are shared with Australia. Another genus, Roupala is exclusively American.

The Chilean Coniferae are mostly southern genera, Podocarpus, Libocedrus, Saxegothaea and Araucaria, the latter, as already mentioned, being another genus which South America shares with Australia. The Chilean species, *A. imbricata,* popularly known as "monkey-puzzle," grows in the mountains of Chile at an altitude of 2,000–3,000 feet.

Central Chile, both in climate and topography, much resembles the corresponding regions of California, and the central valley between the Andes and the coastal hills has been compared with the great central valley of California. There is the same expanse

FIG. 101.—Beech-forest, Western Argentina, elevation 4,000 feet.
Photo., Dr. Bailey Willis.

of open grass-land, with an extensive development of evergreen, often thorny shrubs in the foot-hills, like the chaparral of the foot-hills of the Sacramento and San Joaquin Valleys.

On the coast the rainfall becomes very heavy. Valdivia, lat. 40°, has 100 inches annually, almost the same as on the coast of California in the same latitude north, and the heavy rain-forests of central Chile have their counterpart in the magnificent coniferous forests of northern California, Oregon and Washington. In both regions the climate is a cool and uniform one, which with the abundant moisture results in evergreen forests of the greatest luxuriance.

The constituents of these forests in Chile and North America, however, are very different. While the northern forests are composed almost exclusively of conifers—redwood, spruce, fir, hemlock and cedar, etc., these play a very subordinate rôle in the Chilean coastal forest, where the prevailing trees are beeches and other broad-leaved evergreens, quite wanting in the northern forests. Among the most characteristic of these are the following—*Drimys Winteri* (Magnoliaceae), *Laurelia aromatica* (Monimiaceae), *Myrtus luma*, *Aextoxicum punctatum* (Euphorbiaceae), *Flotowia diacanthoides* (Compositae), *Weinmannia trichosperma* (Cunoniaceae), *Cryptocarya peumus* (Lauraceae). Species of Laurelia and Weinmannia are both important trees of New Zealand. Only a single conifer, *Podocarpus Chilensis*, is found in this forest, and this is not a dominant tree. Among the shrubs are species of Griselinea (Cornaceae), Lomatia and Embothrium (Proteaceae); Escallonia (Saxifragaceae); the latter with handsome glossy foliage and pretty white, pink or crimson flowers, often cultivated in California and other warm temperate regions. Fuchsias are also frequent, as well as evergreen barberries, myrtles, and the less familiar Baccharis, Aristotelia (Tiliaceae), and Pseudopanax. The two latter, with Fuchsia and Griselinia, are characteristic genera of New Zealand.

These cool rain-forests abound in mosses, liverworts and ferns, among the latter a tree-fern (*Alsophila pruinata*), and epiphytes abound, among which the filmy ferns are notable.

Climbing plants are abundant including a scarlet nasturtium (*Tropoeolum speciosum*) and a beautiful climbing lily (*Lapageria rosea*), both occasionally seen in cultivation. Wild yams (Dioscorea), a vine, *Cissus striata*, and a number of less familiar genera occur, and several parasites of the mistletoe family are common.

Within the dark forest flowers are scarce, but in clearings, and at the edge of the forest are many shrubs and herbaceous plants of great beauty. Of the shrubs, the handsome *Sophora tetraptera*, with yellow pea-flowers is noteworthy, as the same species is widespread in New Zealand and also occurs in Lord Howe Island. *Alstroemeria aurantiaca*, a showy lily sometimes seen in cultivation, a raspberry (*Rubus ulmifolius*), a violet, an orchid (*Pogonia tetraphylla*.). Calceolaria, Sisyrinchium, and Calandrinia are some of these flowers of the more open areas. Libertia, a liliaceous genus also found in Australasia, may also be cited.

Ascending the mountains east of Valdivia, the rain-forest is replaced by one in which coniferous trees are more prominent. One of the most important commercially is the "Alerce" (*Fitzroya Patagonica*) whose timber is highly esteemed and which has been pretty well exterminated in many places. Several other coniferous genera occur, viz., Saxegothaea, Podocarpus, Libocedrus, the latter the only genus occurring in the United States. Of the lower shrubs, a species of Gaultheria recalls the "salal" of the Pacific coast, and the little wintergreen of Atlantic North America.

Among the most remarkable of the Chilean plants is *Gunnera Chilensis*, sometimes seen in cultivation. It suggests a gigantic rhubarb with huge leaves 4–5 feet across. A still larger species, *G. manicata* is found in Brazil, and in Hawaii a very similar species, *G. petaloidea* lives in the mountain rain-forest.

South of lat. 43°, there extends a chain of islands characterized by rain-forests in which mosses, liverworts and ferns are developed to an extraordinary degree, forming dense carpets on the forest floor, and covering the trunks and branches with a thick drapery. Tree-ferns, however, are apparently much less abundant than in the rain-forests in the same latitude in New Zealand.

The rain-forest occupies the whole coast of southern Chile to the extreme tip of Fuegia; but with the decreasing temperature there is a marked falling off in the number of species, and the trees become more stunted; but the vegetation is still, for the most part, evergreen, for although the climate is raw and boisterous there is no excessive cold.

The predominant trees are the same as in the forest further north, beeches, Libocedrus, Podocarpus, Weinmannia, Myrtus, Drimys, etc. There are extensive bogs with peat-mosses in which

grow a good many plants closely related to the bogs of the far
north, such as sundews, butter-wort (Pinguicula), marsh-marigold
(Caltha), crowberry (Empetrum), and others. Of the lower evergreen growths are various ferns, including a Gleichenia. Dacrydium and Orobolus are also characteristic genera.

The Chilean flora, as might be expected from the great range of
latitude, shows marked differences between the north and south.
The extreme desert conditions of the north constitute an absolute
barrier against invasion of plants from the moist tropics. This
accounts for the complete absence in Chile of such striking families
as the Araceae, Scitamineae, Bignoniaceae, Malpighiaceae, and
the bamboos. The palms, so extensively developed in tropical
America, are restricted to two species, one of which, *Juania
Australis*, is confined to the island of Juan Fernandez. The
Bromeliaceae, more xerophytic in habit, have a considerable
number of representatives but are much less important than is
the case in most other parts of South America.

On the other hand, owing to the cool and moist coastal climate
of central Chile, many sub-antarctic species extend far northward,
a condition parallelled in California by the southward extension
of many boreal species in the coastal redwood belt. In both regions
there is also a migration southward along the higher parts of the
great Cordillera.

A comparison of the floras of California and Chile show upwards
of 150 genera in common, and although a large part of these are
wide-spread in temperate climates, there are a good many strictly
American genera, and some confined to the Pacific slope. Such,
for example, are many Cacti, the creosote-bush (Larrea), Baccharis, Encelia, Grindelia, Orthocarpus, Mirabilis, and others.

There has been probably a migration in both directions, as some
genera are more characteristic of the north, others better developed
in the southern hemisphere. Thus Calandrinia, which has some
half dozen species in California, has many more in Chile, and also
Australia, and is presumably of southern origin. On the other
hand, Orthocarpus (Scrophulariaceae), with about 30 species in
Pacific North America, is represented by a single species in the
Andes.

While the number of species common to Chile and the Pacific
Coast of North America is small, there are several which could be

PLATE LII.—Vegetation of the southern Cordillera, Patagonia. *Photo., Dr. Bailey Willis.*

mentioned. Thus the Chilean strawberry (*Fragaria Chilensis*) is very common on the cliffs and sand dunes about San Francisco. None of the Chilean conifers belong to northern types. Podocarpus is represented in the West Indies, but otherwise, except for Libocedrus with a solitary species in California, the Chilean conifers belong to strictly austral genera, Araucaria and Fitzroya.

Southern Chile has a flora which is unmistakably related to that of New Zealand and Southern Australia; indeed so intimate is this relationship, that it seems extremely likely that some sort of land connection must at one time have existed between these countries, now so widely severed. Not only are there many genera in common, but some fifty species are cited as belonging to both regions.

Many of the trees characteristic of the forests of sub-antarctic South America and New Zealand belong to the same genera. In both regions the antarctic beeches (Nothofagus) abound, and such genera as Weinmannia, Laurelia, Aristotelia and Drimys, characteristic of New Zealand, but quite unknown in America, except in the Chilean region, indicate that these have reached South America from some southern land which has disappeared, while the presence in Chile of such a striking New Zealand species as *Sophora tetraptera*, already referred to, and the occurrence in New Zealand of three species of the essentially South American genus Fuchsia, make it pretty certain that there must have been some much more intimate connection between South America and Australasia than now exists. So many are the correspondences between the Andean and sub-antarctic floras of South America and those of New Zealand, as to make it practically certain that these regions have been in connection at some former time. Presumably this connection was *via* some extension northward of the existing antarctic continent.

Temperate South America has contributed many ornamental plants to our gardens. From South Brazil and Argentina come the Petunias, Verbenas, and Portulaca; from Chile the showy Calceolarias and Schizanthus of the greenhouses, Salpiglossis and nasturtiums.

The garden fuchsias are derived largely from Chilean species, while in milder climates the pepper tree (*Schinus molle*), the monkey-puzzle (*Araucaria imbricata*) evergreen barberries, especially *Berberis Darwinii*, Escallonias, the heath-like Fabiana, passion-flowers, and the beautiful *Lapageria rosea*, are among a few of the notable horticultural contributions of Chile.

More useful, if not ornamental, is the potato, several species of which are native to Chile and Peru.

The Chilean Oceanic Islands

Off the coast of Chile are two groups of volcanic islands said to be situated on a common submarine ridge. The southern group, Juan Fernandez, lies directly west of Valparaiso, the second, San Ambrosio and San Félix, further north, 900 km. from the coast.

There are three islands in the Juan Fernandez group, two of them, Masatierra and Masafuera, having peaks respectively 1,000 and 1,800 m. in elevation. There is an extensive evergreen forest developed over much of the two larger islands, but in the drier parts the vegetation is to a great extent herbaceous. In the driest districts, especially on rocky slopes and cliffs, are many xerophytes, among them a large bromeliad (*Ochagavia elegans*).[1]

The general character of the forest is much the same as that of the Chilean coast, but there is a very large proportion of endemic species. Perhaps the most notable is a palm (*Juania Australis*), with the exception of *Jubaea spectabilis*, the only Chilean palm.

Ferns abound in the islands, many, like the filmy-ferns, being epiphytes, while tree ferns are also common. On Masafuera the elevated plateau of the interior is covered by an extensive growth of ferns, forming what has been called a "fern-steppe."

According to Drude,[2] of the 102 species of flowering plants in Juan Fernandez, no less than 70 are endemic, and there are 10 endemic genera.

The archipelago of San Ambrosio and San Félix is very barren, and the flora extremely scanty. Professor Bailey Willis, of Stanford University, who recently visited San Felix, which formerly had extensive guano deposits, collected four species, one of which, *Thamnoseris lacerata* (Cichoraceae) is a monotypic species, endemic to the islands.

---

[1] Reicher, *loc. cit.*, p. 267.   [2] *Loc. cit.*, p. 132,

INDEX

Abauria excelsa, 215
Abies, see also *Fir*
A. amabilis, 131
A. concolor, 124, 127, Fig. 41
A. grandis, 119, 131, 139
A. lasiocarpa, 121–131, Fig. 30
A. magnifica, 148
A. pectinata, 46
A. Pinsapo, 58, 62
Abronia, 137
Abyssinia, 170, 171
Acacia, 52, 63, 169, 170, 171, 173, 181,
    189, 243, 257, 259, 316, 318, 332,
    349, 351, 353, 357
A. Arabica, 179
A. giraffae, 173, 318, 320
A. Greggii, 155, Pl. XII
A. horrida, 173
A. Koa, 257
Acanthus, 182
Acer, see also *Maple*
A. circinnatum, 130
A. glabrum, 120
A. macrophyllum, 130
A. Negundo, 140, 144
A. platanoides, 47
A. pseudo-platanus, 47
Aconitum, Aconite, see also *Monk's-hood*, 37
Acrocomia, 269, 294, 295, 303
A. sclerocarpa, 294, 295, Fig. 81
Acrostichum aureum, 113, 159, 219
Adansonia, see *Baobab*
A. digitata, 164
Adder-tongue, see *Erythronium, Ophi-oglossum*
Adenostoma, 141, 144
Adhesive seeds and fruits, 16
Adiantum pedatum, 140
Aeschynanthus, 209, 212, 238
Aesculus, see also *Horse-chestnut*
Ae. Californica, 141
Aetoxicum punctatum, 365
Africa, 157
Afzelia, 206
Agapanthus, 308, 311
Agathis, see also *Kauri*, 24, 215, 223,
    248, 336, 338
A. Australis, 336, 338
A. Palmerstoni, 248
Agave, 57, 112, 156, 205, 303

Ailanthus, 76
Alaria, 91, 128
A. esculenta, 91
Alaska, 28, 33, 37–38, 84, 128
Albany, West Australia, 331
Alberta, 43
Albizzia, 173, 206, 228, 314
A. stipulata, 233
Aleppo Pine, see *Pinus Halepensis*
Alerce, see *Fitzroya*
Aleurites Moluccana, 249, 256, 257,
    Pl. XXVI
Alfalfa, Medicago sativa, 319
Alfilaria, see *Erodium*
Algae, 5, 6, 91–94
    Blue-green Algae, 4, 234
    Brown Algae, 56
    Calcareous Algae, 5
    Coralline Algae, 5
    Red Algae, 56
Algaroba, see *Prosopis*
Algeria, 60–63
Allamanda, 292
Allium, 49, 143
Almond, 52
Alnus, Alder, 35, 41, 47, 129, 140
Alocasia, 238
Aloe, 66, 165, 170, 171, 198, 308, 316,
    318, 319, 320, Pl. XL
A. Schlechteri, 308, Fig. 85
Alpine vegetation
    Alps, 49
    Atlas, 62
    Carpathians, 49
    Pyrenees, 56, 49
    Mt. Rainier, 131
    Rocky Mountains, 31, 120
    Switzerland, 50
    Tyrol, 50
    White Mountains, 31
Alsophila, 168, 185
A. crinita, 193
A. glauca, 206, 228, Fig. 60
A. Kamarunensis, 168
A. pruinosa, 365
Alstroemeria aurantiaca, 366
Altai Mountains, 37, 68
Amaryllis, Amaryllidaceae, 308, 330
A. bella-donna, 308
Amazon, 271, 273, 274, 275, 281
Amecameca, Mexico, 265

371